GARBAGE IN THE CITIES

Garbage in the Cities

REFUSE, REFORM, AND THE

ENVIRONMENT, 1880–1980

By Martin V. Melosi

The Dorsey Press
Chicago, Illinois 60604

7-93 # 18067718

ISBN 0-256-06243-9

Library of Congress Catalog Card No. 87-73417

Printed in the United States of America

1 2 3 4 5 6 7 8 9 0 ML 4 3 2 1 0 9 8

To Jules Karlin, with great respect

Contents

Illustrations

following page 112

An unsanitary open dump in Richmond, Virginia, before 1914.

Dumping ashes and rubbish from barges at Sandy Hook outside New York Harbor about 1900.

Hand-sorting of refuse in New York City (1903).

Immigrants sorting various grades of paper (1916).

Traveling garbage burner in the alleys of Chicago in 1893.

Hydraulic press room in the reduction plant on Barren Island, New York (1903).

George E. Waring, Jr., "The Apostle of Cleanliness."

The annual parade of Colonel Waring's White Wings in 1897.

One of New York City's White Wings shows off his can carrier in 1905.

Headquarters for New York's Juvenile Street Cleaning Leagues (1910).

The Alley "L" Club in Chicago pitches in to clean the streets (1911).

Edith Pierce awards a badge to one of her Junior Sanitary Leaguers of Philadelphia in 1916.

Little Women Civic League of P.S. No. 4, Manhattan.

Poster promoting a cleanup campaign in Reading, Pennsylvania, in 1916.

Flushing the streets in Saint Louis (1905).

Dumping garbage from a horse cart into railroad cars in Saint Louis about 1916.

The incinerator at Montgomery, Alabama, 1911.

The clinkering process at the Montgomery, Alabama, incinerator (1911).

Milwaukee's motor-driven squeegee truck (1916).

Flushing streets by trolley car in 1916.

Advertisement for horse-drawn street-cleaning machines (1912).

Motorized garbage dump trucks in Springfield, Ohio, in 1914.

Preface

THINKING back on my youth, I can recall few occasions when the subject of garbage and rubbish crossed my mind. I do remember how the garbagemen always clanged our galvanized-steel trashcans together at 6:30 in the morning—a reminder that I had better get up to finish the homework I had set aside the night before. I am also reminded of the old joke "What has four wheels and flies?" A garbage truck, of course. And I remember that one of my cousins in San Francisco was a garbageman who eventually became the chairman of the board of San Francisco Sausage Company, which, I might add, makes the best Italian salami in the country.

Not until 1972 did refuse mean anything more to me than an inconvenience. In that year, as a graduate student in history at the University of Texas, I enrolled by impulse in a research seminar on environmental problems offered by H. Wayne Morgan. In his seminar on the Gilded Age the previous semester I had been amazed and utterly intrigued by his discussion of the squalor of the nineteenth-century city. It set me thinking about the impact of the physical environment on human beings. In Morgan's environmental history seminar I chose to write about the problem of refuse in the nineteenth-century city. To this day I do not know my reasons for that topic, other than some encouragement from Morgan and my taste for the unconventional. I transformed that seminar paper into an article, which eventually won a national award. This recognition convinced me that I was not the only historian intrigued by the unusual subject matter. In 1975, after completing my dissertation and accepting a position at Texas A&M University, I decided to follow up that article with a longer, more mature study of the waste problem. I had since broadened my interest in the subject and had become fascinated with the political, economic, social, and physical impacts of pollution on urban life.

The subject of this book, therefore, is a novel one for historians. I have taken my share of jibes and snickers from colleagues and family members. I have been introduced on several occasions with the line "Without any further disposal . . . ." People have teased me about spending six years in graduate school to produce the definitive study on garbage in America. I have been tagged, I suspect permanently, as the "garbage historian." Yet despite the good-natured ribbing, I have sensed a growing interest in urban environmental history over the last decade. Colleagues throughout the country have begun or have completed studies on sewerage, noise, smoke, pure water, and so forth. The time is coming when environmental history as a discipline will give as much attention to the man-made environment as it does to the wilderness and conservation.[1] Curiously, refuse pollution and solid-waste management have attracted widespread attention from many other scholarly and technical disciplines. Technical journals, scientific monographs, and policy studies offer abundant information about the waste problem. The historical perspective is most often missing, however, which leaves substantial room for the historian to make a noteworthy contribution.

Thus *Garbage in the Cities* is the first historical treatment of its kind. It offers an evaluation of the extent and nature of the refuse problem in the United States, and it demonstrates why and how urbanites have confronted that problem. It is my hope that the book will contribute to an understanding of an important city service, refuse management; provide insight about a significant, if mundane, pollution problem; and offer some perspective on the immutable relationships of urbanization, industrialization, and pollution.

[1] For a more thorough discussion of the emergence of urban environmental history, see Martin V. Melosi, "Urban Pollution: Historical Perspective Needed," *Environmental Review* 3 (Spring 1979): 37–45; Martin V. Melosi, "The Urban Physical Environment and the Historian: Prospects for Research, Teaching, and Public Policy," *Journal of American Culture* 3 (Fall 1980): 526–40.

Acknowledgments

I take great pleasure in thanking all the people who made the completion of this book easier than it might have been otherwise. My wife, Carolyn, comes first, because without her love and patience I would accomplish very little. Although my young daughters, Gina and Adria, do not always provide a home environment conducive to thought and reflection, they do give me great joy, which breaks up the tedium of the endless search for an errant footnote or an elusive transition sentence.

Those colleagues, acquaintances, and friends who read and criticized this study deserve special recognition, namely, Sara Alpern, Mary Clare Fabishak, Richard Fenton, Dale Knobel, John Lenihan, Bradley Rice, and Joel Tarr. I hope that I have done them justice. Special thanks must go to others throughout the nation who offered me advice about the form my book should take or suggested valuable sources that I should consult: Michael Robinson and Suellen Hoy, of the Public Works Historical Society; Ralph Black, John Connolly, Carol Lawson, and Tom Williams, of the Environmental Protection Agency; Martin Lange, former commissioner of solid-waste management for New York City; and Neil FitzSimons, of the American Society of Civil Engineers.

The staffs of the following libraries and depositories were generous with their time: Sterling Evans Library, Texas A&M University, College Station; Perry-Castañeda Library, University of Texas, Austin; New York University Library, New York City; Engineering Societies Library, New York City; New York Public Library, New York City; Haven Emerson Public Health Library, New York City; Municipal Reference and Research Center, New York City; National Library of Medicine, Bethesda, Maryland; and the Library of Congress, Washington, D.C.

To the Rockefeller Foundation, and especially Gary H. Toenniessen, assistant director, I owe a huge debt. Their financial support was central to the success of this project. Especially during the summers of 1976 and 1977 they provided the funds necessary to mine the resources of a wide array of libraries and made it possible for me to consult with scholars, engineers, and administrators who broadened my perspective on the subject of this book. The History Department, the College of Liberal Arts, and the University Mini-Grant Committee of Texas A&M University also provided essential clerical support and supplemental funds at crucial times during the preparation of the manuscript. I am permanently indebted to the university for its continual support for my research interests. And one final note of thanks goes to the Texas A&M Research Foundation for its aid in acquiring funding for this endeavor.

Carole Knapp, Mary Wilson, and Rosa Richardson of the History Department staff helped me greatly by retyping what were usually illegible drafts of the manuscript. I only hope that all the people who shared in the preparation of this book share my pleasure in its appearance.

College Station, Texas MARTIN V. MELOSI

GARBAGE IN THE CITIES

Introduction

SINCE human beings have inhabited the earth, they have generated, produced, manufactured, excreted, secreted, discarded, and otherwise disposed of all manner of waste. Among the myriad kinds of rejectamenta, refuse—solid waste—has been one of the most abundant, most cumbersome, and potentially most harmful. Beginning with ancient civiliaztions, there has always been refuse. There has not always been a refuse problem, however, at least not one of the magnitude that has developed in modern times. Simply to equate poor sanitation with the primitiveness of a society is to overlook the major factors that produce a refuse problem with serious health and environmental repercussions. First, refuse is primarily an urban blight. Agrarian societies throughout history have successfully avoided solid-waste pollution: cities and towns have faced the gravest dangers. Although varying in degree and intensity, the urban refuse problem is exacerbated by limited space and dense populations. Second, a "refuse problem" must be perceived by those affected by it. In other words, it must be understood to have negative effects on human life. The problem may be seen at first as merely a nuisance or annoyance and only later as a health hazard or part of a large-scale environmental crisis. It is the modern industrial society, not the ancient primitive society, that has experienced the most intense refuse problem. With the Industrial Revolution in Europe and the United States came the manufacture of material goods on a large scale and the attendant pollutants. With the emergence of modern metropolises people concentrated in urban areas as never before. However, the modern urban-industrial society also developed environmental consciousness and civic awareness.

This book focuses on the refuse problem in industrial America, in which, because of its rapid growth and rising affluence, the magnitude of the waste production has been staggering in the nineteenth and twentieth centuries. Most of the book concentrates on the period between 1880 and 1920, beginning with the time citizens first became aroused about the "garbage nuisance" and ending soon after World War I, when the priorities of war distracted attention from almost every municipal problem. The American experience with refuse pollution during this period was linked, in part, to the European experience, but it was also the result of a unique set of circumstances that produced the affluent, wasteful society whose material progress became the envy of the world.

To place in perspective the nature and extent of the American refuse problem, it will be useful first to trace the impact of waste on human society from ancient times through the Industrial Revolution in Europe. The historic connection betwen refuse and urbanization is apparent within this context, as is the significance of local circumstance and popular attitudes toward waste.

With the transition from hunting and gathering to food producing, around 10,000 B.C., human beings began to abandon the nomadic life for more permanent settlements, thus laying the groundwork for the first urban sites. In time the demands of this new life-style as well as the increased density of the environment, produced many challenges, including the need for improved methods of waste disposal. On-site disposal through natural decomposition would never do; casual rural habits could not be tolerated in crowded urban surroundings. New ways of dealing with waste developed slowly, however. In ancient Troy wastes were left on the floors of homes or simply thrown into the streets. In parts of Africa similar habits prevailed to the point where street levels rose and new houses had to be constructed on higher ground. As Lewis Mumford graphically stated:

For thousands of years city dwellers put up with defective, often quite vile, sanitary arrangements, wallowing in rubbish and filth they certainly had the power to remove, for the occasional task of removal could hardly have been more loathsome than walking and breathing in the constant presence of such ordure. If one had any sufficient explanation of this indifference to dirt and odor that are repulsive to many animals, even pigs, who take pains to keep themselves and their lairs clean, one might also have a clue to the slow and fitful nature of technological improvement itself, in the five millennia that followed the birth of the city.[1]

---

[1]Lewis Mumford, *The City in History: Its Origins, Its Transformation, and Its Prospects*, p. 75. See also E. S. Savas, *The Organization and Efficiency of Solid Waste Collection*,

This bleak portrayal suggests a lack of resolve by ancient civilizations to promote good sanitation. While the general state of uncleanliness was appalling in those times, there were many examples of progress. In the Indus Valley city Mahenjo-Daro (founded about 2500 B.C.) a precedent-setting experiment in central planning led to the construction of homes with built-in rubbish chutes and trash bins. The city also had an effective drainage system and a scavenger service. The residents of other Indian cities, such as Harappa, in the Punjab, equipped their homes with bathrooms and drains. Excavations of ancient Babylon revealed drains, cesspools, and sewage systems. In the Egyptian city Heracleopolis (founded about 2100 B.C.) the wastes in the "non-elite" quarter were ignored, but in the elite and religious quarters efforts were made to collect and dispose of all wastes, which usually ended up in the Nile. In Crete, a most advanced civilization in terms of sanitation, by 2100 B.C. the homes of the Sea Kings had bathrooms connected to trunk sewers, and by 1500 B.C. the island had areas set aside for the disposal of organic wastes. Records of China dating from the second century B.C. indicate forces of "sanitary police" who were charged with removing animal and human carcasses and "traffic police" who oversaw, among other things, street sweeping in the major cities.[2]

Religion, as well as utilitarian and social conventions, played a major role in the establishment of sanitary practices in the ancient world. Most notable were the Jewish laws of cleanliness. About 1600 B.C., Moses wrote a code of sanitary laws that was perpetuated and enlarged upon down through the centuries. Every Jew was expected to remove his own waste and bury it far from the living quarters. The Talmud ordered that the streets of Jerusalem were to be washed daily, a severe law in such an arid region. Like a number of other ancient cities conscious of health and sanitation needs, as early as 800 B.C., Jerusalem also had a sewer system and its own water supply.[3]

---

pp. 11–13; Charles G. Gunnerson, "Debris Accumulation in Ancient and Modern Cities," *Journal of the Environmental Engineering Division, ASCE* 99 (June 1973): 229–43.

[2] George Rosen, *A History of Public Health*, pp. 25–27; Fred B. Welch, "History of Sanitation" (Paper read at the First General Meeting of the "Wisconsin Section" of the National Association of Sanitarians, Inc., Milwaukee, Wisc., December 1944), p. 39; Savas, *Organization and Efficiency*, pp. 11–12. For information about early street paving see "The Early History of Street Paving and Street Cleaning," *Engineering News* 36 (16 July 1896): 47–48.

[3] Savas, *Organization and Efficiency*, p. 12. See also "The Early History of Street Paving and Street Cleaning," p. 47; Welch, "History of Sanitation," p. 39.

The achievements of Mahenjo-Daro, Harappa, and Jerusalem did not produce a universal standard of cleanliness in the ancient world. Into the classical period refuse problems plagued even the high culture of Athens. In the fifth century B.C. garbage and other accumulated waste cluttered the city's outskirts and threatened the Athenians' health. (The municipal dumps bordering the city even became sites for abandoning unwanted babies.) On balance, however, the Greeks made some important contributions to sanitation. About 500 B.C., Greeks organized the first "municipal dumps" in the Western world. The Council of Athens began enforcing an ordinance requiring scavengers to dispose of wastes no less than one mile from the city walls. Athens also issued the first known edict against throwing garbage into the streets.[4]

Rome, because of its size and dense population, faced sanitation problems unheard of in Greece. The city was more effective in dealing with water, sewerage, and some public-health matters than in resolving the refuse problem. In addition to building the famous aqueduct system, the Romans supervised public baths, houses of prostitution, and wine-drinking establishments. They also regulated food vendors. By the end of the reign of Augustus Caesar in A.D. 14, Rome had an effective public-health administration. Refuse collection and disposal, however, though well organized by prenineteenth-century standards, were deficient for the city's needs. The volume of waste was staggering, yet municipal collection was restricted to state-sponsored events, such as parades and gladiatorial games. By law property owners were responsible for adjacent streets, but enforcement of the law was lax. The wealthy employed slaves to collect and dispose of waste, and independent scavengers collected garbage and excrement to be resold as fertilizer. Open dumping remained the standard disposal practice with all its obvious shortcomings. For a city of approximately one and a quarter million people, the waste problem far exceeded the ability to deal with it. Well before the Fall of Rome the city became incredibly unhealthy and dirty. Ironically, as Rome experienced a population reduction to about twenty thousand in the thirteenth century, and as the rest of the Western world similarly "deurbanized," the breakdown of sanitation services had a less widespread, more localized impact. Beyond Europe, especially in the great Islamic cities and in China, there were fairly advanced sanitation systems.[5]

[4] Savas, *Organization and Efficiency*, p. 13; Mumford, *The City in History*, p. 130.
[5] Welch, "History of Sanitation," p. 41; Savas, *Organization and Efficiency*, pp. 13–14;

The persistent clichés about the medieval period as the Dark Ages with recurrent plagues suggest that Europe became a vast garbage dump after the Fall of Rome. Such generalizations are overstated. The population of Europe was scattered and was spared the massive waste problem experienced by Rome in classical times. Despite the crudity of medieval dwellings and living conditions, sparsely populated areas did not have to contend with the refuse pollution experienced in the great cities of the past. With the rise of medieval cities stablelike conditions were gradually improved. According to public-health historian George Rosen, "All the institutions needed for a hygienic mode of life had to be created anew by the medieval municipalities. It was within this urban environment that public health, thought, and practice revived and developed further in the medieval world."[6]

All the basic needs—safe water, sewerage, and so forth—had to be met by a new urban society. The collection and disposal of waste was a particularly difficult problem at a time when rural habits were being reintroduced into town life. Hogs, geese, ducks, and other animals shared the urban habitat with human beings. By the thirteenth century the larger European cities were once again coming to grips with refuse. Cities began paving and cleaning their streets at the end of the twelfth century. Paris began paving its streets in 1184, when, according to contemporary accounts, King Philip II ordered the streets paved because he was annoyed by the offensive odors emanating from the mud in front of his palace. Augsburg became the first city in Germany to pave its streets, though not until 1415. Street cleaning at public expense came some time later, in Paris not until 1609. In the German principalities street-cleaning work was often assigned to Jews and to the servants of the public executioner. It was hardly an ennobling profession.[7]

Waste collection and dumping in medieval cities have a varied history. In 1388 the English Parliament banned waste disposal in public watercourses or ditches. Paris had a most unusual experience with the refuse problem. In 1131 a law was passed prohibiting swine from running loose in the streets after young King Philip, son of Louis the Fat, was killed in a

---

Rosen, *A History of Public Health*, p. 48. See also Katie Kelly, *Garbage: The History and Future of Garbage in America*, pp. 16–18.

[6] Rosen, *A History of Public Health*, pp. 56–57.

[7] "The Early History of Street Paving and Street Cleaning," pp. 47–48; Rosen, *A History of Public Health*, pp. 57–58.

riding accident caused by an unattended pig. The monks of the Abbey of Saint Anthony protested the law, and were granted a dispensation because their herds of swine were a major source of income. The controversy over allowing animals to run free raged on for years, however. Until the fourteenth century Parisians were allowed to cast garbage out their windows, and although several attempts were made at effective collection and disposal, by 1400 the mounds of waste beyond the city gates were so high that they posed an obstruction to the defense of Paris. One ingenious regulation provided that whoever brought a cart of sand, earth, or gravel into the city had to leave with a load of mud or refuse. Little by little the people of medieval Europe were becoming aware of waste as a health hazard. Public resistance to new regulations was strong, however, and primitive collection and disposal methods were widespread. No adequate solution was in sight. Exacerbating the problem was the steady transition of the medieval towns into modern cities, with multistory tenements, high concentrations of people and business establishments, and growing quantities of inorganic as well as organic wastes.[8]

Until the transition of Europe from a predominantly agrarian to an urban industrial society in the nineteenth century, the refuse problem remained much as it had been in the Middle Ages. Although the Renaissance brought a revival of classical art to Europe and heralded a new era, early modern Europe did not undergo a sufficient physical or demographic change to influence the development of new methods to cope with waste. Change was gradual until the onset of the Industrial Revolution. Only in the major cities could the rudiments of a sanitation system be found. Most people continued to discard garbage and rubbish in helter-skelter confusion. In Edinburgh, regarded by many as the filthiest city in all of Europe, citizens cast garbage into the streets in the evening, hoping that the scavengers would collect it the next morning. At Naples the breakwater sheltering moored vessels was so badly clogged by 1597 that city leaders almost decided to build a new breakwater rather than clean the old one. Cities continued to pass laws and ordinances against the most unsanitary practices, but to little avail. The plagues that invaded Europe between 1349 and 1750 provided some inducement for better sanitation, but responsibility largely remained an individual matter well into the nineteenth century.[9]

---

[8] Savas, *Organization and Efficiency*, pp. 14–15; Mumford, *The City in History*, pp. 290–92; "The Early History of Street Paving and Street Cleaning," p. 48.

[9] Savas, *Organization and Efficiency*, pp. 16–17; Rosen, *A History of Public Health*,

The Industrial Revolution, which originated in England in the mid-eighteenth century, brought down the old order in Europe, replacing it with a new one characterized by vast economic expansion and rapid urbanization. The major physical consequence of the Industrial Revolution was an environmental crisis in the cities. As never before, urbanites were forced to confront massive pollution in many forms. In this context the refuse problem emerged as a major blight.

Historian Eric E. Lampard suggested that the Industrial Revolution was "a particular form of social change" and that its occurrence "transcends explanation in purely economic terms." To understand the depths of its impact, one must realize how completely the Industrial Revolution changed the lives of Europeans and other peoples. Lampard argued that the first phases of the Industrial Revolution produced a kind of "disorder" rather than an instantaneous new order, that the gradualness of the change was what most distressed and bewildered town and country people alike.[10] During the transition from a preindustrial to an industrial society dislocations, distress, instability, and uncertainty of change shook the people to their roots. The transition from rural to urban, from agrarian to industrial, had a similar impact on the physical environment.

The effect of the Industrial Revolution on urban society was not all negative, but its imprint on the physical city was tragic. Mumford has written that "industrialism, the main creative force of the nineteenth century, produced the most degraded urban environment the world had yet seen; for even the quarters of the ruling classes were befouled and overcrowded."[11] Asa Briggs, in more measured but also critical words, observed:

The worst aspects of nineteenth-century urban growth are reasonably well known. The great industrial cities came into existence on the new economic foundations laid in the eighteenth century with the growth in population and the expansion of industry. The pressure of rapidly increasing numbers of people, and the social consequences of the introduction of new industrial techniques and new ways of organizing work, involved a sharp break with the past. The fact that the new techniques were introduced by private enterprise and that the work was organzied for other people not by them largely determined the reaction to the break.[12]

pp. 122–23; Charles Singer, et al., eds., *The Industrial Revolution, 1750 to 1850*, vol. 4 of *A History of Technology*, pp. 505–506; Kelly, *Garbage*, p. 20.

[10] Eric E. Lampard, "The Social Impact of the Industrial Revolution," in Melvin Kranzberg and Carroll W. Pursell, Jr., eds., *The Emergence of Modern Industrial Society, Earliest Times to 1900*, vol. 1 of *Technology in Western Civilization*, p. 305.

[11] Mumford, *The City in History*, p. 447.

[12] Asa Briggs, *Victorian Cities*, p. 18.

He went on to say, "The priority of industrial discipline in shaping all human relations was bound to make other aspects of life seem secondary." Neglect of the physical environment was to be expected in a society in which priorities were shaped by an "industrial discipline."

The demographic shift in England most profoundly affected city growth and led to serious problems of overcrowding. The English were the world's first urbanized society. Twenty percent of the population lived in cities and towns of 10,000 or more by 1801, with one-twelfth of the people residing in London. By 1851 more than half of the English were city dwellers. At the beginning of the nineteenth century only the Netherlands was more urbanized. During the reign of Queen Victoria (1837–1901) the population of Great Britain doubled, and the 1901 census indicated that 77 percent of the country's 36 million citizens lived in urban areas.

The inability to house such a growing population had led to serious overcrowding and sanitary problems. In 1843 in one section of Manchester there was one toilet for every 212 people. "It was impossible," Lampard wrote, "for the nineteenth-century market-economy to house the growing, urbanizing, population in any but the most rudimentary way. Public and philanthropic efforts could do little more than advertise the 'problem.'" Although the housing crisis eased somewhat after the turn of the century, all manner of structures, including cellars and other dank places, were converted for human habitation. In Liverpool one-sixth of the population lived in underground cellars. As late as the 1930s, London had 20,000 basement dwellings considered unfit for occupation. Many dwellings had insufficient ventilation, inadequate privies, and little or no sunlight.[13]

The crush of people and the concentration of industry in and around cities produced living and working conditions of incredible deprivation, especially for the poor and the working class. The pages of Charles Dickens overflow with graphic images of the wretchedness of life in the industrial city. Stinking water, smoky skies, ear-shattering din, and filthy streets made living conditions grim. Conditions in the factory were no better. The factory was "a new kind of prison; the clock a new kind of jailer."[14] The

---

[13] Eric E. Lampard, "The Urbanizing World," in H. J. Dyos and Michael Wolff, eds., *The Victorian City; Images and Realities*, 1:4, 10–13, 21–22; H. J. Habakkuk and M. Postan, *The Industrial Revolutions and After: Incomes, Population, and Technological Change*, vol. 6 of *The Cambridge Economic History of Europe*, p. 274; Mumford, *The City in History*, pp. 461–65.

[14] Habakkuk and Postan, *The Industrial Revolutions and After*, p. 276.

lessons of good sanitation and public health learned over the years were forgotten or ignored. Nuisance laws were rarely enforced, public health laws went unheeded, and in some quarters cleanliness was all but forgotten.[15]

The life of the urban poor and the working class reveals the neglect of sanitation and proper collection and disposal of waste. It suggests but one dimension of the growing waste problem in industrial-urbanized societies. As Lampard noted, industrial-urban nations are "effluent" societies.[16] The growing production and consumption of goods made the scale and magnitude of the waste problem much greater than that encountered by previous cultures. Even if sanitary standards were improved to the point of rendering the unhealthy safe and the dirty clean, rising affluence, which brought still more production, would produce an ever larger quantity of waste. The growth to maturity of an industrial society, therefore, was no guarantee that the refuse problem would decline, even though sanitary conditions might improve. The moderate rise in the standard of living and the improvement in living conditions in England by the time of the Great Exhibition in London in 1851 did not signal an end to the waste problem. Changes for the better simply meant that the most immediate unpleasant effects of the Industrial Revolution were subsiding.

In the middle to late nineteenth century England could boast about reversing some of the most debilitating physical defects of the industrial city, especially poor sanitary and health conditions. The grimness of the industrial city could not be neglected forever. When the subtle became painfully obvious, when the affluent were touched by some of the same misfortunes as those of the suffering poor, something had to be done. Several forces converged to halt the downward spiral of the environment. One of the most important was the "service revolution." City services had been established over time to meet the most pressing needs: fire and police protection, water supplies, and even waste collection—largely by scavenging. Their growing size and the extent of their problems required industrial cities to provide many citywide services that had previously been provided selectively by volunteers or paid agents. Several scholars have argued that, along with the rise of laissez-faire capitalism, the nineteenth century also

[15] Briggs, *Victorian Cities*, pp. 20, 144; Lampard, "The Urbanizing World," pp. 19–22; Mumford, *The City in History*, pp. 462–63, 476–79.

[16] Lampard, "The Urbanizing World," pp. 43–45; Lampard, "The Social Impact of the Industrial Revolution," p. 317.

experienced a kind of "municipal socialism," that is, a demand for services provided by the city rather than the individual. Although some scholars have exaggerated the range and quantity of services provided by this municipal socialism, the needs of the large, heterogeneous industrial city did force a rethinking of ways in which those needs could be met. One of the results of the new emphasis on city-wide services was the development of rudimentary public works and public-health agencies or departments.[17]

Another essential factor—perhaps the most essential factor—in bringing about the first effort to improve sanitation in the industrial city was the emergence of modern public-health science. Surveys undertaken by the Poor Law Commission, first in London and then throughout England, evaluated the health of the working population. In 1842 the commission published a report under the primary authorship of Edwin Chadwick, on the sanitary conditions of this population. The most significant feature of the report was the conclusion that disease, especially communicable disease, was related in some way to filthy environmental conditions (the exact connection would not become clear until the advent of the germ theory of disease). The establishment of the Sanitary Commission in 1869 and subsequent enactment of public-health laws provided the foundation for environmental sanitation that led to a reduction in urban disease. With the advent of modern science and information-gathering procedures brought to bear on public health, conditions in industrial England began to improve. Similar programs in other parts of Europe and in the United States signaled a new "age of sanitation." As will be seen later, the emergence of bacteriological science and the rise of the germ theory of disease led to the discrediting of environmental sanitation as the sole means of curbing communicable diseases. Nonetheless, these first steps offered immediate and in some cases dramatic relief from some of the ravages of the urban environment. The industrial city had not been brought under control, but at least the most obvious environmental hazards were being dealt with.[18]

While Europe was in the midst of its Industrial Revolution, the United

---

[17] R. M. Hartwell, "The Service Revolution: The Growth of Services in Modern Economy," in Carlo M. Cipolla, ed., *The Industrial Revolution, 1700–1914*, vol. 33 of *The Fontana Economic History of Europe*, pp. 364–67; Savas, *Organization and Efficiency*, pp. 19–20.

[18] J. C. Wylie, *The Wastes of Civilization*, pp. 50ff.; Briggs, *Victorian Cities*, p. 19; Rosen, *A History of Public Health*, pp. 214–17, 252–59; Anthony N. B. Garvan, "Technology and Domestic Life, 1830–1880," in Kranzberg and Pursell, *The Emergence of Modern Industrial Society*, pp. 555–56; Welch, "History of Sanitation," pp. 43–45.

States was emerging as a national entity. Many of the difficult lessons learned in the industrial cities of Europe had little applicability in the colonial society of North America. Some aspects of the European experience with sanitation problems were transmitted to the New World, but not in ways that would help Americans avoid those problems. The evolution of American society established a different context for dealing with health and sanitation, out of time with European experiences and condition, if not always out of step with the problems themselves.

Preindustrial America was a highly decentralized society, but from the beginning it had some form of urban life. Indeed, cities and towns played central roles in establishing American traditions, in fostering a strong economy, and in providing staging areas for territorial expansion. The importance of American cities and towns was disproportionate to their size. From the early seventeenth century until the eve of America's own industrial revolution in the mid-nineteenth century, the total urban population remained small, as did the physical dimensions of the cities. The first federal census of 1790 showed that city dwellers represented only 5.1 percent of the population, and only two cities exceeded 25,000. By 1840 the urban population had increased to 10.8 percent, and only New York exceeded 250,000. Between 1790 and 1840, however, the number of cities increased from 24 to 131.[19]

What distinguished the American experience with sanitation problems from the European experience during a comparable period of growth were dimensions of space and magnitude. In the American colonies the abundance of land and natural resources such as water supplies mitigated against massive sanitation problems even in cities and towns. Since no American city reached the size of London during that period, the need to deal with health and sanitation problems on a grand scale did not materialize. That is not to say that American cities were free of refuse and poor sanitation—only that any parallels between the two societies must be drawn with an understanding of local conditions. Americans cities periodically experienced appalling sanitary and health problems. Carl Bridenbaugh wrote that in colonial times the casting of rubbish and garbage into the streets was "a confirmed habit of both English and American town-dwellers." In the dirtiness of streets, however, "colonial villages vied with, but

---

[19] U.S. Bureau of the Census, *Characteristics of the Population*, vol. 1 of *Census of Population: 1960*, pt. A, pp. 1-14, 1-15, table 8; David R. Goldfield and Blaine A. Brownell, *Urban America: From Downtown to No Town*, pp. 13–21.

never equaled, the filthiness prevalent in contemporary English towns,"
though the swine roaming the streets scavenging for food and causing
obstructions to people and horses were reminiscent of scenes in most European villages.[20] In eastern cities, where crowding became a chronic problem as early as the 1770s, the streets reeked with waste, wells were polluted, and deaths from epidemic disease mounted rapidly. Even in the
burgeoning cities in the West and South problems were sometimes legion.
As late as the 1860s, Washingtonians dumped garbage and slop into alleys
and streets, pigs roamed freely, slaughterhouses spewed nauseating fumes,
and rats and cockroaches infested most dwellings—including the White
House. No wonder the infant mortality rate was very high in the capital
city.[21]

Because of the time differential, preindustrial American cities benefited earlier and more quickly from sanitary sciences than did their counterparts in Europe. The connection between filth and disease was dogma. In
colonial cities removal of waste and street cleaning were considered effective ways of preserving public health as well as eliminating nuisances. By
the mid-nineteenth century several cities had established boards of health
and had passed ordinances against indiscriminate dumping of refuse and
the free roaming of animals.[22]

These measures alone were not enough to curb the problem of waste
and to maintain consistently high standards of sanitation. First, environmental sanitation alone could not protect cities from epidemics; until
the development of the science of bacteriology, cities were impotent to
deal with them. Second, ordinances were not reinforced with adequate
inspections, surveillance, or policing to ensure citizens' compliance.

[20] Carl Bridenbaugh, *Cities in the Wilderness: The First Century of Urban Life in America, 1625–1742*, pp. 18, 85–86. See also Carl Bridenbaugh, *Cities in Revolt: Urban Life in
America, 1743–1776*, pp. 32–33, 239–40.

[21] Sam Bass Warner, Jr., *The Private City: Philadelphia in Three Periods of Its Growth*,
p. 16; Charles E. Rosenberg, *The Cholera Years: The United States in 1832, 1849, and 1866*,
pp. 112–13, 184; Bessie Louise Pierce, *The Beginning of a City, 1673–1848*, vol. 1 of *A History of Chicago*, pp. 204–205, 338–39; Constance McLaughlin Green, *Washington: Village
and Capital, 1800–1878*, p. 211.

[22] John Duffy, *A History of Public Health in New York City, 1625–1866*, pp. 180–93;
356–75; Sidney I. Pomerantz, *New York, an American City, 1783–1803: A Study of Urban
Life*, pp. 270–76, 295–96, 344; John B. Blake, *Public Health in the Town of Boston,
1630–1822*, pp. 18, 100–104, 156–63; Bayrd Still, *Milwaukee: The History of a City*, pp. 103,
239–40; Bridenbaugh, *Cities in the Wilderness*, p. 85; Bridenbaugh, *Cities in Revolt*, pp.
30–32, 240.

City leaders' concern for cleanliness was not always matched by their constituents'.[23]

The quality of sanitation in preindustrial America was determined largely by local circumstances. Some city leaders had the foresight to place a high priority on city cleanliness, while others ignored the problem. Epidemics ravaged several cities, while others were spared because of their relative isolation or because of attention to comprehensive sanitary measures. While rudimentary public-works systems emerged in several of the larger or more progressive communities, individuals or private scavengers handled the waste problems in many towns and villages. For the most part the citizens of preindustrial America lacked the environmental consciousness that would encourage the institutionalization of sanitary programs. Little progress was made in establishing clear lines of responsibility for collection and disposal of refuse, except perhaps in New York and Boston, and even in New York advances were slow in coming. The burghers of New Amsterdam had been among the first to pass laws against casting waste into the streets (1657), but the condition of the streets remained the responsibility of the householders. In the late eighteenth and early nineteenth centuries New York established municipal control over several sanitary services, but jurisdictional disputes between state and local governments and between city and individuals continued. The time for comprehensive community-wide programs and general environmental reform had not yet arrived. Americans must have found it difficult to comprehend the massive pollution problems confronting industrial London. They must have found it even more difficult to anticipate that the same problems would threaten them in the not-too-distant future.[24]

The impact of the Industrial Revolution on American cities was no less staggering than its impact on European cities had been. Like Europe, the United States experienced an environmental crisis, though with its own

[23] Blake, *Public Health in the Town of Boston*, pp. 157–58.

[24] Bridenbaugh, *Cities in the Wilderness*, pp. 18, 165–67, 239, 321ff; Blake, *Public Health in the Town of Boston*, pp. 15–16, 103–104, 209–10; Duffy, *A History of Public Health in New York City, 1625–1866*, pp. 180–93, 356–90; Pomerantz, *New York, an American City*, pp. 251, 269–76, 295–96, 344; Bridenbaugh, *Cities in Revolt*, pp. 31–33, 240; Green, *Washington*, pp. 93–94, 211, 254–55; Still, *Milwaukee*, pp. 239–40; William E. Korbitz, ed., *Urban Public Works Administration*, pp. 9–96; Ernest S. Griffith, *History of American City Government: The Colonial Period*, pp. 261–91; American Public Works Association, *Street Cleaning Practice*, Rodney R. Fleming, 3d ed., pp. 2–3 (hereafter cited as APWA); APWA, *Street and Urban Road Maintenance*, pp. 5–6.

unique characteristics. Also like Europe, the United States was confronted
with a waste problem that had two distinctive dimensions. One was linked
to the physical distress caused by overcrowding, poor sanitation, and primitive methods of collection and disposal; the other was tied to the rising
affluence of the people, which would have a longer-range impact. Both, of
course, were triggered by the Industrial Revolution and the emergence of a
metropolitan society that changed the substance and style of American life.

The Industrial Revolution in the United States had no greater impact
than in its transformation of the country into an urban nation. As early as
1820 there was a significant link between urban development and industrial
growth. Between 1840 and 1920—the period of the first major wave of industrialization—the urban population grew from 1,845,000 to over 54 million, that is, from 10.8 percent of the population to a little more than 51
percent. This represented at least 29 percent growth in the urban population each decade and as much as 92.1 percent growth between 1840 and
1850. The number of urban areas also grew at a fast pace—from 131 in
1840 to 2,722 in 1920, extending across the country.[25]

During this period of remarkable growth the industrial city was the
dominant urban form, especially between 1870 and 1920. Densely populated, physically expansive, and economically vital, the industrial city was
characterized by urban sprawl, an ever-rising skyline, and specialized land
use in the form of well-defined business and residential districts. Relatively new cities with strong industrial economies such as Cleveland, Pittsburgh, and Milwaukee, began experiencing rapid population growth and
economic prosperity. Industrialization also transformed many older commercial or preindustrial cities, such as Boston, Baltimore, Philadelphia,
and New York, which also attracted factories.[26]

Industrial cities paid a high price for their rapid population growth
and economic dynamism. Not unlike their counterparts in Europe, they
suffered an environmental crisis characterized by crowded tenement districts, chronic health problem, billowing smoke, polluted waterways, traffic congestion, unbearable noise, and mounds of putrefying garbage.
Americans were unprepared to deal with the magnitude of these pollutants

[25] U.S. Bureau of the Census, *Characteristics of the Population*, pt. A, pp. 1-14, 1-15,
table 8.
[26] Sam Bass Warner, Jr., *The Urban Wilderness: A History of the American City*, pp.
55–112; Maury Klein and Harvey A. Kantor, *Prisoners of Progress: American Industrial Cities, 1850–1920*, pp. 68–108.

and the rapid transformation of the United States into an urbanized nation. Several factors converged to create this environmental crisis. By 1885 the need for a plentiful and inexpensive source of energy to run factories and to heat homes had led to the extensive use of coal. Bituminous (soft) coal was the most widely used; only a small portion of it was consumed in the generating of power and heat, and most of the residue went directly into the air, encrusting buildings, clothing, and the lungs of city dwellers.[27]

The concentration of factories in and around cities added to environmental problems. Iron and steel mills, textile mills, and chemical plants were often constructed near waterways, sources of the large quantities of water needed for conversion to steam or for the manufacture of chemical solutions. Waterways also proved useful for disposing of wastes. A study made in 1900 suggested that 40 percent of the pollution load on American rivers was industrial in origin. Manufacturers contributed substantially to land pollution as well, dumping heaps of rubbish, garbage, slag, ashes, and scrap metal on available vacant land. Slaughterhouses and other animal-processing industries dumped animal wastes in open pits or on vacant lots; tanning companies polluted waterways by washing hides in them. The noise produced by large factories could deafen workers and disrupt surrounding residential neighborhoods.[28]

The numbers of factories and the dense concentration of industries around cities turned many nuisances into full-fledged environmental disasters. By 1899, 40 percent of the 500,000 industrial establishments in the country were factories. At least three-fourths of American manufacturing was concentrated in New England, the Middle Atlantic states, and the north central states. By 1900, thirty-four of the forty-four states were manufacturing more than 50 percent of their goods in urban areas; in eighteen states more than 75 percent of the products came from urban factories. Industrial specialization added to this high concentration. For instance, the highly polluting iron-and-steel industry was concentrated in the greater Pittsburgh area, and, not surprisingly, the amount of smoke was stifling.

[27] Sam H. Schurr and Bruce C. Netschert, *Energy in the American Economy, 1850–1975*, pp. 57–83; Joseph M. Petulla, *American Environmental History*, pp. 149–51, 189–91.
[28] APWA, *History of Public Works in the United States, 1776–1976*, ed. Ellis L. Armstrong, Michael C. Robinson, and Suellen M. Hoy, p. 410; Robert R. Russel, *A History of the American Economic System*, p. 183; Raymond W. Smilor, "Cacophony at 34th and 6th: The Noise Problem in America, 1900–1930," *American Studies* 28 (Spring 1977): 28–29; Mumford, *The City in History*, p. 459.

Chicago, Saint Louis, and Kansas City led the nation in slaughtering and meatpacking, and the citizens suffered a great deal from the festering wastes and noxious odors.[29]

Massive human concentrations in the industrial cities exacerbated the environmental crisis. The rapid population growth of the United States and its cities during this period is well known. Between 1850 and 1920, while the world population increased by 55 percent, the population of the United States soared by 357 percent. As stated earlier, the most phenomenal growth occurred in the cities, primarily because of immigration and rural-to-urban migration. During this period nearly 32 million people entered the United States, most of them from southern and eastern Europe. By 1910, 41 percent of American city dwellers were foreign-born. About 80 percent of the new immigrants settled in the Northeast. Migration from rural areas of the country was also impressive. Although statistics are scant, a conservative estimate is that 15 million rural people moved to the cities between 1880 and 1920. During those years the rural population fell from 71.4 percent to 48.6 percent.[30]

Statistics can measure the magnitude of these shifts in population, but they cannot measure the human dimension of the attendant environmental crisis. City dwellers in the industrial cities lived and worked in oppressive social and physical surroundings. It is almost impossible to comprehend the overcrowding in some cities. From 1820 to 1850 the average block density in lower Manhattan increased from 157.5 to 272.5 persons. In 1894, New York City's Sanitary District A averaged 986.4 people an acre in thirty-two acres, which translated to 300,000 people in a space of five or six blocks. Bombay, India, the next-most-crowded area in the world, had 759.7 people an acre; Prague, the European city with the worst slums, had 485.4 people an acre.[31].

Jane Addams, in *Twenty Years at Hull-House*, recalled the seeming disregard for the crowded and inferior living condtions of those years:

The mere consistent enforcement of existing laws and efforts to their advance often placed Hull-House, at least temporarily, into strained relations with its neighbors. I recall a continuous warfare against local landlords who would move wrecks of old houses as a nucleus for new ones in order to evade the provisions of the

[29]Martin V. Melosi, "Environmental Crisis in the City: The Relationship between Industrialization and Urban Pollution," in Martin V. Melosi, ed., *Pollution and Reform in American Cities, 1870–1930*, pp. 6–9.

[30]Ibid., pp. 9–10.

[31]Ibid., p. 11.

building code, and a certain Italian neighbor who was filled with bitterness because his new rear tenement was discovered to be illegal. It seemed impossible to make him understand that the health of the tenants was in any wise as important as his undisturbed rents.[32]

Jacob Riis, in *How the Other Half Lives*, wrote:

Thousands were living in cellars. There were three hundred underground lodging-houses in the city when the Health Department was organized. Some fifteen years before that [about 1852] the old Baptist Church in Mulberry Street, just off Chatham Street, had been sold, and the rear half of the frame structure had been converted into tenements that with their swarming population became the scandal even of that reckless age.[33]

Appalling stories of overcrowding, like the one about the thirty-three Serbian workers and their boss who lived in a five-room house, or the common practice of keeping farm animals in basements and even slaughtering them there, were all too familiar.[34]

In such surroundings health problems, disease and high mortality rates were to be expected. Typhoid spread throughout New Orleans from sewage standing in unpaved streets. In 1873, Memphis lost nearly 10 percent of its population to yellow fever. Mortality figures for "Murder Bay," a black district in Washington, D.C., not far from the White House, were twice as high as those for white neighborhoods. The residents of that slum lived in ghastly surroundings, picking their dinners out of garbage cans and dumps. By 1870 conditions in New York City had deteriorated so badly that infant-mortality rates were 65 percent higher than those of 1810. Correlations between living conditions and disease in tenements led to some understanding of the debilitating effects of a bad environment on health, but improvements would not come quickly.[35]

Even the well-to-do were not completely insulated from the environment of the industrial city. The crush of human beings, the concentration of factories, and the expansion of the city affected everyone. Even the

[32] Jane Addams, *Twenty Years at Hull-House*, p. 209.

[33] Jacob Riis, *How the Other Half Lives*, pp. 9–10.

[34] David Brody, "Slavic Immigrants in the Steel Mills," in Thomas R. Frazier, ed., *The Private Side of American History*, (New York: Harcourt Brace Jovanovich, 1975), p. 133; Addams, *Twenty Years at Hull-House*, pp. 207–209; Riis, *How the Other Half Lives*, p. 8.

[35] Thomas C. Cochran and William Miller, *The Age of Enterprise: A Social History of Industrial America*, p. 262; Roy Lubove, *Twentieth-Century Pittsburgh: Government, Business, and Environmental Change*, p. 18; Klein and Kantor, *Prisoners of Progress*, pp. 314–28.

wealthy banker had to endure the trip from his country estate to his downtown office. Engulfed in the problems of the cities, Americans, like their earlier counterparts in Europe, found it all but impossible to cope with them as individuals. The new urban environment challenged every Jeffersonian notion of individuality and self-reliance. Yet the need to confront the most immediate environmental problems was at hand, and urbanites had little choice but to do so.

The first efforts to resolve the environmental crisis were directed piecemeal at the most obvious concerns. Thus the needs for sources of pure water and adequate sewerage received top priority because they affected citizens collectively and were vital for good health. To the credit of many cities, effective programs to tap pure-water sources and construct modern sewer systems were under way by the 1870s. Efforts to control smoke pollution and excessive noise lagged far behind and did not gain momentum until the mid-1890s. Such problems were more elusive, more difficult to gauge and measure, and even more difficult to monitor and control. Smoke had come to symbolize material progress and the economic activity vital to the growth of industrial cities and the nation. Noise also seemed to indicate a society on the move. Only when the skies remained black with soot and the din made it difficult to think, eat, or sleep did the reformers gain public and official support.[36]

The refuse problem gained public recognition as an environmental issue soon after the efforts to assure clean water and adequate sewerage in the early 1880s and just before the first attempts to abate smoke and excessive noise in the mid-1890s. At first it was considered a mere nuisance, but by the 1890s the "garbage problem" was recognized as a major pollutant of the industrial era. The following chapters will describe the extent of the problem, discuss how it was perceived by contemporaries, and demonstrate how reformers tried to resolve it. We will also see how American cities, between 1880 and 1920, began coping effectively with the immediate threats caused by refuse but failed to confront the more fundamental problems associated with the production of wastes. Not until the 1960s and 1970s did Americans begin to link the resolution of the refuse problem to American affluence and the consumption of goods.

[36] For a more thorough discussion of these pollution problems see Melosi, *Pollution and Reform in American Cities, 1870–1930*.

1

Out of Sight, Out of Mind: The Refuse Problem in the Late Nineteenth Century

In the late nineteenth century urban America discovered the "garbage problem." In an 1891 issue of *Harper's Weekly* an observer noted, "As the world grows older it becomes not only conscious of new problems which it has to solve, but it becomes more keenly conscious of the importance of old ones which it has only imperfectly met."[1] The refuse problem attained such massive proportions in the industrial United States that even the most insensitive city dweller could no longer ignore it. Heaps of gargage, rubbish, and manure cluttered alleys and streets, putrefied in open dumps, and tainted the watercourses into which refuse was thrown. Recognition that refuse was a serious problem was the first important step toward resolving it. Although lacking reliable statistics about sanitary conditions and sophisticated scientific knowledge, nineteenth-century Americans began to realize that mounds of garbage, rubbish, and other discards were not simply eyesores but unnecessary encumbrances and potential health hazards.

A budding environmental consciousness that made urbanites sensitive to impure water supplies, poor drainage and sewerage, and smoky skies also influenced their thinking about solid wastes. As the "garbage nuisance" came to be seen as a serious environmental problem, the impulse for reform acquired broad dimensions. First, the traditional acceptance of individual responsibility for refuse collection and disposal made way for an acceptance of community responsibility. Second, some measure of civic protest against the most serious sanitation problems and civic involvement in promoting municipal cleanliness were seen as necessary to persuade of-

---

[1] G. T. Ferris, "Cleansing of Great Cities," *Harper's Weekly* 35 (10 January 1891): 33.

ficials to act in the best interests of the community. Third, engineers re-evaluated prevailing collection and disposal methods and frequently offered technical and administrative alternatives meant to provide solutions to the problem. Little by little nineteenth-century Americans confronted the complexities of a nagging environmental problem and opened the door for more sophisticated reform measures in the twentieth century. Solutions were difficult to achieve, but a start was made.

The extent of the refuse problem in the years after the Civil War was an indicator of the rapid urban growth of the nineteenth century and the dense concentration of people at the core of the cities. At a meeting of the American Public Health Association (APHA) in 1879, the Reverend Hugh Miller Thompson described a dumping ground in New Orleans sited on the edge of the swamp:

Thither were brought the dead dogs and cats, the kitchen garbage and the like, and duly dumped. This festering, rotten mess was picked over by rag-pickers and wallowed over by pigs, pigs and humans contesting for a living in it, and as the heaps increased, the odors increased also, and the mass lay corrupting under a tropical sun, dispersing the pestilential fumes where the winds carried them.[2]

In 1891 the head of the Street Department of Boston bemoaned how the city's streets, once "models of cleanliness," had been rapidly deteriorating of late. "The reason why the streets had grown more filthy from year to year," he said, "was easily discovered. The system of cleaning in vogue, while it answered for twenty years ago, had been entirely outgrown. Notwithstanding the enormous growth of the city, the system has never been changed to keep pace with this growth."[3]

Contemporary statistics help the modern reader visualize the staggering quantities of refuse that brought the problem to public attention (it should be noted, however, that many of the data from the nineteenth century were based on estimates and indicated only the amount of refuse actually collected, not the great volumes that remained in the streets and alleys). For example, Boston authorities estimated that in 1890 scavenging teams collected approximately 350,000 loads of garbage, ashes, street sweepings, and other debris. In Chicago about 225 street teams gathered approximately 2,000 cubic yards of refuse daily. Seasonal variations in the

---

[2]The Rev. Hugh Miller Thompson, "Disposal of City Garbage at New Orleans," *Sanitarian* 7 (November 1879): 545.

[3]Boston, Street Department, *Annual Report* (1891), pp. 119–20.

amounts and kinds of wastes complicated the picture. In Manhattan at the turn of the century scavengers averaged 612 tons of garbage daily; during July and August the volume increased to 1,100 tons daily. Transportation of wastes to dumping sites was easier in the summer months, and the warm weather made mandatory the frequent collection of rapidly putrefying offal. Also, in the summer larger quantities of produce and dairy products were available to urbanites. For example, New Yorkers consumed approximately 750,000 watermelons during the warmer months of each year in the 1890s. Something had to be done with the rinds.[4]

Surveys conducted during the first two decades of the twentieth century offer some of the earliest statistical evidence of the mounting refuse problem in the United States. Table 1 shows the amount of garbage (organic waste) collected in eighteen major cities in 1916. In most of the major cities the amount of refuse collected yearly ranged from one-half to three-quarters ton per capita.[5] Between 1900 and 1920 each citizen of Manhattan, Brooklyn, and the Bronx annually produced about 160 pounds of garbage, 1,231 pounds of ashes, and 97 pounds of rubbish. One expert estimated that each American contributed approximately 100 to 180 pounds of garbage, 300 to 1,200 pounds of ashes, and 50 to 100 pounds of rubbish yearly. By comparison, European city dwellers produced substantially less refuse than their American counterparts. A 1905 study indicated that fourteen American cities averaged 860 pounds of mixed rubbish per capita per year, while in eight English cities the amount was 450 pounds per capita, and in seventy-seven German cities, 319 pounds.[6] Franz Schneider, Jr., research associate of the Sanitary Laboratory of the Massachusetts Institute of Technology, imaginatively calculated that if the entire year's refuse of New York City was gathered in one place "the resulting mass would equal in volume a cube about one eighth of a mile on an edge. This surprising vol-

[4]"Disposal of Refuse in American Cities," *Scientific American* 65 (29 August 1891): 136; John McGaw Woodbury, "The Wastes of a Great City," *Scribner's Magazine* 34 (October 1903): 392; Henry Smith Williams, "How New York Is Kept Partially Clean," *Harper's Weekly* 38 (13 October 1894): 973.

[5]Rudolph Hering and Samuel A. Greeley, *Collection and Disposal of Municipal Refuse*, p. 13; H. de B. Parsons, *The Disposal of Municipal Refuse*, p. 27.

[6]These figures are meant only to demonstrate the relatively large quantities of urban refuse produced in the United States, not to describe European conditions. See Hering and Greeley, *Collection and Disposal of Municipal Refuse*, pp. 13, 28, 70; Rudolph Hering, "Disposal of Municipal Refuse," *Transactions of the American Society of Civil Engineers* 54 (1904): 265–308.

TABLE 1
Tons of Garbage Collected in Eighteen Major Cities, 1916

City (Population)	Garbage Collected (Tons)	Garbage Collected per Capita (Tons)
Baltimore, Md. (593,000)	37,915	0.064
Boston, Mass. (781,628)	52,650	0.067
Bridgeport, Conn. (172,113)	19,897	0.116
Cincinnati, Ohio (416,300)	40,692	0.098
Cleveland, Ohio (674,073)	59,708	0.089
Columbus, Ohio (220,000)	20,393	0.093
Dayton, Ohio (155,000)	16,621	0.107
Detroit, Mich. (750,000)	72,785	0.097
Grand Rapids, Mich. (140,000)	8,678	0.062
Indianapolis, Ind. (271,758)	23,267	0.086
Los Angeles, Calif. (600,000)	51,062	0.085
New Bedford, Mass. (118,158)	10,162	0.086
New York, N.Y. (5,377,456)	487,451	0.091
Philadelphia, Pa. (1,709,518)	101,678	0.059
Pittsburgh, Pa. (579,090)	73,758	0.127
Rochester, N.Y. (275,000)	30,782	0.112
Toledo, Ohio (220,000)	23,971	0.109
Washington, D.C. (400,000)	46,293	0.116

SOURCE: Rudolph Hering and Samuel A. Greeley, *Collection and Disposal of Municipal Refuse* (New York, 1921), pp. 13, 28.

ume is over three times that of the great pyramid of Ghizeh, and would accommodate one hundred and forty Washington monuments with ease."[7]

Horses, still the major means of individual and commercial transportation in the late nineteenth century, rivaled human beings in creating waste problems. At the turn of the century there were 3 to 3½ million horses in American cities. In New York City alone there were about 120,000; in Chicago, something over 83,000. Engineers estimated that the normal, healthy city horse produced over twenty pounds of manure and gallons of urine daily, most of which ended up in the streets. Cumulative totals of manure produced by horses were staggering: 26,000 horses in Brooklyn produced about 200 tons daily; 12,500 horses in Milwaukee produced 133

[7]Franz Schneider, Jr., "The Disposal of a City's Waste," *Scientific American* 107 (13 July 1912): 24.

tons. Even when provisions were made for carting off the manure and depositing it beyond the city limits, a considerable amount spilled from the wagons and remained in the streets until street cleaners made their rounds. On unpaved streets the manure was ground into the dirt. The manure in Brooklyn, one observer noted, "was removed promptly by farmers in the early spring; but as summer advanced and it was not needed for the crops, it was allowed to accumulate."[8]

The proliferation of horsecars for mass transit in the 1850s exacerbated the problem. By the mid-1880s, 100,000 horses and mules were pulling 18,000 horsecars over 3,500 miles of track nationwide. The horses' discharges not only cluttered the streets and corroded the metal streetcar tracks but also threatened the health of city dwellers. Stables were notorious breeding places for disease. Unbearable as well was the stench coming from the stables and manure pits that many horsecar companies maintained within the city limits as sources of additional income. Since the life expectancy of a city horse was only about two years, carcasses were plentiful and had to be disposed of. New York City scavengers removed 15,000 dead horses in 1880. As late as 1912, when motor vehicles dominated the streets, Chicago scavengers still had to remove 10,000 dead horses.[9]

The arrival of the electric streetcar and the automobile appeared to be the panacea for the horse problem. The Automobile Chamber of Commerce, whose interests were clearly linked to promoting motor vehicles, declared that the replacement of Chicago's 80,000 horses with motor trucks and automobiles would not only improve the city's sanitation problem but also save the city a million dollars a year in street cleaning.[10] Whether these figures could be trusted is a matter for speculation, but street cleaners enthusiastically heralded the arrival of the automobile as the means of their salvation. Little did they realize what the transition from animal power to mechanical power signaled for the city's physical environment. Trading manure and horse carcasses for hydrocarbons, noxious fumes, and waste heat from internal-combustion engines was no bargain.

[8]Joel A. Tarr, "Urban Pollution: Many Long Years Ago," *American Heritage* 22 (October 1971): 65–69, 106; "Disposal of Refuse in American Cities," p. 52; "Clean Streets and Motor Traffic," *Literary Digest* 49 (5 September 1914): 413.

[9]American Public Works Association, *History of Public Works in the United States, 1776–1976*, p. 164 (hereafter cited as APWA); John Duffy, *A History of Public Health in New York City, 1866–1966*, p. 127; Tarr, "Urban Pollution: Many Long Years Ago," pp. 67–69; "Clean Streets and Motor Traffic," p. 413.

[10]"Clean Streets and Motor Traffic," p. 413.

With so much organic waste accumulating in the cities, giving off foul odors and attracting flies and rats, urbanites could not avoid recognizing a connection between refuse and health hazards. Contemporary sanitary science seemed to confirm the connection. In the mid-nineteenth century experiments in England and in the United States demonstrated that there was some relationship between communicable diseases and putrefying wastes. The efforts of British lawyer-turned-sanitarian Edwin Chadwick led the way for new sanitation laws in England and inspired American health officials to consider refuse collection and disposal from the perspective of improving health conditions. The prevailing wisdom at midcentury was that disease was caused by environmental factors. The "miasmic," or filth, theory of disease dominated American thinking on sanitation into the 1890s. According to the theory, gases emanating from putrefying matter or sewers were the cause of contagious diseases, and city cleanliness, proper drainage and sewerage, and adequate ventilation of buildings would suffice in arresting them. "Environmental sanitation," which included the proper removal of solid wastes, seemed to offer an immediate and effective solution to many city health problems. According to medical historian Howard D. Kramer, "A sanitary program based on these beliefs won considerable popular support and scored several major victories." Among those victories were the New York Metropolitan Health Law (1860); the creation of state boards of health, beginning with the Massachusetts board in 1869; the founding of the APHA in 1872; and the establishment of the short-lived National Board of Health in 1879.[11]

Environmental sanitation as the means of ridding the cities of death and pestilence had some serious drawbacks, however. In the 1880s the discovery of specific pathogenic organisms—bacteria—enabled public-health officers and sanitarians to understand the actual causes of many contagious diseases. In the twentieth century the "germ theory" of disease eventually replaced older notions about the relationship between filth and disease and led to the implementation of bacteriological laboratories as the

---

[11]Howard D. Kramer, "The Germ Theory and the Public Health Program in the United States," *Bulletin of the History of Medicine* 22 (May–June 1948): 233–47. In response to the disastrous yellow fever epidemic of 1878, health reformers were able to secure from Congress the first national quarantine act and the creation of the National Board of Health. Neither proved effective. In 1883 Congress eliminated the appropriation of the National Board of Health and it collapsed. See John Duffy, "Social Impact of Disease in the Late 19th Century," in *Sickness and Health in America: Readings in the History of Medicine and Public Health*, ed. Judith Walzer Leavitt and Ronald L. Numbers, pp. 399–400.

chief means of controlling epidemics. The views of "anticontagionists," advocates of the miasmic theory, fell into disrepute, and environmental sanitation came to be considered far less important as a means of controlling disease.[12]

Municipal cleanliness through environmental sanitation, though it did not fully explain the nature of disease transmittal, was a worthwhile goal with a beneficial purpose, especially in light of the deplorable state of public health in nineteenth-century American cities.[13] It inspired a rudimentary environmental awareness, akin to modern ecological concepts, which gave impetus to refuse-management reform and provided a rallying point for attracting more advocates. Contemporary accounts confirm the growing perception of refuse as a health problem of serious consequence by the 1880s. One observer considered clean streets an important "sanitary objective."[14] Referring to street conditions in Boston, an engineer noted that, street cleaning "having been found to have so large an influence on the health and mortality of a community, a mere occasional attempt to clear up what street litter we cannot climb over is not sufficient."[15] In 1892, in the wake of a cholera epidemic in New York City, *Engineering News* asserted:

. . . When we consider that the sanitary wellbeing of two millions of people may depend upon the manner in which this refuse is disposed of, it is seen that some intelligent solution of this complex problem must be reached, and our city authorities can not afford to allow matters to relapse into old ruts as soon as the present cholera agitation is over. It is no case for cheese-paring or economy, and when it is once realized that a large sum of money must be spent for this public life insurance it is certain that men can be found to point out the means.[16]

If the magnitude of the urban refuse problem did not convince city officials that effective sanitation measures were needed, the rising con-

[12]Kramer, "Germ Theory," pp. 233–47; James H. Cassedy, *Charles V. Chapin and the Public Health Movement*, pp. 39–61; Duffy, *Public Health in New York City*, pp. 91–111; Henry I. Bowditch, *Public Hygiene in America*, pp. 29–41.

[13]For sources dealing with public health problems in nineteenth-century cities, see Martin V. Melosi, "Urban Pollution: Historical Perspective Needed," *Environmental Review* 3 (Spring 1979): 37–45.

[14]Gen. Emmons Clark, "Street-cleaning in Large Cities," *Popular Science Monthly* 38 (April 1891): 748.

[15]Henry B. Wood, "Street Work in Boston," *Journal of the Association of Engineering Societies* 11 (August 1892): 433–34.

[16]"City Refuse Disposal," *Engineering News* 28 (6 October 1892): 325. See also John S. Billings, "Municipal Sanitation in Washington and Baltimore," *Forum* 15 (August 1893): 727–37.

cerns over the health question did. As one writer noted about conditions in New York City in 1894: "It is quite in order that New York should be grappling with the garbage problem at this time, for almost every other large city in the civilized world is in a similar predicament. . . . the garbage problem is the one question of sanitation that is uppermost in the minds of local authorities."[17] City officials also realized that the complexities of urban life in the late nineteenth century made collection and disposal of refuse by private citizens impractical. In 1893 a special sanitary committee in Boston asserted:

> The means resorted to by a large number of citizens to get rid of their garbage and avoid paying for its collection would be very amusing were it not such a menace to public health. Some burn it, while others wrap it up in paper and carry it on their way to work and drop it when unobserved, or throw it into vacant lots or into the river. . . . the destruction of garbage by individual householders in any large city is too dangerous an experiment to be seriously considered by any intelligent community.[18]

But cities in post–Civil War America were only beginning to take charge of their own affairs and demand "home rule" from rural-dominated state legislatures. That made the offering of necessary services slow in coming.[19]

Of course, even before the Industrial Revolution several of the largest communities had provided rudimentary sanitation services or at least had contracted out some of the work; however, the question of who was ultimately responsible for collection and disposal of refuse was not yet decided by the 1880s and 1890s. Because of the impracticality of private action, the major cities especially were compelled to choose between two available alternatives. They could either contract the service by taking bids from private scavenging companies or establish a municipal service. The contract system was initially more popular because it required little or no capital outlay by the city, while still allowing for a modicum of municipal supervision. Advocates of the contract system, moreover, feared that mu-

---

[17] Henry Smith Williams, "The Disposal of Garbage," *Harper's Weekly* 38 (1 September 1894): 835.

[18] City of Boston, Joint Special Committee on the Disposing of City Offal, *Report of the Joint Special Committee on the Disposing of City Offal*, p. 17.

[19] In the late nineteenth and early twentieth centuries the efforts of many cities to move away from state interference in their affairs resulted in frequent demands for municipal "home rule." This movement took many forms, including efforts to increase the appointive power of mayors and to gain control of various service departments. See Charles N. Glaab and A. Theodore Brown, *A History of Urban America*, pp. 174–76.

nicipally operated services bred political corruption. An editorial in *Engineering News* in 1890 suggested that for New York City "[a] little less Tammany v. County Democracy and a little more organized muscle would work wonders in cleaning our streets."[20] The contract system was also touted as an incentive for free enterprise in the cities. The New York Street Cleaning Department reintroduced the contract system of street cleaning in 1890 after a long period of municipal control. Soon afterward the following appeared in *Engineering News*:

Properly administered and stringently enforced, a contract means the immediate discharge of all labor that does not turn money into the contractor's pocket by the vigorous use of muscle; the man must work or the master cannot meet his engagements and liabilities, and as long as the contractor is made to feel that his contract price will be his sole return for service, and that he will be strictly held to the specifications of that contract, the public can depend upon him to manage the labor and hold the Commissioner responsible for the class of work performed. Under this condition of affairs responsibility can be fixed, and as every citizen would be an inspector, the citizen knows who to howl at if things go wrong.[21]

Faith in the contract system was not shared by all city officials and concerned citizens. In the 1890s, especially, the contract system came under severe criticism as reformers looked to municipal ownership of utilities and municipal operation of services to cure many of the city's physical and social ills. The attack on the contract system was particularly strong in Chicago. As the head of the Chicago Board of Health stated in his 1892 report:

One sentence will almost express it—there are few if any redeeming qualities attached [to the contract system]. No matter what guards are placed around it, the system remains vicious. If the contractor intends to approach his duty, the men he employs are not to be depended upon; he can not follow each one; the result is bad service. You ask the remedy. I reply, let the city purchase its own plant and do the work; at the end of the year you have at least the plant to show for the investment— at present nothing but the remembrance of how this man or that man has neglected your alley.

The Civic Federation of Chicago charged that the contractors collecting the garbage were swindling the city and completing only half the work prom-

[20] *Engineering News* 23 (4 January 1890): 13.
[21] *Engineering News* 23 (15 February 1890): 156. See also Washington, D.C., Health Department, *Report of the Health Officer* (1882), p. 10; Saint Louis, Health Department, *Annual Report* (1894), p. 9; (1895), p. 9.

ised.[22] While in Chicago the debate over the contract system focused on the questions of efficiency and economy of service, in other cities the health issue dominated the controversy. In its 1895 report the Board of Health of Newton, Massachusetts, contended that, since it was the responsibility of the city to care for its citizens' health, sanitary services should not be left to the mercy of profit-motivated contractors.[23]

The controversy over the contract system was not resolved in the nineteenth century, because municipal conditions varied so greatly that a consensus seemed impossible. Future debates over the best approach would focus on the relative cost of each system, the effectiveness of the methods employed, and the degree of municipal control. For the present, however, previous practice dictated the method employed. The 1880 United States census, the first census in which comprehensive urban statistics were compiled, reveals no national trend favoring one system over the other. In only 48 of 199 cities surveyed was there a municipal system for collection and disposal of garbage and ashes. Only 38 cities employed the contract system, while 59 cities left the responsibility to private parties.[24] As figure 1 indicates, however, larger cities (those with populations over 30,000) were more likely to have a formal, citywide system of collection than were smaller cities (those with populations under 30,000). Furthermore, smaller cities were more likely to favor private collection than were larger cities. These findings tend to reinforce the contention that urban growth and expansion had a major impact on the extension of services.[25]

There was a much more significant trend toward municipal responsibility for street cleaning than there was for refuse collection and disposal. Data from the 1880 census indicate that 140 (or 70 percent) of the 199 cities surveyed had municipal street-cleaning services.[26] That is largely attributable to the accessibility of streets to all citizens. These "arteries" (a popu-

[22] Chicago, Department of Health, *Annual Report* (1892), pp. 15–16; *Engineering News* 33 (3 January 1895): 1. See also George E. Hooker, "Cleaning Streets by Contract—A Sidelight from Chicago," *Review of Reviews* 15 (March 1897): 437–41.

[23] City of Newton, Mass., *Report of the Board of Health upon the Sanitary Disposition of Garbage and Other Municipal Waste, and the Reorganization of the Department* (1895), pp. 3–4.

[24] U.S. Department of the Interior, Census Office, *Report on the Social Statistics of Cities, Tenth Census, 1880*, comp. George E. Waring, Jr.

[25] Good examples of this phenomenon can be found in Sam Bass Warner, Jr., *Streetcar Suburbs: The Process of Growth in Boston, 1870–1900*.

[26] U.S. Department of the Interior, Census Office, *Report on the Social Statistics of Cities, Tenth Census, 1880*.

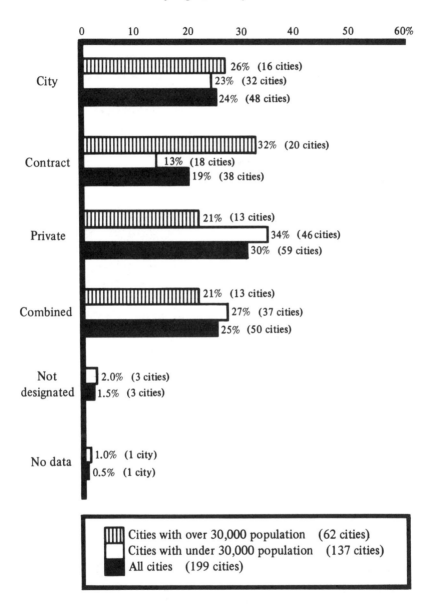

FIG. 1. Responsibility for collection of garbage and ashes, percentage and number of cities, 1880. *Source*: U.S. Department of the Interior, Census Office, *Report on the Social Statistics of Cities, Tenth Census, 1880*, compiled by George E. Waring, Jr. (Washington, D.C., 1886).

lar contemporary term for streets as parts of the "urban organism"), which allowed human beings, animals, and goods to move from one place to another, had to be free of obstacles. The question of ultimate responsibility for street cleaning was more easily determined because the streets had no clear territorial limits and thus transcended individual responsibility. Also, during the late nineteenth century, streets were undergoing a major change in use. As historian Clay McShane noted, streets traditionally served "vital neighborhood and family social uses. Pushcart vendors brought their wares to urban housewives, whose mobility was limited by the slow, expansive transportation system of the era. Surviving lithographs and photos show great herds of children playing in the streets, generally the only available open spaces." By 1900, however, streets were designed to cope with the heavy volume of traffic or provide a means for removing the vast quantities of horse manure.[27] Efforts to pave more street with materials which could withstand the burdens of heavy transportation use may have permitted city bureaucrats to lose sight of the important original purpose of city streets but brought attention to the need for an effective city street-cleaning program.

In the growing urban bureaucracies after midcentury environmental sanitation initially became the province of municipal health authorities.[28] The 1880 census reveals that at least 94 percent of the cities surveyed had a board of health, a health commission, or a health officer. Of these authorities 46 percent had some direct control over the collection and disposal of refuse.[29] As table 2 shows, larger cities were more likely to give their health boards and commissions direct control over these services.

There is no evidence, however, that late-nineteenth-century health boards were capable of effective reform of collection and disposal practices. For instance, few sanitary authorities in 1880 operated without overt political interference. Physicians and sanitarians dominated few boards of health. In fact, some boards had no physicians as members. Without the communities' best-qualified public-health experts in positions of immedi-

[27] Clay McShane, "Transforming the Use of Urban Space: A Look at the Revolution in Street Pavements, 1880–1924," *Journal of Urban History* 5 (May 1979): 283.

[28] Cassedy, *Charles V. Chapin and the Public Health Movement*, pp. 44–45; Wilson G. Smillie, *Public Health: Its Promise for the Future*, pp. 351–52; William F. Morse, "Methods of Collection and Disposal of Waste and Garbage by Cremation" (Paper read at the Sanitary Convention of State and Local Boards of Health of Pennsylvania, Erie, Pa., 1892), p. 3.

[29] See U.S. Department of the Interior, Census Office, *Report on the Social Statistics of Cities, Tenth Census, 1880*.

TABLE 2
Responsibility for Refuse Collection and Disposal, 1880

Cities with Sanitary Authorities, by Population (Number of Cities)	Percentage		
	Full or Some Authority	Little or No Authority	No Data
Under 30,000 (127)	38	61	1
30,000–99,999 (40)	55	45	
Over 100,000 (20)	75	25	

SOURCE: U.S. Department of the Interior, Census Office, *Report on the Social Statistics of Cities, Tenth Census, 1880*, compiled by George E. Waring, Jr. (Washington, D.C.), 1886.

ate authority over health matters, considerations other than health could influence the boards' actions. Also, with the limited funds which most cities provided to their boards—most boards lacked operating budgets or salaried employees and received funds only in times of epidemics or other emergencies—few could establish long-range programs for the protection of health or for environmental sanitation. The boards of health were susceptible to the whims of the city councils or state legislatures which dominated them. Most often their effectiveness was limited to cataclysmic events and epidemics, with meager resources for anything else.

Public-health officers and sanitarians, nevertheless, dominated the thinking about collection and disposal practices in the United States during the 1880s and 1890s. Considered as a health problem, refuse could no longer be regarded simply as a nuisance. In 1887, citing the unsatisfactory state of collection and disposal methods throughout the nation, the APHA appointed a Committee on Garbage Disposal, headed by the eminent sanitarian Dr. S. S. Kilvington. The major task of the committee was to determine the extent of the refuse problem in the United States. The committee spent ten years at its assignment, gathering statistics from every major city in the country, examining European methods, and analyzing American practices.[31] Efforts such as these demonstrated the degree to which the health question infused refuse reform with a sense of direction and purpose.

[30] Ibid. See also Smillie, *Public Health*, p. 352.
[31] American Public Health Association, *A Half Century of Public Health*, ed. Mazyck P. Ravenel, pp.190–91; Hering and Greeley, *Collection and Disposal of Municipal Refuse*, p. 2.

Warnings by sanitarians and public-health officers about the potential health hazards associated with accumulating waste soon began raising public consciousness about the need for better sanitation. Concern about the waste problem was reflected in most of the newspapers, popular magazines, and technical and professional journals of the day. Publications as diverse as *Harper's Weekly*, *Munsey's Magazine*, *Scientific American*, and *Engineering News* featured articles deploring the "garbage problem" or "filthy streets." A writer for *Harper's Weekly* asked: "What shall be done with the garbage? This is one of the great problems in the administration of modern cities."[32] A commentator in *Scientific American* stated: "The disposal of the refuse in cities, while it has been a problem in the sanitation of our larger towns, is yet to be solved. There is probably not a city of any size in the United States where the disposal of wastes is satisfactory or conducted in such a manner as to meet the demands of cleanliness and hygiene."[33]

Citizens' neglect of sanitation matters was a popular theme in the newspapers and magazines. One writer asserted: "The average citizen, accustomed to endure nuisances as a humpback carries his deformity, saunters along sublimely indifferent to foul smells, obstructed sidewalks, etc."[34] John S. Billings, however, founder of the Army Medical Library and *Index Medicus*, believed that public apathy was making way for civic awareness. "Quite recently," he stated, "there seems to be a growing interest in sanitary matters in our cities, and people are asking whether the city is in good condition to resist the introduction or spread of cholera, and to what extent it is worth while to expend money to secure pure water, clean streets, odorless sewers, etc."[35]

Increasingly during the 1880s and 1890s protest against inadequate refuse collection and disposal was becoming a primary function of many citizens' groups and civic organizations. They too relied heavily on the health argument to justify their dissent. In 1881, the Citizens' Committee of Twenty-one of New York City circulated petitions, held mass meetings, and met

[32] G. W. Hosmer, "The Garbage Problem," *Harper's Weekly* 38 (11 August 1894): 750.

[33] "Disposal of Refuse in American Cities," p. 136. For an extensive listing of contemporary periodical articles dealing with the refuse problem, see Robert C. Brooks, *A Bibliography of Municipal Problems and City Conditions*.

[34] Ferris, "The Cleansing of Great Cities," p. 33.

[35] John S. Billings, "Municipal Sanitation: Defects in American Cities," *Forum* 15 (May 1893): 305.

with city officials to change the method of street cleaning, which the committee believed "was one better calculated to advance political interests than to secure cleanliness and health."[36] At about the same time, the Citizens' Association of Chicago was calling for similar changes. By 1893 organized protest against unsanitary conditions had multiplied greatly. The Municipal Order League of Chicago (primarily a women's organization) had formed in 1892, according to the Board of Heath, "to assist the civil authorities, not to theorize, publicly suggest impracticable and impossible socialisms." During the year the league distributed twenty thousand printed cards to be hung in kitchens throughout the city; the cards contained suggestions for the disposal of wastes and outlined local ordinances about refuse. Several "improvement associations" formed in neighborhoods throughout Chicago to promote civic responsibility with respect to waste disposal. The *Chicago Herald* sponsored a Public Improvement Bureau. Several times a week the *Herald* printed blank forms on which citizens were to write complaints. The forms were collected and forwarded to the appropriate city department.[37]

In the struggle for sanitation reform the Ladies' Health Protective Association of New York City (LHPA) was possibly the most influential civic group in the country. Organized in 1884, the association was the outgrowth of the efforts of fifteen women of the exclusive Beekman Hill area to force the removal of a large, stench-ridden manure pile from their neighborhood. Ultimately the LHPA undertook several projects, including school and slaughterhouse sanitation, street-cleaning reform, and improvement in refuse-disposal methods.[38] Although influenced by national trends in public health, the LHPA was a community organization without extensive medical or technical expertise—something that could be also said of most other civic groups. For that reason the LHPA often stated its protests in aesthetic rather than scientific or medical terms. As an organization dominated by

[36] New York City, Citizens' Committee of Twenty-one, *Statement and Report of the Citizens' Committee of Twenty-one Respecting the Efforts to Procure Reform in the System of Cleaning the Streets of the City of New York*.

[37] Citizens' Association of Chicago, *Annual Report* (1880), pp. 16–18; Chicago, Department of Health, *Annual Report* (1892), pp. 29–31. See also *Engineering News* 33 (3 January 1895): 1.

[38] Mary E. Trautmann, "Women's Health Protective Association," *Municipal Affairs* 2 (September 1898): 439–43; Duffy, *Public Health in New York City, 1866–1966*, pp. 124, 130, 132.

middle- and upper-middle-class women, who perceived their reform efforts as an extension of their roles as housewives and mothers, the LHPA
also couched its protests in domestic terms:

Even if dirt were not the unsanitary and dangerous thing we know that it is, its
unsightliness and repulsiveness are so great, that no other reason than the superior
beauty of cleanliness should be required to make the citizens of New York, through
their vested authorities, quite willing to appropriate whatever sum may be necessary, in order to give to themselves and to their wives and daughters, that outside
neatness, cleanliness and freshness, which are the natural complement and completion of inside order and daintiness, and which are to the feminine taste and perception, simply indispensable, not only to comfort but to self-respect.[39]

Probably because of, rather than in spite of, its layman's outlook about the
problem of waste, the LHPA put sanitation into terms which many citizens
and political leaders could understand and appreciate. The association's
successful efforts in lobbying for improved sanitary measures in New York
City largely grew out of its ability to popularize the health concerns of sanitarians and public-health officers. Similar groups in other cities followed
the lead of the LHPA.[40] The heightened awareness of sanitary problems in
the 1880s and 1890s ultimately led to criticism of the inadequate collection
and disposal practices of the time. The methods that cities relied on were
so primitive that the best one could expect was frequent removal of the
garbage and trash from the immediate range of human senses. In other
words, a philosophy of "out of sight, out of mind" prevailed. Much of the
refuse was simply removed from a location to create a nuisance or health
hazard in another. Disposal methods fell into two categories: indiscriminate discharging and utilitarian application. In the first category dumping
of refuse on open land or into water was the most common practice; the
second category included use of organic matter for fertilizer, animal feed,
road surfaces, and land fill (See fig. 2 to 4).

    Whatever the method of disposal, few precautions were taken to en-
sure that it was sanitary. Even utilitarian practices, which offered a means

[39] New York Ladies' Health Protective Association, *Memorial of the New York Ladies'
Health Protective Association To the Hon. Abram S. Hewitt on the Subject of Street-Cleaning*,
pp. 4–5. See also Suellen M. Hoy, " 'Municipal Housecleaning': The Role of Women in Improving Urban Sanitation Practices, 1880–1917," in Martin V. Melosi, ed., *Pollution and Reform in American Cities, 1870–1930*, pp. 173–98.

[40] See Philadelphia, Department of Public Works, Bureau of Street Cleaning, *Annual
Report* (1893), p. 58; Mrs. C. G. Wagner, "What Women Are Doing for Civic Cleanliness,"
Municipal Journal and Engineer 11 (July 1901): 35; Edith Parker Thomson, "What Women
Have Done for the Public Health," *Forum* 24 (September 1897): 46–55.

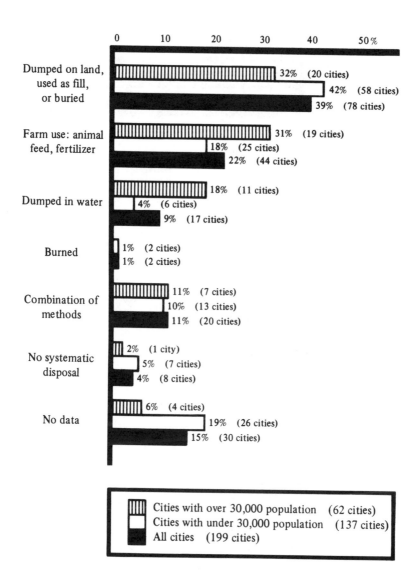

FIG. 2. Garbage disposal methods, percentage and number of cities, 1880. *Source*: U.S. Department of the Interior, Census Office, *Report on the Social Statistics of Cities, Tenth Census, 1880*, compiled by George E. Waring, Jr. (Washington, D.C., 1886).

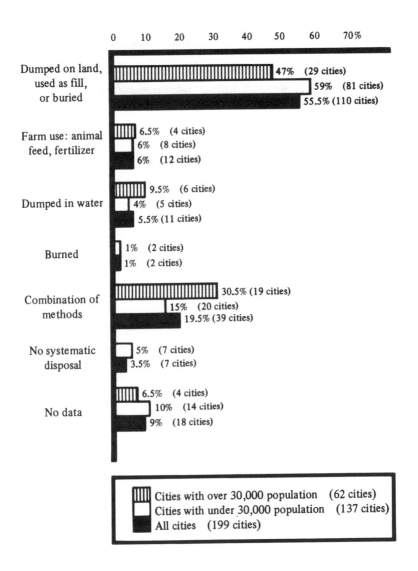

FIG. 3. Street sweeping disposal methods, percentage and number of cities, 1880. *Source*: U.S. Department of the Interior, Census Office, *Report on the Social Statistics of Cities, Tenth Census, 1880*, compiled by George E. Waring, Jr. (Washington, D.C., 1886).

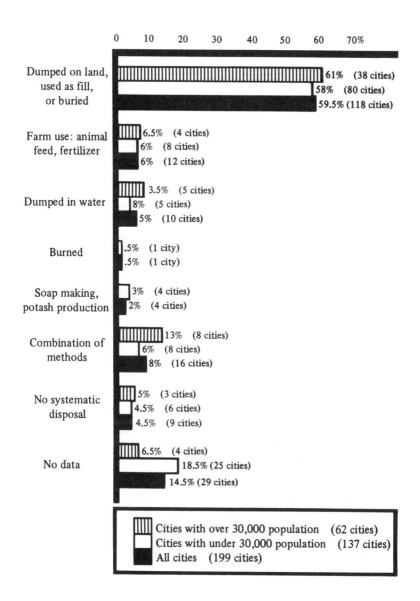

FIG. 4. Ash disposal methods, percentage and number of cities, 1880. *Source*: U.S. Department of the Interior, Census Office, *Report on the Social Statistics of Cities, Tenth Census, 1880*, compiled by George E. Waring, Jr. (Washington, D.C., 1886).

of solving the problem by recycling some wastes, frequently created new sanitation problems. Untreated organic material used for filling potholes in roads and other depressions created serious health hazards. Waste used for agricultural purposes—fertilizing or animal feed—often was handled without proper safeguards. The transfer of garbage from the city to the farms sometimes required an intermediary stop at a "swill yard" within the city limits, where the waste was unloaded for farmers to cart away. These swill yards were dangerous breeding grounds for disease and, like open dumps, emitted a revolting stench. The common practice of feeding garbage to swine and other animals also became questionable; studies indicated that the meat or products of animals fed on garbage might not be fit for human consumption. Investigations in the mid-1890s in New England revealed that cases of trichinosis among hogs fed with garbage increased form 3 to 17 percent over a three-year period and that the annual mortality from hog cholera increased alarmingly.[41] The major cause of the health problems was not the feeding of organic matter to animals but rather the unsophisticated manner in which refuse was transported and utilized.

Utilitarian methods of waste disposal theoretically offered cities the means of ridding themselves of unwanted materials while at the same time converting a liablity of urban life into an asset for the countryside. Unfortunately this expectation did not materialize in the nineteenth century. The quantity of refuse was so great that cities could not give it away, let alone sell it to farmers, as had been the earlier custom. The cost of transporting refuse from cities to countryside and the rapid decomposition of organic materials meant that only farms close to urban centers could use the wastes for feed or fertilizer. Rapid urban growth coupled with constriction of rural areas further complicated the situation.[42]

Since urban wastes were diverse as well as plentiful, no universally accepted methods of collection and disposal had developed. In addition to organic wastes—garbage, manure, human excrement, dead animals—there were also tons of coal and wood ashes, street sweepings, wastepaper, cans, old shoes, and other assorted rejectamenta. Some waste, such as

---

[41] City of Newton, Mass., *Report of the Board of Health*, (1895), p. 5; Philadelphia, Bureau of Health, *Annual Report* (1892), pp. 18–19; Chicago, Department of Public Works, *Annual Report* (1889), pp. 23–24; Detroit, Board of Health, *Annual Report* (1882), p. 115.

[42] See Joel A. Tarr, "From City to Farm: Urban Wastes and the American Farmer," *Agricultural History* 49 (October 1975): 598–612.

kitchen and restaurant garbage, had to be collected more frequently than rubbish. A scavenger could hardly employ the same method for collection of manure that he used for wastepaper or discarded clothing. Cities had to contend with very basic and often perplexing questions in disposing of their refuse. Should solid wastes be separated in the homes and business establishments for ease of disposal? Was some of the material salvageable or recyclable? Was disposal of separated or mixed refuse more economical? How could the city or a contractor best employ human labor in the collection and disposal of waste? What about mechanical devices? Were there sufficiently effective techniques for the disposal of the various kinds of waste? Indeed, the questions were as difficult to pose as to answer. Unfortunately, city officials had little success with either questions or answers throughout much of the nineteenth century.

If convenient utilitarian methods of disposal were unavailable, most cities ignored the more complex alternatives and resorted to dumping their refuse wherever space allowed. The open dump and the watercourses became the most expedient, but hardly the best, places for disposal. Before the turn of the century, however, many city officials were forced to confront the cost of expedience. For example, many cities, especially those not situated along waterways, dumped refuse on vacant lots or near the "least desirable" neighborhoods. Protests from the unfortunates who lived near the putrefying mounds often went unheard or were ignored. As the concentration of people in the inner cities became acute in the 1880s and 1890s, and as more dumps were created to meet the needs of the rapidly multiplying population, widespread outcries were heard, and these outcries could not easily be ignored. City officials were also faced with a new problem: rapidly multiplying commercial and residential building programs and high land values made it difficult to acquire new dumping sites. As the health officer of Washington, D.C., stated in his 1889 report:

Appropriate places for [refuse] are becoming scarcer year by year, and the question as to some other method of disposal . . . must soon confront us. Already the inhabitants in proximity to the public dumps are beginning to complain. . . . I can not urge too strongly upon the Commissioners the necessity for action in this direction. The waste that is taken from yards and dwelling places must be provided for, and that provision should not be longer delayed.[43]

[43] Washington, D.C., Health Department, *Report of Health Officer* (1889), p. 31. See also Boston, Board of Health, *Annual Report* (1883–84), p. 56; Baltimore, Department of Street Cleaning, *Annual Report* (1882), p. 11; *Annual Report* (1887), pp. 19–20.

By far the most pernicious method of disposal was the dumping of refuse into lakes, rivers, harbors, and even the open sea. The logic of such a method was painfully simple, as the Reverend Mr. Thompson noted about New Orleans's use of the Mississippi:

At 4 p.m. each day a tug picks up the scows, tows them two miles down the river below the city, where the garbage is dropped into the stream, and disappears into the devouring jaws of gar, pike, codfish and the other greedy denizens of the great stream, which attend in countless numbers at their daily dinner hour. What is spared by them is whirled away into the waters, and not a trace of any part of the offensive matters can be discovered four miles below.[44]

In 1886, New York City dumped 1,049,885 of its 1,301,180 cartloads of refuse into the ocean and for many years continued to rely on ocean dumping as a primary means of disposal. In Chicago the lack of "convenient and suitable" dumping grounds led the city to dispose of much of its waste in Lake Michigan, three miles from the mouth of the Chicago River.[45]

Such a disposal method had many repercussions. Cities which dumped their refuse in rivers had to contend with constant complaints from cities downstream. New York dumped so much of its waste into the Atlantic that the approaches to the harbor were often clogged, and the public and private beaches on the New Jersey shoreline looked like cesspools. It was not uncommon for swimmers to be nudged by mattresses and old shoes—which most certainly gave them a fright. Besides the obvious nuisances, untold damage was done to marine ecology in many waterways polluted with refuse. As one commentator lamented in an 1894 issue of *Harper's Weekly*:

All in all . . . dumping at sea is not a cheap method of garbage disposal. Even if it were cheap, however, it is not a commendable or even a permissible method of disposal. It has been adopted as a makeshift by New York as by many other seaport cities because it seemed easiest in the beginning, but it can nowhere be regarded as a finality.[46]

[44] Thompson, "Disposal of City Garbage at New Orleans," p. 546.

[45] New York City, Department of Street Cleaning, *Annual Report* (1886), p. 23; "City Refuse Disposal," *Engineering News* 28 (6 October 1892): 325; Chicago, Department of Public Works, *Annual Report* (1882), p. 25.

[46] Williams, "How New York Is Kept Partially Clean," p. 974. See also Hosmer, "The Garbage Problem," p. 711; New York State Assembly, Committee on the Affairs of Cities, *Report to the Assembly of the State of New York, April, 1880, as to the Present System of Street Cleaning in the City of New York, and the Means Whereby a More Efficient and Economical Method of Doing the Work May Be Secured*, p. 50; "The Disposal of Garbage and Other City Refuse," *Engineering News* 32 (26 July 1894): 72–73.

The crudeness of the disposal methods of the nineteenth century were finally becoming recognized—at least by a few—for what they were.

Street cleaning fared better than refuse removal in the nineteenth century, but its effectiveness varied widely from city to city. As historian Lawrence H. Larsen wrote, "Although Americans living in the nineteenth century boasted of many aspects of their growing urban mosaic, hardly any talked in glowing terms about the cleanliness of their streets."[47] Gone from most cities by 1880 were the herds of swine which had been used as inexpensive scavengers. The system which replaced them, however, hardly solved the problem of dirty streets. The 1880 census suggests that approximately 84 percent of the cities surveyed relied on hand sweeping to keep the streets clean.[48] This method could be effective if carefully maintained, but unfortunately many cities did not clean their streets regularly, except for the major business thoroughfares. Few cities even bothered to clean their streets in the winter. Although most cities had some sort of antilittering ordinance, citizens rarely obeyed them, and policemen rarely felt compelled to enforce them.[49] It was easy to blame the dirty streets on the most convenient scapegoats, as *Popular Science Monthly* did in 1891:

In those cities and parts of cities where the people of the laboring class and the poor are crowded in tenement-houses, and where a considerable part of the population is foreign-born and from countries where personal and public cleanliness have not been enforced by proper police regulations, it is no trifling task to secure cleanliness of the streets.[50]

To charges that their streets were not adequately cleaned, city officials responded by claiming that inadequate funding or physical problems associated with poor street pavement were responsible. The 1887 annual report of the Boston Board of Health asserted that the three major causes of inadequate street sanitation were poor paving, the continual digging up of streets for pipelaying, and an insufficient work force.[51] There was consid-

---

[47] Lawrence H. Larsen, "Nineteenth-Century Street Sanitation: A Study of Filth and Frustration," *Wisconsin Magazine of History* 52 (Spring 1969): 239–40.

[48] Statistics gleaned from U.S. Department of the Interior, Census Office, *Report on the Social Statistics of Cities, Tenth Census, 1880.*

[49] See "Street Department Notes," *Municipality and County* 1 (April 1895): 155; Boston, Street Department, *Annual Report* (1891), p. 128. See also U.S. Department of the Interior, Census Office, *Report on the Social Statistics of Cities, Tenth Census, 1880.*

[50] Clark, "Street-Cleaning in Large Cities, " p. 748.

[51] Boston, Board of Health, *Annual Report* (1887), p. 36.

erable substantiation for these claims. Street paving was primitive in the nineteenth century. Before the widespread use of asphalt, sweeping was difficult. In 1880 more than half of urban streets were unpaved (see table 3),[52] and as late as 1909 only one-third of city streets were asphalt.

Funds for street cleaning were inadequate. Street department budgets rarely kept up with the rapid growth of the industrial cities, and allocations for street cleaning had to compete with the costs of street construction and maintenance—both vital to urban growth. In forty major cities surveyed in the 1890 census, the average percentage of the street budget earmarked specifically for cleaning was 17.5 percent, with the rest of the budget going for construction and maintenance. The extremes, however, were great. Newark spent 60 percent of its street budget on cleaning, while Memphis spent slightly over 1 percent.[53]

As the number of streets multiplied, the meager street-cleaning force was spread over an ever-larger area. City officials had to choose between cleaning all the streets sporadically or concentrating on the main thoroughfares and ignoring the rest. With either choice the result was inadequate service. For example, as Boston began absorbing its suburbs, such as Brighton and West Roxbury, the street-cleaning force was inadequate to meet the new demands. The Boston Board of Health complained that the printed list of streets to be swept rapidly became obsolete "owing to the impossibility of covering the entire area laid out, and the work was largely done by general orders to work where the dirt was the greatest." During those times of the year when the main streets were relatively clean in the central city, the whole Boston street-cleaning crew was transferred to the suburbs for a quick cleaning. During the winter months the force was used primarily to collect ashes and neglected street cleaning almost entirely.[54]

Increases in the street-cleaning budget were no assurance of clean streets. The cost per capita for street cleaning varied widely across the country, with little or no correlation with the cleanliness of streets. One survey indicated that in the 1880s citizens of Buffalo, New York, paid on an average of 5 cents a year for street cleaning while New Yorkers paid 71 cents a year. Translated into cost of street cleaning per mile, people in Buf-

[52] McShane, "Transforming the Use of Urban Space," pp. 279–82.

[53] U.S. Department of the Interior, Census Office, *Report on the Social Statistics of Cities in the United States, Eleventh Census, 1890*, comp. John S. Billings, p. 18.

[54] Boston, Board of Health, *Annual Report* (1891), pp. 120–21.

TABLE 3

Comparison of Paved to Unpaved Streets and Alleys in Fifty of the Largest U.S. Cities, 1890

City	Total Length of Streets and Alleys (Miles)	Total Length of Paved Streets and Alleys (Miles)	Percentage of Paved Streets and Alleys
Albany, N.Y.	140	55	39.3
Allegheny, Pa.	138	73	52.9
Atlanta, Ga.	200	29	14.5
Baltimore, Md.	780	459	58.8
Boston, Mass.	408	408	100.0
Brooklyn, N.Y.	653	375	57.4
Buffalo, N.Y.	372	194	52.2
Cambridge, Mass.	79	24	30.4
Camden, N.J.	100	31	31.0
Chicago, Ill.	2,048	629	30.7
Cincinnati, Ohio	503	284	56.5
Cleveland, Ohio	462	69	14.9
Dayton, Ohio	325	49	15.1
Denver, Col.	756	0	0.0
Detroit, Mich.	614	160	26.1
Fall River, Mass.	106	3	2.8
Grand Rapids, Mich.	149	89	59.7
Indianapolis, Ind.	400	234	58.5
Jersey City, N.J.	165	52	31.5
Kansas City, Mo.	383	51	13.3
Los Angeles, Calif.	800	84	10.5
Louisville, Ky.	314	183	58.3
Lowell, Mass.	104	19	18.3
Memphis, Tenn.	90	35	38.9
Milwaukee, Wis.	419	249	59.4
Minneapolis, Minn.	1,025	27	2.6
Nashville, Tenn.	251	147	58.6
Newark, N.J.	186	48	25.8
New Haven, Conn.	140	32	22.9
New Orleans, La.	635	109	17.2
New York, N.Y.	575	358	62.3
Omaha, Nebr.	508	52	10.2
Paterson, N.J.	207	55	26.6
Philadelphia, Pa.	1,151	750	65.2

TABLE 3 (*Continued*)

City	Total Length of Streets and Alleys (Miles)	Total Length of Paved Streets and Alleys (Miles)	Percentage of Paved Streets and Alleys
Pittsburgh, Pa.	356	143	40.2
Portland, Oreg.	220	64	29.1
Providence, R.I.	168	122	72.6
Reading, Pa.	72	47	65.3
Richmond, Va.	106	69	65.1
Rochester, N.Y.	255	72	28.2
St. Louis, Mo.	1,061	422	39.8
St. Paul, Minn.	970	41	4.2
San Francisco, Calif.	342	192	56.1
Scranton, Pa.	125	7	5.6
Seattle, Wash.	65	9	13.8
Toledo, Ohio	438	60	13.7
Trenton, N.J.	100	7	7.0
Washington, D.C.	235	163	69.4
Wilmington, Del.	78	33	42.3
Worcester, Mass.	145	145	100.0

SOURCE: U.S. Department of the Interior, Census Office, *Report on the Social Statistics of Cities in the United States, Eleventh Census, 1890*, compiled by John S. Billings (Washington, D.C., 1895), pp. 58–62.

falo paid $34 a mile, and New Yorkers paid a staggering $1,870 a mile.[55] Graft and corruption played a large part in this disparity. In an 1895 article in *Harper's Weekly*, F. W. Hewes charged the New York municipal government under Tammany Hall domination with mishandling of Street Cleaning Department funds. In Hewes's survey no city spent one-fifth as much as New York, and the streets were still deplorable. Similar charges had been raised earlier with the same conclusion: the Street Cleaning Department was rife with corruption and manned by political appointees.[56]

[55] Chicago, Department of Public Works, *Annual Report* (1894), p. 11. See also "Cost of Street Cleaning in Various Cities," *Engineering News* 33 (11 April 1895): 247.

[56] F. W. Hewes, "Street Cleaning," *Harper's Weekly* 39 (9 March 1895): 233–34. See also *Engineering News* 23 (4 January 1890): 12–13; "Street Cleaning Statistics," *Municipality and County* 1 (April 1895): 153; Duffy, *A History of Public Health in New York City, 1866–1966*, pp. 51–69.

As city authorities began to recognize the inadequacies of collection and disposal methods, they turned to municipal or sanitary engineers for answers. At first municipal engineers offered as a solution the adaptation of British and Continental disposal technologies, giving considerably less attention to collection practices. Like sanitarians and civic leaders they considered refuse a health problem, but one which could be resolved through technical processes. As the field of sanitary engineering matured in the early twentieth century, faith in a technical solution to the refuse problem would give way to a more comprehensive approach.[57] In the meantime, American engineers marveled at the way many European countries had apparently solved their waste problems efficiently and "scientifically," especially through the use of fire as a "disinfectant." Burning waste at high temperatures seemed to be the perfect disposal method—no stench-ridden dumps, no pollution of streams and other watercourses, no unsanitary landfills. One doctor called cremation of garbage "a great sanitary device." Another physician, from Wheeling, West Virginia, stated that the health department of his city had experimented with incineration of wastes and concluded that "at last we have secured a means of entirely destroying these substances and their power to do evil."[58] In 1888, Dr. Kilvington told an audience attending the annual meeting of the APHA:

Everywhere interest in the question of cremation is awakening, and the present points to the future—a near future—in which every city, large or small, upon the American continent will consider the crematory a necessary part of its municipal outfit; forward to a time when our cities will be redeemed from the curse of accumulating waste, when the rivers will be unpolluted by the sewage which now converts them into common sewers, when the cess-vault and the garbage-pit and the manure heap and even the earth cemetery will be abandoned, when the age of filth-formation will be superseded by the era of filth-destruction, when fire will purify alike the refuse of the living and the remains of the dead—but also is it allotted to each one of us to help to bring in the coming of this sanitary consummation.[59]

The Europeans' technical expertise and leadership in the practice of

[57] See Stanley K. Schultz and Clay McShane, "To Engineer the Metropolis: Sewers, Sanitation, and City Planning in Late-Nineteenth-Century America," *Journal of American History* 65 (September 1978): 389–411.

[58] J. Berrien Lindsley, "On the Cremation of Garbage," *Journal of the American Medical Association* 11 (13 October 1888): 514; George Baird, "Destruction of Night-Soil and Garbage by Fire," American Public Health Association, *Public Health: Papers and Reports* 12 (1886): 120 (hereafter cited as APHA).

[59] S. S. Kilvington, "Garbage Furnaces and the Destruction of Organic Matter by Fire," in APHA, *Public Health: Papers and Reports* 14 (1889): 170.

cremation and other new sanitation techniques was predictable. London and other European cities had been grappling with the problem of waste long before the United States was founded, and, furthermore, they did not have land or water available for dumping. Out of necessity less primitive methods had to be invented. The first systematic cremation of refuse at the municipal level was tested in Nottingham, England, in 1874. In Manchester two years later Alfred Fryer built an improved "destructor" (Americans used the terms "garbage furnace," "cremator," and "incinerator" to describe their systems), which became the model for much subsequent development of the technology. Fryer's effort marked the beginning of large-scale implementation of incinerating devices throughout England and the rest of Europe. The success of the British method of disposal led to the construction of cremators and incinerators in the United States. In 1885, Lieutenant H. J. Reilly of the United States Army built the first American garbage furnace on Governor's Island, New York. In 1886–87 engineers installed the first municipal cremators in Wheeling, West Virginia; Allegheny, Pennsylvania; and Des Moines, Iowa.[60]

Municipal officials throughout the country quickly took note of these experiments, and orders for incinerators were brisk. The Engle Sanitary and Cremation Company of Des Moines was an early pioneer in the field. By 1894 it had installed incinerators in cities throughout the country, from Portland, Oregon, to Coney Island, New York, and from Milwaukee, Wisconsin, to Saint Augustine, Florida. They also constructed an incinerator for exhibition at the Chicago World's Fair and built several systems for cities in Latin America.[61] Regulated disposal by fire was hailed as a technological panacea, though some engineers and scientists cautioned against expecting too much from the cremation method, or from any other single method of disposal.[62] In 1890 the Boston Health Department acknowledged

[60]Walter Francis Goodrich, *Refuse Disposal and Power Production*, pp. 3, 9–10; Chamber of Commerce of the United States, Construction and Civic Development Department, *Refuse Disposal in American Cities*, p. 15; William F. Morse, "The Disposal of the City's Waste," *American City* 2 (May 1910): 23; W. Howard White, "European Garbage Removal and Sewage Disposal," *Transactions of the American Society of Civil Engineers* 15 (December 1886): 869.

[61]William Mayo Venable, *Garbage Crematories in America*, p. 88; "Garbage-cremation," *Science* 12 (7 December 1888): 265–66; William F. Morse, "The Utilization and Disposal of Municipal Waste," *Journal of the Franklin Institute* 158 (July 1904): 25–42.

[62]See "City Refuse Disposal," *Engineering News* 28 (6 October 1892): 325; George H. Rohé, "Recent Advances in Preventive Medicine," *Journal of the American Medical Association* 9 (2 July 1887): 5–6; Thomas H. Manly and Douglas H. Stewart, "The Economical and

that burning waste was the "best and safest" means of disposal but, because of the high cost of commercial cremators, recommended burning
waste in home kitchens.[63] That, of course, was a highly impractical solution for most urbanites. Yet there was a finality about burning waste that
was attractive to many city dwellers, no matter what the procedure or
method.

In addition to cremation, other technological breakthroughs from Europe were attracting attention as alternatives to primitive methods of disposal. In 1896 a company in Buffalo, New York, introduced the so-called
Vienna, or Merz, process for the extraction of oils and other by-products
through the compression of city garbage. The "reduction process," as it
became known, offered cities a method of disposal which provided recoverable and resalable materials from waste. Utilization of waste was an old
idea, but reduction was a new development. By-products could be sold
commercially as lubricants, perfume base, or fertilizer. Cities which adopted this process, such as Saint Louis, Detroit, Buffalo, and Milwaukee,
sought a means of recovering some of the costs of disposal through the sale
of the by-products. Thus reduction offered another dimension to disposal
methods. Some cities employed both reduction and incineration in an
effort to convert what waste they could into profitable by-products and
burn what was not commercially viable.[64]

Thus in the 1880s the refuse problem finally came to the attention of
American city dwellers. Sanitarians and public health officers gave compelling health reasons for concern about it, civic groups offered aesthetic
reasons for improvement in its collection and disposal, and engineers provided new technologies to eliminate it. Yet little real progress was made in

---

Efficient Disposal of the Household Garbage of New York," *Sanitarian* 34 (February 1895):
106; Chicago, Department of Health, *Annual Report* (1888), p. 11; New York City, Department of Street Cleaning, *Annual Report* (1887–88), pp 17–18.

[63] Boston, Health Department, *Annual Report* (1890), pp 76–77.

[64] See Douglas H. Stewart, "The Gold in Garbage," *Journal of the American Medical
Association* 25 (21 September 1895): 484–86; "The Merz System of Garbage Utilization in
Four American Cities," *Engineering News* 32 (1 November 1894): 354–59; "The Report of
the New York Garbage Commission," *Engineering News* 32 (29 November 1894): 452;
Charles V. Chapin, *Municipal Sanitation in the United States*, pp. 703–706. See also "The
New York Garbage Deodorizing Plant at Riker's Island," *Engineering News* 32 (2 August
1894): 90; "Garbage Utilization at Cincinnati and New Orleans," *Engineering News* 36 (8
November 1896): 236–38; "The Utilization of New York City Garbage," *Scientific American*
77 (14 August 1897): 102; Saint Louis, Department of Health, *Annual Report* (1895–96), pp.
31–32; Chicago, Department of Health, *Biennial Report* (1897–98), pp. 28–29.

bringing the refuse problem under control. Hope and expectation had yet to be translated into practice. Public awareness was crucial, but even more crucial was the willingness to commit municipal funds to provide adequate sanitary services for all sectors of the constantly expanding cities and workable systems of refuse management to contend with the ever-increasing volume and complex array of wastes. Furthermore, public awareness had to evolve into public responsibility; citizens had to become convinced that proper sanitation was a personal as well as a municipal obligation. With the appointment of Colonel George E. Waring, Jr., as street-cleaning commissioner of New York City in 1895, came the first practical, comprehensive system of refuse management in the United States.

2

The "Apostle of Cleanliness" and the Origins of Refuse Management

ON October 1, 1898, Spanish and American diplomats met in Paris to negotiate a treaty ending the four-month war between their countries. The brief but significant conflict toppled the anemic Spanish Empire in the Caribbean and the Pacific, leaving the Philippine Islands, Guam, Puerto Rico, and Cuba under American control. Fearing a yellow-fever epidemic in occupied Cuba, President William McKinley appointed the noted sanitary engineer Colonel George E. Waring, Jr., as special commissioner of the United States government to investigate health conditions in Havana as a preliminary step toward the establishment of a comprehensive system of sanitation there. While he was in Havana, Waring contracted yellow fever and died on October 29, soon after returning to New York City.[1]

The reaction to Waring's death was emotional and heartfelt. At Cooper Union on November 22 a memorial service was held at which several prominent civic and political leaders praised the public servant. As the *New York Times* reported:

More than 5,000 men, women, and children assembled within the walls of Cooper Union last night to pay tribute to the memory of Col. George E. Waring, Jr., Commissioner of Street Cleaning during the administration of ex-Mayor Strong. In eulogistic speeches the good deeds of the dead man were told and retold by those who had been his close friends during his life.[2]

Among those who took the podium were Jacob A. Riis, the famous muckraking journalist; Felix Adler, a leader in humanistic religion and founder

---

[1] George A. Soper, "George Edwin Waring," *Dictionary of American Biography* (New York: Charles Scribner's Sons, 1936), 19:456. See also *New York Times*, 28 October 1898, p. 1; 29 October 1898, p. 7; 30 October 1898, pp. 1, 18; 31 October 1898, p. 1.

[2] *New York Times*, 23 November 1898, p. 6.

of the Ethical Culture Society; Seth Low, president of Columbia University, labor reformer, advocate of Negro rights, mayor of Brooklyn from 1881 to 1885 (and to be mayor of New York City from 1901 to 1903); Carl Schurz, lawyer, newspaperman, reformer, political orator, and former Republican senator from Missouri; and William Strong, former mayor of New York City, under whom Waring had served as street-cleaning commissioner. The New York State Chamber of Commerce established a permanent memorial to Waring raised by public subscription. Interest on the $100,000 collected was paid to his widow and daughter during their lifetimes and then reverted to Columbia University to establish the Waring Memorial Fund for instruction in municipal affairs.[3]

Tributes in many of the popular periodicals and newspapers of the day extolled the contributions Waring had made to the promotion of sanitation. Albert Shaw, editor of *Review of Reviews*, an ardent Progressive and an admirer of Waring, called the fallen municipal engineer "the greatest apostle of cleanliness." In her eulogistic poem, which appeared in the *Century*, Helen Gray Cone described him as "Fever-Slayer, yet slain by the breath abhorred." The *Outlook* declared that Waring's work in New York City had been "epoch-making." Arturo Fernandis, president of Cuba, wrote to Mrs. Waring that her husband was "[a] notable figure among brilliant personalities who by his skill and knowledge was preeminent in the mighty American Union." One of the colonel's admirers, an embittered antiimperialist, reckoned that Waring was a victim of American expansionism. "Waring was sent to Cuba," he declared, "on an errand as foolish as most of the 'expansionist' policy. . . . If we knew the things which make for our peace and prosperity, we should regard the life of a man like Waring as of more value to the American people than the whole island of Cuba and all that it contains."[4]

Sudden death has a way of making martyrs out of public figures. Certainly the testimony of Waring's friends and admirers exaggerated the ac-

[3] Soper, "George Edwin Waring," p. 456; Albert Shaw, *Life of Col. Geo. E. Waring, Jr.: The Greatest Apostle of Cleanliness*; Richard W. G. Welling, Miscellaneous Papers, New York Public Library, Manuscript Division; *Newport News*, 23, 28, November 1898; *New York Times*, 23 November 1898, p. 6; 24 November 1898, p. 7.

[4] Shaw, *Life of Col. Geo. E. Waring, Jr.*; Helen Gray Cone, "Waring," *Century Illustrated Monthly Magazine* 59 (February 1900): 547; "George E. Waring," *Outlook* 60 (5 November 1898): 564–65; *Newport News*, 22 November 1898; 25 November 1898; "Colonel Waring," *Nation* 67 (3 November 1898): 326–27. See also William Potts, "George Edwin Waring, Jr.," *Charities Review* 8 (1898): 461–68; W. P. Gerhard, "A Half Century of Sanitation," pt. 2, *American Architect and Building News* 63 (4 March 1899): 67.

complishments of the man. Yet there was something about his career as sanitary engineer, agriculturalist, popular writer, and public official which made his death a public as well as a personal loss. Despite his widely publicized flamboyance, his public posturing and theatrics, his drive for personal recognition and material wealth, Waring was a pioneer in the field of sanitary engineering, an important urban environmental reformer, and the father of modern refuse management. His brief stint as street-cleaning commissioner of New York from 1895 to 1898 formed a bridge between the primitive collection and disposal practices of the nineteenth century and the increasingly sophisticated methods of the twentieth century.

Waring's career spanned the second half of the nineteenth century, a time of radical changes in the nation. In keeping with the times, as the United States was transforming itself from a rural, agrarian society into an urban, industrial one, he shifted his career from farming to municipal engineering. He was, therefore, a transitional figure with one foot in the past and one in the future.

Born in Poundridge, New York, on July 4, 1833, Waring spent much of his boyhood in nearby Stamford, Connecticut. He had a typical middle-class upbringing; his father was a manufacturer of stoves and agricultural implements in Stamford. He was educated in both public and private schools in the 1840s, and after graduation from Bartlett's School, in Poughkeepsie, New York, he spent a year in the hardware business and about two years managing a rural gristmill. In 1853, Waring became a student of the renowned agricultural scientist James J. Mapes, who conducted many experiments in farming techniques and edited the *Working Farmer*. Through Mapes's guidance young Waring launched on a career in scientific agriculture, which provided him with extensive practical training in several areas, including drainage engineering, and brought him into contact with influential people in rural New York and New England. He lectured throughout Maine and Vermont on scientific-farming techniques during the winters of 1853 to 1855. In 1855 he became manager of Horace Greeley's farm near Chappaqua, New York. He held that position for two years and then accepted a similar position on Frederick Law Olmsted's farm on Staten Island in 1857.[5]

Waring had published his first book, *The Elements of Agriculture*, in

---

[5] *National Cyclopedia of American Biography* (New York: James T. White & Co., 1929), 6:157; *New York Times*, 30 October 1898, p. 2; Neil FitzSimons, "Pollution Fighter: George Waring" (manuscript), p. 2.

1854. In it he had lauded the virtues of scientific methods of agriculture, encouraging farmers to employ modern "book methods" to increase crop yields, preserve soil fertility, and utilize manure properly. The book stressed the idea that human beings could harness nature for their own uses: "[The practical farmer] knows nothing of the first principles of farming, and is successful by the 'indulgence' of nature, not because he understands her, and is able to make the most of her assistance." Waring's assertion that human beings could play a significant role in improving the physical environment grew out of his belief that scientific methods could help control a malevolent nature.[6]

Waring's association with the noted landscape architect Frederick Law Olmsted also helped shape his environmentalism and proved to be a significant turning point in his career as an engineer. Accoring to Olmsted's biographer Laura Wood Roper, in initiating the rural-park movement in the United States, Olmstead had tried "to humanize the physical environment of the cities and to secure precious scenic regions for the use and enjoyment of all the people."[7] When he set about constructing Central Park in the late 1850s, he looked to his personal friend and employee George Waring to help with the project. In August, 1857, he appointed Waring to the post of drainage engineer and charged him with responsibility for most of the agricultural work in the park. Waring received such high praise for his efforts that he obtained several other urban assignments and soon abandoned most of his farming activities. His friendship with Olmsted and their professional association not only influenced Waring's new career orientation but also made him more sensitive to the need for his engineering skills in improving living conditions in the city. Several years after Central Park was completed, when Waring was street-cleaning commissioner of New York City, he publicly expressed gratitude to Olmsted for his influence upon his career.[8]

The Civil War temporarily halted Waring's promising engineering career. In May, 1861, he was commissioned a major in the Garibaldi Guards (the Thirty-ninth New York Volunteers), who acquired the nickname "Organ Grinders" because of their red blouses and Bersagliere hats. Waring served briefly with the Army of the Potomac at the First Battle of Bull Run

[6] George E. Waring, Jr., *The Elements of Agriculture*, pp. 279–85. See also Martin V. Melosi, *Pragmatic Environmentalist: Sanitary Engineer George E. Waring, Jr.*, p. 6.

[7] Laura Wood Roper, *FLO: A Biography of Frederick Law Olmsted*, p. xiv.

[8] Ibid., pp. xiii–xiv, 139, 148, 462. See also Soper, "George Edwin Waring," p. 456; Albert Fein, *Frederick Law Olmsted and the American Environmental Tradition*, pp. 28–29.

and then was sent to Saint Louis to recruit troops for General John C. Frémont. He organized a battalion of cavalry, the Frémont Hussars, who were
deployed against guerrillas striking in Missouri during the summer of 1861.
In January, 1862, the Hussars were consolidated with other units to form
the Fourth Missouri Cavalry, at which time Waring was commissioned a
colonel. He served with the Fourth Missouri until 1864, primarily in the
southwestern part of the state.[9]

Waring's appreciation for military principles, decorum, and discipline
never deserted him, nor did the title "Colonel," which he bore until his
death. Like many other young men who survived the war, he looked back
on his military experience with nostalgia tinged with bravado. Several
years after the war he said:

It is a pleasant thing to be a colonel of cavalry in active field service. There are
circumstances of authority and responsibility that fan the latent spark of barbarism
which, however dull, glows in all our breasts, and which generations of republican
civilization have been powerless to quench. We may not have confessed it even to
ourselves; but on looking back to the years of the war, we must recognize many
things that patted our vanity greatly on the back,—things so different from all the
dull routine of equality and fraternity of home, that those four years seem to belong
to a dream-land, over which the haze of the life before them and of the life after
them draws a misty veil.[10]

A sense of duty, authority, and discipline remained with him after the war.
As he stated in the *Outlook* in 1898: "The most complete and lasting happi-
ness of which we are capable comes from a sense of duty done."[11] Certainly much of his pomposity and arrogance was an outgrowth nurtured by
the military bearing he cultivated during the Civil War, but so was his faith
in his organizational ability and administrative skills, which served him
well in his later career.

After being mustered out of the service in 1865, Waring set out to
build a successful business career. Some abysmal failures in oil and coal
ventures sent him back to scientific agriculture. In 1867 he assumed the
management of Ogden Farm near Newport, Rhode Island, a position he
held for ten years. He plunged vigorously into his work and became particularly interested in husbandry and horticulture. In 1868 he organized the

---

[9] "The Military Element in Colonel Waring's Career," *Century Illustrated Monthly
Magazine* 59 (February 1900): 544–47; Soper, "George Edwin Waring," p. 456; Roper,
FLO, p. 162.

[10] George E. Waring, Jr., *Whip and Spur*, pp. 67–68.

[11] George E. Waring, Jr., "Education at West Point," *Outlook* 59 (6 August 1898): 825.

American Jersey Cattle Club and edited the *Herd Book*; two years later he introduced the trophy tomato to horticulturalists. One commentator observed: "[The tomato] was practically unknown as a table luxury a quarter of a century ago. Its usefulness began with the production of the variety called the trophy. And the trophy tomato was one of Colonel Waring's contributions to agriculture and to modern luxury of life."[12]

In the late 1860s and early 1870s, Waring's interest in agriculture faded once again, and he gave more attention to engineering problems such as drainage and sewerage. He gave up all his gardening operations in 1872, and by 1877 he had abandoned farming entirely. His book *Draining for Profit and Draining for Health* appeared in 1867. A practical guide to the construction of drainage systems, it was the first of several books and articles that he wrote on the subject during the 1870s and 1880s. In the 1870s he began accepting commissions to build drainage and sewerage systems on the East Coast. He constructed sewer systems for Ogdenburg, New York, in 1871; for Saratoga Springs, New York, in 1874; and for Lenox, Massachusetts, in 1875–76. At Lenox, Waring built the first "separate system" in the United States.[13] The separate system, also called the "Waring system," channeled rainwater and raw sewage into different pipes for ease of disposal. Although it was a source of much controversy in the engineering community, the separate system brought the colonel to the forefront of the nation's sewerage designers.[14]

Waring's design and construction of a separate system in Memphis, Tennessee, brought him widespread attention but also embroiled him in

[12] *Newport News*, 6 December 1898. See also *National Cyclopedia of American Biography*, 6:157.

[13] *National Cyclopedia of American Biography*, 6:157; Waring, *Sewerage and Land-Drainage*, p. 108. Additional works on drainage and sewerage written by Waring in the 1870s and 1880s include *The Sanitary Condition of City and Country Dwelling Houses*; "House-Drainage and Sewerage" (Paper read at the Philadelphia Social Science Association, 1878); "The Draining of a Village," *Harper's Magazine* 59 (June 1879): 132–35; "Recent Modifications in Sanitary Drainage," *Atlantic Monthly* 44 (July 1879): 56–62; "The Sewering and Draining of Cities" (Paper read at the American Public Health Association, Nashville, Tenn., 1879); "Suggestions for the Sanitary Drainage of Washington City," *Smithsonian Miscellaneous Collections* 26 (1880): 1–23; "Storm-water in Town Sewerage" (Paper read at the American Public Health Association, New Orleans, La., 1881); "Sanitary Drainage," *North American Review* 137 (July 1883): 57–67; *How to Drain a House*; *The Disposal of Sewage, and the Protection of Streams Used as Sources of Water Supply*.

[14] For the fullest treatment of the separate system and Waring's association with it, see Joel A. Tarr, "The Separate vs. Combined Sewer Problem: A Case Study in Urban Technology Design Choice," *Journal of Urban History* 5 (May 1979): 308–39.

one of the greatest controversies of his professional career. For years Memphis had suffered from inadequate sewerage and had been decimated by yellow-fever epidemics. In 1879, Waring was appointed to a special commission of the National Board of Health charged with examining conditions in the city. He learned that in two short years yellow fever had claimed approximately five thousand victims and that in the resulting panic two-thirds of the city's 40,000 residents had fled. After considering several plans for a sewerage system for Memphis, the commission awarded the contract to Waring over the opposition of several civil engineers. The project was carried out in 1880. Many contemporaries lauded the new system, claiming that it was responsible for saving the city from ruin. Civic leaders from other urban areas, impressed by the favorable publicity which the Memphis system received, sought out the colonel to have him build separate systems for their cities.[15]

Waring and his separate system were not without their detractors. Some engineers preferred the combined system, which employed a single large pipe for carrying rainwater and sewage to its final destination. An investigation of European sewerage systems, conducted for the APHA in 1880 by the noted sanitary engineer Rudolph Hering, indicated that both systems were equally sanitary but that the combined system was cheaper for densely populated cities while the separate system was cheaper for less heavily populated cities. The debate raged on as engineers defended their favorite methods. Waring held the American rights to the separate system, and some charged him with harboring crass financial interest in promoting it rather than having a genuine commitment to it as the most sanitary disposal method. "The Memphis system," one critic stated, "was the most conspicuous [of the various separate systems], although a comparative failure, a fact which the people of the city naturally suppressed for business reasons for many years."[16] Although they were overstated, charges

[15] George E. Waring, Jr., "The Memphis System of Memphis and Elsewhere" (Paper read at the American Public Health Association, Mexico City, 1893); Waring, "The Sewering and Draining of Cities"; Soper, "George Edwin Waring," p. 456; William Henry Corfield, *The Treatment and Utilization of Sewage*, 3d ed., p. 199; Harold W. Babbitt, *Sewerage and Sewage Treatment*, p. 3; Detroit, Board of Health, *Annual Report* (1882), p. 115; Charles N. Glaab and A. Theodore Brown, *A History of Urban America*, pp. 165–66; Tarr, "The Separate vs. Combined Sewer Problem," pp. 315–18.

[16] Leonard Metcalf and Harrison P. Eddy, *Sewerage and Sewage Disposal*, pp. 11–12. See also James H. Cassedy, "The Flamboyant Colonel Waring: An Anti-Contagionist Holds the American Stage in the Age of Pasteur and Koch," *Bulletin of the History of Medicine* 36 (March–April 1962): 168–70.

that Waring gained financial advantage from his engineering accomplishments is not without justification. His promotion of the "earth closet" is a
good example. In the 1860s, Waring publicized the earth closet as a revolutionary innovation in household sanitation, even after the water closet had
proved to be more efficient and practical for American homes. He not only
tenaciously defended the device but also tried to induce his friends, even
Olmsted, to invest in it.[17]

Waring's commitment to his sanitary principles was not guided exclusively or even primarily by materialistic interests, however. His engineering
accomplishments and his writings demonstrate his growing commitment to
the positive implications of environmental sanitation. His service as a special government agent charged with compiling social statistics of cities for
the tenth United States census (1880) gave him broad insight into urban
problems throughout the country. His association with the ill-fated National Board of Health also gave him access to a cross section of public-
health officers, engineers, and sanitarians, as well as adding a national perspective to his views on health and sanitation.[18] His environmentalism
quickly moved beyond the small towns of New England and the Middle
Atlantic states to the major urban centers of the nation. By the mid-1890s
his reputation as a national leader in sanitary reform was widely accepted;
his list of publications on sewerage, drainage, and general sanitation multiplied rapidly. He also continued to ride the crest of popularity generated by
several travel accounts of jaunts to Europe and by guides on horsemanship
and bucolic narratives which he churned out in abundance.[19] By most measures, and despite personal and professional rivalries with other engineers,
Waring was a success.

The colonel had a unique opportunity to test his expertise in sanitation

[17] See George E. Waring, Jr., *Earth-Closets: How to Make Them and How to Use Them*;
Cassedy, "The Flamboyant Colonel Waring," p. 165; Roper, *FLO*, pp. 320, 324.

[18] See U.S. Department of the Interior, Census Office, *Report on the Social Statistics of
Cities, Tenth Census, 1880*; George E. Waring, Jr., "The National Board of Health," *Atlantic
Monthly* 44 (December 1879): 732–38. An interesting sidelight on Waring's work on the tenth
census is that he selected George Washington Cable, the Creole novelist, as an assistant on the
project. See Charles Philip Butcher, *George Washington Cable*, (New York: Twayne Publishers, 1962), pp. 60–63; Arlin Turner, *George W. Cable: A Biography* (Durham, N.C.:
Duke University Press, 1956), pp. 108–12.

[19] Waring's popular works include *Whip and Spur; A Farmer's Vacation* (Boston: J. R.
Osgood & Co., 1876); *The Bride of the Rhine* (Boston: J. R. Osgood and Co., 1878); *Tyrol
and the Skirt of the Alps* (New York: Harper and Brothers, 1879); *Ruby* (Boston: J. R. Osgood
and Co., 1883); *Vix* (Boston: J. R. Osgood and Co., 1883); *The Saddle-Horse* (New York:
Orange Judd Co., 1881).

as street-cleaning commissioner of one of the world's great cities. In 1894 the Committee of Seventy—leaders of the civic reform movement in New York City—successfully engineered the defeat of Tammany Hall in the mayoral race and elected their candidate, William L. Strong, who had been a bank president, corporate director, and successful dry-goods merchant. According to historian Justin Kaplan: "It was confidently expected that Strong would apply to the affairs of the city the business virtues by which he had amassed a personal fortune of about a million dollars. (It was at the counting table, the faith of the day ran, that philosopher-kings were to be trained.)"[20] Although politically naïve and lacking the experience of a seasoned veteran of the wards, Strong was honest and attempted to move municipal government beyond the personal rule of Tammany Boss Richard Croker. Strong failed to achieve many structural changes in city government, but he was able to enlist a few potent reformers, who brought some acclaim to what was otherwise a lackluster administration. Police Commissioner Theodore Roosevelt and Street-Cleaning Commissioner George Waring were the bright spots of the Strong administration (Gifford Pinchot, the noted conservationist, declined the post of park commissioner). Apparently Roosevelt had been offered the street-cleaning post first, but had declined in favor of the appointment as police commissioner, which proved to be a stepping-stone to the governorship of New York. With the endorsement of people such as Francis Kinnicutt, of the Street Cleaning Aid Society, Waring was offered the post of street-cleaning commissioner.[21] At the time Waring was assistant engineer for New Orleans. "I made it a condition of my acceptance," he later noted, "that I should be entirely exempt from interference and free of all political obligations. I would undertake to clean the streets if I could do it in my own unhampered way, and not otherwise."[22]

At first the New York press mocked the appointment. Waring was often photographed astride his well-groomed steed, sporting his expertly waxed handlebar mustache and dressed in riding togs, pith helmet, and riding boots. He gave the appearance of a parody of the military officer he had

[20] Justin Kaplan, *Lincoln Steffens: A Biography*, p. 73.

[21] John Duffy, *A History of Public Health in New York City, 1866–1966*, pp. 108–109; Roper, *FLO*, p. 462; Theodore Roosevelt, *Theodore Roosevelt: An Autobiography*, p. 168; Richard Skolnik, "George Edwin Waring, Jr.: A Model for Reformers," *New York Historical Society Quarterly* 52 (October 1968): 357.

[22] George E. Waring, Jr., "The Cleaning of the Streets of New York," *Harper's Weekly* 39 (29 October 1895): 1022.

been during the war. Those who were aware of his professional background, however, looked with great favor on the appointment. *Engineering News* noted that the appointment "insures the services in this important department of a man of marked executive capacity and one aggressive in methods and well posted in the sanitary engineering of cities."[23] As streets became cleaner and garbage was more efficiently disposed of, the initial criticism turned to lavish praise. The former cavalry officer, drainage engineer, and agriculturalist ultimately found his most appreciative audience in New York City.

In his tenure as street-cleaning commissioner, Waring applied everything he had learned about sanitation. He implemented a wide variety of reforms, many of which had been attempted piecemeal in the previous thirty or forty years. At the core of his views on sanitation was an adherence to Hippocrates' adage "Pure air, pure water, and a pure soil" and the belief that cleanliness was a gauge of civilization. "There is no surer index of the degree of civilization of a communtiy," he said, "than the manner in which it treats its organic wastes."[24] Waring's environmentalism, however, rested upon the filth theory of disease. Many of his writings emphasized various aspects of that flawed view of disease transmittal, expecially the dangers of "sewer gas," which he held responsible for many of the health problems of the day.[25] "This much decried and insidious sewer-gas," he exclaimed in 1880, "is probably entitled to most of the blame it receives for its own direct action, and to as much more from the fact that it so often acts as a vehicle for the germs, or causative particles of specific diseases."[26] Never an original thinker on matters of health and untrained in medicine, Waring accepted the prevailing wisdom of the health experts of his day. Since the contagionist theory and the implementaion of bacterio-

[23] *Engineering News* 33 (3 January 1895): 8. See also Martin V. Melosi, " 'Out of Sight, Out of Mind': The Environment and the Disposal of Municipal Refuse, 1860–1920," *Historian* 35 (August 1973): 626–27; "Hitch Your Wagon to a Star," *Garden and Forest* 9 (24 June 1896): 251–52.

[24] George E. Waring, Jr., *The Causation of Typhoid Fever*, p. 7; Waring, *Sewerage and Land-Drainage*, p. 21.

[25] "Sewer gas" was a term applied to the odoriferous gases emanating from decomposing matter.

[26] Waring, "Suggestions for the Sanitary Drainage of Washington City," p. 12. See also Waring, "Storm-water in Town Sewerage"; Waring, *How to Drain a House*, pp. iii–vi, 1–11, 69–71; Waring,"Sanitary Drainage," *North American Review* 137 (July 1883): 57–67; Waring, "Village Sanitary Work," *Scribner's Monthly* 14 (June 1887): 176–77; Cassedy, "The Flamboyant Colonel Waring," p. 166; Glaab and Brown, *A History of Urban America*, p. 165.

logical laboratories did not become widespread until after Waring's death, it is somewhat unfair to criticize him for not abandoning the anti-contagionist point of view. Had he lived beyond 1898, he might have become willing to discard the filth theory for the more sophisticated germ theory. In fact, some of the colonel's later writings indicate that he had begun to recognize the role of bacteria in causing infection and disease.[27]

Despite his advocacy of an outdated theory of disease, Waring instinctively recognized many of the potential dangers of unsanitary surroundings. In *Sewerage and Land-Drainage* he wrote: "While we know, thus far, relatively little of the exact causes of disease, our knowledge at least points out certain perfectly well-established truths. One of them is that man cannot live in an atmosphere that is tainted by exhalations from putrefying organic matter, without danger of being made sick—sick unto death."[28] He may have attributed too much to sanitary reform as a cure-all for disease, but his environmentalism was built on a relatively broad base which recognized that human beings deserved unpolluted surroundings for aesthetic as well as physical reasons and that citizens should not shirk their responsibility for preserving a livable environment. He asserted:

It has hitherto been—and, in fact, it still is—the practice of the world to consider its wastes satisfactorily disposed of when they are hidden from sight. In spite of an almost universal outcry about sewer-gas, filth diseases and infective germs, the great mass, even of those who join in the cry, pay little heed to defects in the conditions under which they are living so long as they are not reminded by their eyes or their noses that their offscourings are still lurking near them.[29]

In the long run Waring would be better known for his deeds than for his words. His reformist credentials were built on action rather than on medical or scientific expertise or discovery. Toward that end he had emphasized the need to muster human resources to solve sanitation problems. In his early writings he stressed the responsibility of the individual for improving household health conditions. He soon came to believe that programs of community action were essential for solving health problems beyond the home, and he advocated programs to educate not only the gen-

[27] Waring, "Partial Purification of Sewage," *Engineering News* 31 (4 January 1894): 15–16; George E. Waring, Jr., *Modern Methods of Sewage Disposal*, pp. 1–19, 30–33, 41–47, 54–57, 214–15, 239–43; Waring, *The Disposal of Sewage, and the Protection of Streams Used as Sources of Water Supply.*

[28] Waring, *Sewerage and Land-Drainage*, p. 22.

[29] Waring, "Out of Sight, Out of Mind," *Century Illustrated Monthly Magazine*, 47, n.s. 25 (April 1894): 939.

eral public but social and political leaders as well. He once observed, "Until we can convince the country physician that his most important obligation to his community lies in a supervision of the conditions under which it lives, it is hardly worthwhile to waste breath upon the average members of the community."[30] In Waring's mind community action had to be guided from the top by a social, political, and technical elite trained to solve health problems and responsible for encouraging citizens to do their part. His advocacy of elitist guidance was a further indication of his pragmatism. The simplest way to initiate change, he believed, was to inspire those in positions to effect those changes. Before taking control of the New York Street-Cleaning Department, Waring had organized several "village improvement associations." The purpose of such an association was to improve the appearance of the village, which should be "a wholesome, cleanly, tidy, simple modest collection of country homes, with all of its parts and appliances adapted to the pleasantest and most satisfactory living of its people."[31] These associations were the archetypes of his civic-involvement programs in New York City. Throughout his career the marshaling of people to solve problems was at least as important to Waring as technological innovation—a view his fellow engineers rarely shared.

As street-cleaning commissioner, Waring did more than simply adapt village programs to the conditions of the big city. In 1881, in a long two-part article in *Scribner's Monthly* entitled "The Sanitary Condition of New York," the colonel demonstrated his understanding of the complexities of large cities. He analyzed the causes of New York's sanitary problems and proposed some remedies. He suggested that the city had some "remarkable natural advantages," such as its location near the sea, its natural drainage, and its prevailing winds, and he concluded that the "causes of unhealthfulness" were "removable." Always the pragmatist, he knew that "the city cannot be torn down, and its sewers and drains dug up, and the whole work begun 'de novo.'" Instead, Waring suggested, the city should make the best possible use of the existing drains, pave the streets adequately for proper drainage, implement an effective street-cleaning program, discharge waste more efficiently, conserve the water supply, and institute

[30]George E. Waring, Jr., "The Sanitary Condition of City and Country Dwelling Houses" (Paper read at the American Public Health Association, Boston, Mass., 1876), pp. 5–21.

[31]George E. Waring, Jr., *Village Improvements and Farm Villages*, p. 17. See also George E. Waring, Jr., "Village Improvement Associations," *Scribner's Monthly* 14 (May 1877): 97–98.

household sanitation programs. Although Waring tended to oversimplify the physical condition of the city, he nonetheless grasped the totality of its sanitation needs and offered realistic solutions to many of the problems. Indeed, many of the solutions he suggested in 1880 would become part of his reform program in 1895.[32]

From his first day on the job as street-cleaning commissioner, Waring practiced the art of the possible. He recognized that his immediate task was to gain control of a department which had been little more than a source of patronage for Tammany Hall. "[The department] was hardly an organization," he stated. "There was no spirit in it; few of its members felt secure in their positions; no sweeper who was not an unusually powerful political worker knew at what moment the politician who had got him his place would have him turned out to make room for another." Waring vowed to put "a man instead of a voter" behind each broom and to expel the political cronies who would not accept his leadership. Claiming not to have any specific grudge against those who supported Tammany, he retained almost half of the current employees. It was reported that a superintendent in charge of snow removal hired during the previous administration was summoned to the new commissioner's office. The colonel told the man that he had been accused of being a "rank Tammany man." "Whenever you want my resignation, it is at your service," the indignant man replied. "Don't be quite so fast," Waring said. "Let me hear your version of the case." The superintendent spoke up: "Do you know what a Tammany man is? It is a man who votes for his job. I have been a Tammany man, and a faithful one. I have worked for the organization; I have paid regular contributions to it. But I am a Waring man now." Detecting a smile on the colonel's face, he added: "Don't misunderstand me. If Tammany comes into power again, I shall be a Tammany man again." Impressed by the man's candor, Waring kept him on.[33]

Instances of Waring's benign treatment of Tammany men did not con-

[32] Waring, "The Sanitary Condition of New York," pt. 1, *Scribner's Monthly* 22 (May 1881): 64–75; pt. 2, *Scribner's Monthly* 22 (June 1881): 179–89.

[33] George E. Waring, Jr., *Street Cleaning and the Disposal of a City's Wastes*, pp. 15–18. See also George E. Waring, Jr., "The Cleaning of a Great City," *McClure's Magazine* 9 (September 1897): 911–15; E. Burgoyne Baker, "The Refuse of a Great City," *Munsey's Magazine* 23 (April 1900): 84; Skolnik, "George Edwin Waring, Jr.," pp. 359–60. For more detailed descriptions of Waring's sometimes unusual political views, see George E. Waring, Jr., "Government by Party," *North American Review* 163 (November 1896): 587–94; George E. Waring, Jr., "The Drink Problem in New York City Politics," *Outlook* 60 (15 October 1898): 436–40.

vince the political machine that the new commissioner posed little threat to them. Quite the contrary. As a major figure in Mayor Strong's reform government Waring was a constant target for Tammany attacks. In April, 1895, critics charged the colonel with a conflict of interest. Apparently his engineering firm, Waring, Chapman, and Farquar, had connections with the Sanitary Security Company, which inspected and certified houses for compliance with municipal sanitation ordinances. Waring was cleared of that charge. On several other occasions Tammany-connected individuals accused him of increasing the cost of administering the department without apparent increase in benefit to the community. Waring dealt with this and other accusations with little difficulty. In 1897, however, he brought charges of malicious libel against Boss Richard Croker. The source of the alleged libel was a campaign document printed in the *New York Morning Telegraph* accusing Waring of inefficiency, use of public property for private purposes, gross extravagance in public office, and speculation with municipal funds.[34] The stormy relationship between Waring and the machine lasted until 1898, when Tammany successfully turned out Strong's reform administration and the colonel lost his job.[35]

Waring's eventual reorganization of the Street-Cleaning Department was well received by all but those intimately tied to the machine. Given his penchant for military discipline and his faith in engineering expertise, it is not surprising that he selected graduates from technical schools or men with military backgrounds for supervisory positions in the newly structured department. "Knowing that organizations of men are good or bad according to the way in which they are handled," he said, "that 'a good colonel makes a good regiment,' I paid attention first to those at the top—to the colonels." In establishing his departmental elites, he chose young men from schools throughout the country. Several of his district supervisors and his master mechanic were young—the superintendent of final disposition was twenty-five years old.[36]

[34]*New York Times*, April 28, 1895, p. 19; October 31, 1897, p. 3; November 29, 1897, p. 6; "Col. Waring on Street Cleaning," *City Government* 4 (June 1898): 223; "Hon. William S. Andrews and Col. George E. Waring, Jr., on the Cost of Street Cleaning in New York City," *Municipal Record and Advertiser* 1 (26 June 1897): 15.

[35]Waring had a penchant for embroiling himself in political controversies. For instance, he created a furor when he declared that the Grand Army of the Republic was an aggregation of "pension bummers." See *New York Times*, April 23, 1895, p. 2.

[36]Waring, "The Cleaning of a Great City," p. 916; Waring, *Street Cleaning*, pp. 19–20; Waring, "Street Cleaning," *City Government* 3 (October 1897): 118.

The most far-reaching personnel changes came in the lower echelons, among the street cleaners. Waring believed that human labor was superior to machines for keeping the street clean and that an efficient work force was essential for effective operation of the department. He was also aware that the street cleaners were the most immediate contact between the department and the citizens. The public was certain to gauge the department's success by the work of the street crews. Using his natural talent for public relations, Waring sought not only to create an efficient force but also to give the street cleaners what would be called today a change of image. Few people saw much nobility in street-cleaning, especially since the workers were often drawn from some political roster or from members of the lowest economic station. Relying on his Civil War background, Waring organized his more than two thousand workers into a "military" unit. They were issued uniforms, were required to attend morning roll calls, and were subject to fines or dismissal for breaches of an elaborate set of rules ranging from absence without authorization to entering a saloon during working hours. In a speech delivered in 1897, Waring said:

One of the [department] rules that was made in reference to the men was, that no man should go into a liquor saloon in uniform or during working hours. (Applause) I was told recently by a gentleman who owns a block on East River, near one of our dumps, where 150 laborers go five or six times a day, that before I "ruined" him he had four liquor saloons rented there at $1,000 each; but now three of them are closed and the other paid only $300 rent.[37]

Waring's most dramatic attempt at image molding for his street cleaners was dressing them in white uniforms. What appeared at the time a foolish stunt proved to be a master stroke. According to municipal law the street crews must be uniformed so they could be distinguished as city workers. Under the previous administration they had worn overalls and brown jumpers and caps with the department's initials. Waring wanted something more eye-catching, something that would have a greater impact on the public. After considering various combinations, he recalled, "at last I suggested to my wife I would try white. My wife, who was a frank person, said that I was a fool!" Nevertheless, he tested the white uniforms in a single district and liked the results so well that he ordered all the sweepers to purchase white uniforms and caps (later cork helmets). As impractical as the uniforms seemed, the public quickly began identifying the workers

[37] Waring, "Street Cleaning," p. 118; Waring, *Street Cleaning*, pp. 19–43; Baker, "The Refuse of a Great City," p. 84.

with doctors, nurses, and others in the health professions. This was the image Waring was striving for.

His theatrics did not stop with the uniforms. Simultaneously he instituted city-wide parades to show off his legions of "White Wings," as they became known. In May, 1896, he staged the first of several annual parades. Leading the columns of about fourteen hundred sweepers and six hundred drivers (the latter dressed in brown) and twenty-three bands as they marched down Fifth Avenue was the colonel himself, astride his mount. Some sweepers carried their brooms, some pushed carts, and a few carried a banner proclaiming "Four Hundred And Twenty Miles of Streets Cleaned Every Day." The White Wings were first met with hisses and boos, but by the time the spectacle of two thousand workers and twenty-three bands passed the mayor in review, the applause of the crowd was uproarious. An editorial in *Garden and Forest* declared: "[The parade] was an inspiring sight when it was recalled through what a storm of distrust and abuse Colonel Waring had to make his way when he proposed to turn politics out of his department, and especially when he put his men in uniforms—and white uniforms at that." In this circus atmosphere Waring had brought his department to the attention of the public.[38]

Public approbation was not all that Waring sought in reorganizing and reorienting his work force. He also wanted to build an espirit de corps among his men that would result in more effective street cleaning. Of course, the uniforms, parades, and other military trappings could not by themselves produce the desired results. Waring the pragmatist knew that theatrics had limits; they would not get his men to perform their tasks, nor would rigid discipline without compensation. Consequently, he initiated some significant labor reforms in the department. First, he increased salaries to sixty dollars a month (two dollars a day)—almost double the pay of most unskilled laborers. He also instituted an eight-hour day. After studying the Belgian method of "arbitration and conciliation" and examining labor conditions among masons and bricklayers in the United States, he instituted a rather elaborate system of grievance committees and arbitration boards to hear complaints and pass judgment on disciplinary matters. Waring's reforms were not instituted out of altruism. He realized that his workers would respond better to material rewards than to moralizing, and also, being a man who could not tolerate opposition to his authority, he

[38] "Hitch Your Wagon to a Star," pp. 251–52; Waring, "Street Cleaning," p. 118; Waring, "The Cleaning of a Great City," p. 917; Potts, "George Edwin Waring, Jr.," p. 465.

wanted his workers beholden to him and not to aggressive labor leaders. Thus there were clear limits to his perception of labor reform. In the press he often exaggerated the dedication and loyalty of his employees, failing to mention the inevitable strikes and nagging grievances that rack every large, diverse organization. Despite his sometimes autocratic manner (or paternalism), Waring's efforts helped improve markedly the image of the street cleaner in the eyes of the public and, most important, helped make the streets much cleaner.[39]

Street cleaning in New York, as in every other large city, required constant attention. The streets were crudely constructed, littering was acceptable public behavior, only the main thoroughfares or streets in fashionable neighborhoods received regular service, and horse manure was everywhere. Under Waring's guidance the department undertook a systematic sweeping program that relied on the army of White Wings rather than technical innovations, such as machine sweepers. Although a number of cities had come to the conclusion that sweeping machines were the best way to cut costs and perform the cleaning task effectively, Waring continued to place his faith in hand sweeping.[40] He also objected to the clouds of dust which the rotary sweepers stirred up and to the way the machines obstructed the streets at night, when most of the sweeping had to be done.

Waring's street-sweeping program required almost 60 percent of his work force and accounted for 40 percent of his department's budget. New York had 433 miles of paved streets, on which 1,450 sweepers worked, which meant that each sweeper was theoretically responsible for about a

---

[39] George E. Waring, Jr., "The Labor Question in the Department of Street Cleaning of New York," *Municipal Affairs* 1 (September 1897): 515–24; Waring, *Street Cleaning*, pp. 24–43; Charles Zueblin, *American Municipal Progress*, rev. ed., p. 76; *New York Times*, July 28, 1895, p. 5; Skolnik, "George Edwin Waring, Jr.," pp. 360–61.

[40] Sometimes the faith in hand sweeping got a little out of control. In an effort to increase the number of sweepers in his force within his budgetary limits, Waring recommended this exploitative plan to the members at the Good Government Club: "Another suggestion I wish to make to you is that the city employ, instead of 2,500 men, 5,000 persons to clean the streets. The present force constitutes a sort of labor aristocracy, each member of which makes about $780 a year, probably the best pay for common labor in the world. I see no objection to this, excepting that the city has to pay it. Now I suggest that we employ 5,000 men, women, and boys to do this work. Good drivers and experienced sweepers would receive about their present pay while the 1,500 boys and the 1,000 women would make about 50 cents a day. There are plenty of foreign women who would be glad to work three or four hours in the early morning at sweeping, and plenty of boys who would do the cart work in the day time. I would employ only one person in every family so that 5,000 families would be helped, each receiving about $160 a year from the work." *New York Times*, June 8, 1895, p. 7.

third of a mile of street. In actual practice, however, each sweeper was responsible for an area of about seven miles. To organize the sweeping, the department set up a city-wide district system with inspectors and supervisors in each district. Under this system streets could be cleaned one to five times a day, depending on the need. Part of Waring's success was due to the vast resources available to him for the task, though he often initiated public debates with the city comptroller over appropriations and other budgetary matters. Nonetheless, his organizational skills in establishing his cleaning system offered a good example to other cities interested in initiating or upgrading street-cleaning systems.[41]

Snow clearing was an annoying street-cleaning problem for northern cities, but Waring's restructured department met the challenge. One ardent admirer declared:

Presently the snow came [in the winter of 1896]. Under former regimes the populace would have trampled through the slush for weary weeks. But long before the snow had ceased falling the streets were full of wagons and carts. . . .

Military orders had been given for each [worker] to report at his particular station as soon as the snow should reach two inches in depth. Presto! The invading army took possession of the streets, and in a space of time that seemed almost incredible the obstruction had been removed. The streets were dried out by the first sun, and it was necessary to go to Central Park to discover that the sleighing was excellent.[42]

The department applied the same degree of vigor to dealing with snow that it did to street sweeping. Waring often boasted that "[in] five consecutive *weeks* of 1895 more snow was removed, and for less money, than in all of the five *years* beginning with 1889." In one day Waring's crew removed 55,773 loads of snow. In an uncharacteristic response to the success of the snow-removal program, Waring stated:

I have been told by the president of the United States Rubber Company that this snow removal, together with the abolition of mud from the streets at all seasons, has cost that company $100,000 per year by reason of the decreased demand for

[41] Waring, *Street Cleaning*, pp. 37–42; Zueblin, *American Municipal Progress*, pp. 75–76; Waring, "Street Cleaning," pp. 118–19; Waring, "The Cleaning of the Streets of New York," *Harper's Weekly* 39 (26 October 1895): 1024; Waring, "Cleansing of Cities and Public Health," *Engineering Magazine* 8 (February 1895): 810; Waring, "The Relations of Good Paving to Street Cleaning," *Engineering Magazine* 12 (February 1897): 781–85; Skolnik, "George Edwin Waring, Jr.," p. 365.

[42] John Brisben Walker, "Great Problems in Organization: The Street-Cleaning Work of Colonel Waring in New York," *Cosmopolitan Magazine* 26 (December 1898): 235. See also Potts, "George Edwin Waring, Jr.;" p. 466.

rubber boots and shoes. What this means to the poorer people of the city, as compared with their previous suffering, need not be said.[43]

H. L. Stidham, the department's snow inspector, claimed that for the crowded tenement dwellers snow clearing meant improved health. His reasoning was somewhat specious:

> With the crowding of the immense tenement population into that human beehive, the East Side, there had been an actual bulging out from the houses to the now clean asphalt streets. Whether it be winter or summer, the people must have this additional room opened up for them, and a delay in the removal of the almost knee-deep snow and befouled slush is at the cost of much sickness, and probably many lives, each winter.[44]

Street cleaning and snow removal were only two responsibilities of the department. It also had complete charge of the collection and disposal of refuse. As with street cleaning, Waring discovered that the methods employed before 1895 were primitive and that the service was erratic. Although he introduced few revolutionary programs in those areas, he did apply his organizational skills to coordinating the collection and disposal programs, a task no one had been willing to attempt until that time. He was extremely critical of random methods of waste collection and disposal: "The 'out-of-sight, out-of-mind' principle is an easy one to follow, but it is not an economical one, nor a decent one, nor a safe one."[45] Waring realized that refuse was diverse in type, requiring various methods to achieve success. His goal was to collect household refuse quickly and efficiently, to recover whatever economic value the discarded material might have, and to dispose of the remainder in ways appropriate to its composition.

His most ambitious project was to devise a program for efficient collection of household and commercial wastes. "Source separation," which had been advocated for years but never attempted on a large scale, was attractive to him as an answer to New York's collection problem. The rationale for the system was that mixed refuse limited the options for disposal while separation of wastes at the source allowed the city to recover a portion of its costs of collection through the resale of some items and the reprocessing of others. Furthermore, Waring believed that the street crews

[43] Waring, "The Cleaning of a Great City," p. 921. See also Waring, "The Cleaning of the Streets of New York," pp. 1022–23.

[44] Waring, *Street Cleaning*, p. 91.

[45] Waring, "The Disposal of a City's Waste," *North American Review* 161 (July 1895): 52.

could handle the wastes more easily if they were separated. His plan for "primary separation" required each householder and business establishment to keep garbage (organic waste), rubbish, and ashes in separate containers until the department collected them. In 1896, Mayor Strong assigned forty policemen to the Street-Cleaning Department to explain the separation plan to every householder and businessman and assure compliance with the new ordinance. Waring's program also ended New Yorkers' long-standing practice of placing refuse containers on the sidewalks where they could easily be tipped over. All receptacles now would have to be kept within a "stoop line." As might be expected, there was considerable public resistance to primary separation; citizens were becoming conditioned to accepting sanitation programs as a municipal rather than a personal responsibility—an ironic twist considering the effort that had been made to encourage that point of view. Under the Waring program those who resisted complying with the rules were sometimes fined and even arrested. Despite the initial unpopularity of the plan, by 1898 it had proved to be fairly successful and was receiving much acclaim from city leaders, if not from an obdurate public.[46]

Because of their complexities, the utilization and disposal of refuse proved to be Waring's most difficult problems. While he achieved some success in these areas, he was not able to establish a completely efficient and economical system of final disposition of waste during his tenure as commissioner. He did, however, make substantial progress by experimenting with various methods in the hope of finding a practical solution to the city's monumental disposal problems. He especially made progress in reducing the amount of waste New Yorkers dumped in the ocean. Until Waring's time the city's dry waste was dumped ten miles beyond Sandy Hook, where the tide was supposed to carry it out to the open ocean. Waring believed that sea dumping was "theoretically a perfect disposal" but that it did not work in practice. The obvious sign of its failure was the abundant debris cluttering the beaches of Long Island and New Jersey—at least until the residents of several fashionable estates screamed for relief.[47]

---

[46] Waring, "The Disposal of a City's Waste," pp. 51–56; Waring, "The Cleaning of a Great City," p. 919; Waring, *Street Cleaning*, p. 43; John McGaw Woodbury, "The Wastes of a Great City," *Scribner's Magazine* 34 (October 1903): 388–89. For good background on the history of resource recovery and source separation in the United States, see Suellen M. Hoy and Michael C. Robinson, *Recovering the Past: A Handbook of Community Recycling Programs, 1890–1945*.

[47] "The Fouling of the Beaches," *Harper's Weekly* 42 (2 July 1898): 663; Waring, "The

Unlike some of his engineering colleagues and some city officials, Waring was not persuaded that any one method offered a ready solution. He was especially skeptical of cremation as a panacea, considering it "a costly and a wasteful process." Incineration, he argued, "is an art which has reached a high degree of development, and which in its best form and under proper guidance may be accepted as good, from a sanitary point of view, and as being practically free from offense. At the same time, cremation means destruction and loss of matter which may be converted into a source of revenue."[48] If there was any consistent element in his disposal plans, it was to recycle or utilize waste economically to recover some of the money the city invested in disposal. Municipal leaders usually responded favorably to his plan to recover expenditures and granted most of his requests for appropriations even when they became substantially higher.

The colonel advocated or attempted various programs of resource recovery or waste utilization which matched specific kinds of refuse with appropriate disposal methods. Beyond the obvious reasons for such an approach was an effort to increase municipal authority over services generally provided in the private sector. For example, the city's push-cart men had made a living by collecting discards which could be resold to junk stores. Waring argued that "public authorities might with advantage take control of the whole business of the collection of rubbish. This would probably be necessary to the securing of the great pecuniary return." Waring justified this plan by arguing that the "push-cart man who jangles his string of bells through the streets" carried on "a more or less illicit traffic with domestic servants." The city fathers would be not only enriching the public coffers but also increasing "the public safety."[49]

Waring also attempted to usurp the work of "scow trimmers," who rummaged through the heaps of waste on the dumping scows searching for rags, shoes, carpets, paper, and anything else with a resale value. Until 1878 the city had paid the trimmers for their services, allowing them to keep what they salvaged. From 1878 to 1882 the city curtailed the subsidies but allowed the scavengers to take what they wanted. Beginning in 1882,

---

Disposal of a City's Waste," pp. 53–54; Waring, "The Cleaning of a Great City," pp. 918–19.

[48] Waring, "The Utilization of City Garbage," *Cosmopolitan Magazine* 24 (February 1898): 406–408.

[49] Waring, "The Disposal of a City's Waste," pp. 51–56.

the city charged a flat rate for the privilege of trimming, realizing that the business had become a going concern with heated competition among rival scavenging crews. Most of the trimmers were Italian immigrants, organized into crews by local padrones. According to Waring, Italians were "a race with a genius for rag-and-bone picking and for subsisting on rejected trifles of food." Prejudice aside, the colonel saw an opportunity to bring the city into the arrangement in a more forthright manner and recommended that the city take over the operation completely. He said:

Dickens' "Golden Dustman" and the accounts of the rag-pickers of Paris have made us familiar with the fact that there is an available value in the ordinary *rejectamenta* of human life. We learn by the work of the dock Italian of New York that to regain this value is a matter of minute detail; it calls for the recovery of unconsidered trifles from a mass of valueless wastes, and the conversion of these into a salable commodity.[50]

In a short time the city took most of the resulting profits from scow trimming, and in January, 1898, Waring established the first rubbish-sorting plant in the United States.[51] His schemes for resource recovery demonstrate the thoroughness of his commitment to sanitation as a municipal responsibility—for better or for worse.

As with rubbish, he devised methods for the utilization of garbage, ashes, and street sweepings. Although he never became interested in waste cremation, he was enthusiastic about experiments in garbage reduction that coincided with his philosophy of utilization of waste. During his tenure as street-cleaning commissioner New York City had a contract with the Sanitary Utilization Company, which extracted grease, other liquids, and dry residuum (for use as fertilizer) from the city's waste at its plant on Barren Island. Waring also encouraged further experimentation to find more efficient and economical methods of reducing waste and utilizing the by-products. Eventually he hoped that this process would also be placed under municipal control.[52]

A long-term advocate of land reclamation for agricultural and other purposes, Waring saw the possibility of using ashes and street sweepings for landfill. Under his direction a bulkhead was constructed around a shoal

[50]Ibid., p. 51. See also "Garbage," *Municipality and County* 1 (April 1895): 164; Waring, "The Cleaning of a Great City," pp. 917–18.

[51]Rudolph Hering and Samuel A. Greely, *Collection and Disposal of Municipal Refuse*, p. 299.

[52]Waring, "Utilization of City Garbage," pp. 408–11; Waring, "The Cleaning of a Great City," p. 919.

at Riker's Island in the East River for the purpose of beginning a fill. Dumping scows regularly steamed to the island to dump loads of ashes and street sweepings. The city also provided fill material at no cost to private owners of shore flats and participated in experiments to turn ashes and organic materials into fireproofing blocks.[53]

Waring was never content simply to make the Street-Cleaning Department a servant of the people. Throughout his term of office he used his position as commissioner to persuade citizens that sanitation was not only a municipal responsibility but also a community and an individual responsibility for which the department simply provided the leadership. His White Wings parades were meant to stimulate public interest in the work of the department, his program of primary separation demanded individual commitment to proper collection and disposal methods, and his public addresses and publications spoke of civic pride and civic duty. Beyond these efforts Waring actively sought to involve specific segments of the population in his sanitation campaign. At utilizing human resources Waring was a master. As he said in October, 1896:

I believed that if the people were once interested in [the refuse problem], and it were known that it was possible to disregard the ideas of the politicians, they would show such a desire for reform in this particular, that political influence would have no weight against them.

This was the reason I did so many things that were considered "injudicious," "dramatic," and, perhaps even foolish. My plan was to force the department on to the attention of the people in every possible way, and I knew that the easiest way to do this was to introduce the personal element, and to make myself as Commissioner as conspicuous as I could.[54]

To that end Waring formed an advisory committee of civic leaders to help him analyze sanitation conditions and offer possible solutions. He also regularly appeared before groups such as the Good Government Club, the City Improvement Society, the Ladies' Health Protective Association, the University Settlement, the College Settlement, and the Committee of Seventy. All the groups tried to help the department in its work.[55]

---

[53] Waring, *Street Cleaning*, pp. 68–73; Waring, "The Disposal of a City's Waste," p. 56; Waring, "The Cleaning of a Great City," pp. 919–20; "The Delehanty Dumping-Scow," *Harper's Weekly* 40 (24 October 1896): 1051; Waring, *Draining for Profit and Draining for Health*, p. 150.

[54] *New York Times*, Sunday Supplement, October 11, 1896, p. 2.

[55] Skolnik, "George Edwin Waring, Jr.," pp. 365–66; Cassedy, "The Flamboyant Colonel Waring," p. 171.

His most celebrated and innovative effort to encourage public involvement was the establishment of the Juvenile Street Cleaning League. Taking note of the participation of children in New York's Civic History Club and other patriotic organizations, Waring concluded that "it seemed possible to enlist their interest in the cleanliness of the city." He had several goals in mind in establishing the league. First, the children of the city could act as eyes, ears, and noses for the department in discovering unsanitary conditions and their perpetrators. The colonel assumed that the young league members might have greater success than adults in gaining the cooperation of litterers. Second, Waring hoped to educate the children in the ways of sanitation and civic pride: "[The children] are being taught that government does not mean merely a policeman to be run away from, but an influence which touches the life of the people at every point."[56] He hoped that the message would ultimately find its way to the parents. The popular but simplistic notion that citizens in working-class ethnic neighborhoods were the least sanitary and most prone to littering led the department to initiate the league on New York's East Side. As David Williard, a Street-Cleaning Department supervisor, observed:

> To arouse a civic pride among New Yorkers is not distinctly within the province of the Department of Street-Cleaning. It is desirable, however, that an interest in the observation of the simple necessary rules of the Sanitary Code be awakened in the minds of at least the ignorant foreign population crowded into the East Side districts. To use for this end the influence of the children, who are recognized by their parents as superior to them in education and intelligence, is not a new idea, but one practically untried to any extent.[57]

Waring argued, "If nothing is gained to the city except in a negative way, at least the neutrality of thousands of children has been purchased and the streets are the cleaner from the fact that so many are kept from making them dirty."[58]

After a slow start the Juvenile Street Cleaning League became a rousing success. In 1896, Waring directed Reuben S. Simons to seek the permission of the New York City Department of Education to deliver addresses on sanitation in the public schools and to try to organize the children into neighborhood leagues. Coaxing the boys and girls to join was no simple task; many of them were averse to volunteering for fear the depart-

---

[56] Waring, "The Cleaning of a Great City," p. 922.
[57] Waring, *Street Cleaning*, p. 177–86; Baker, "The Refuse of a Great City," p. 90.
[58] Waring, *Street Cleaning*, p. 186.

ment wanted to use them as spies. After intensive proselytizing, several groups were formed at settlements and in the public schools. In a very short time there were forty-four leagues with 2,500 participants; by 1899 there were seventy-five leagues and 5,000 participants.[59]

Waring could not resist the temptation to organize the leagues along military lines. The members held weekly meetings, took a civic pledge, wore little white caps, and were issued badges. The leagues even established a ranking system—"helpers," "foremen," "superintendents"—depending on the services the children provided to the city. League members, sometimes five hundred strong, marched in parades as the White Wings had marched before them. At their meetings the children sang songs with obvious messages, to the tunes of "Baby Mine," "As We Go Marching On," and so forth. Here is a sample stanza from "And We Will Keep Right On":

> There's a change within our city, great improvements in our day;
> The streets' untidy litter with the dirt has passed away.
> We children pick up papers, even while we are at play;
> And we will keep right on.[60]

The duties of the league members were rigidly outlined. Each week all the boys and girls were to record the number of people they had spoken to about sanitation, the number of bonfires they had extinguished, and the number of fruit peels they kicked into the gutter. The weekly reports were filled with good deeds done and diligence to duty. One youngster wrote:

Col. Waring.

Dear Sir:—While walking through Broome St., . . . I saw a man throughing a mattress on the street. I came over to him and asked him if he had no other place to put it but here. He told me that he does not no [sic] any other place. So I told him in

---

[59] Reuben S. Simons, "The Juvenile Street Cleaning Leagues of New York," *American City* 3 (October 1910): 163–66.

[60] Waring, *Street Cleaning*, p. 181. The rest of the stanzas are as follows:

> No longer will you see a child fall helpless in the street
> Because some slippery peeling betrayed his trusting feet;
> We do what we are able to make our sidewalks neat;
> And we will keep right on.

> And all the people far and near, in sunshine or in rain,
> Rejoice to see our cleaner streets, and find the reason plain;
> We children take a hand to keep our thoroughfares so clean;
> And we will keep right on.

a barrel, he then picked it up and thanked me for the inflammation I gave him. I also picked up 35 banana skins, 43 water mellion shells, 2 bottles, 3 cans and mattress from Norfolk St.

Metropolitan League[61]

The Juvenile Street Cleaning League was one more example of Waring's efforts to bring the work of his department directly to the notice of the community at large. As farfetched as the idea seemed at first, it effectively publicized the need for civic involvement in resolving sanitary problems in particular and community-wide social problems in general. Although there is no way of quantifying the degree of success the leagues achieved, the response of the press and city officials from around the nation was very favorable. The participation of so many youngsters indicated that the colonel reached them in some basic way. Impressed by the results, other cities around the country, including Philadelphia, Brooklyn, Pittsburgh, Utica, and Denver, established their own juvenile leagues. In 1916, Philadelphia's leagues had ten thousand members. Unfortunately, the Juvenile Street Cleaning League of New York was disbanded in 1900, largely because of the lack of enthusiastic leadership which Waring had offered. It was revived in 1909, when followers of Waring again promoted it. Ultimately it grew to three hundred leagues throughout the city.[62]

Colonel Waring's whirlwind approach to reforming the Street-Cleaning Department ended abruptly when Tammany Hall succeeded in turning out Mayor Strong in 1898. Much of what Waring had accomplished was undone or neglected (at least temporarily) under machine rule.[63] Yet Waring's comprehensive program, despite his untimely death, received extensive national attention and inspired the implementation of similar programs in many cities.[64]

Waring had been able to produce a workable model for sanitary re-

[61] Ibid., p. 184; see also pp. 177–83; Potts, "George Edwin Waring, Jr.," p. 467.

[62] Simons, "The Juvenile Street Cleaning Leagues of New York," pp. 163–66; Skolnik, "George Edwin Waring, Jr.," pp. 366–67; Zueblin, *American Municipal Progress*, p. 76.

[63] See Woodbury, "The Wastes of a Great City," pp. 387–90.

[64] Zueblin, *American Municipal Progress*, pp. 75–76, 82; Delos F. Wilcox, *The American City: A Problem in Democracy*, pp. 118, 224; George A Soper, *Modern Methods of Street Cleaning*, p. 165; John A. Fairlie, *Municipal Administration*, pp. 258–59; "Tammany and the Streets," *Outlook* 66 (20 October 1900): 427–28; "Street Cleaning," *Outlook* 66 (20 October 1900): 426–27; "The Disposal of New York's Refuse," *Scientific American* 89 (24 October 1903): 292–94; Woodbury, "The Wastes of a Great City," p. 387; Baker, "The Refuse of a Great City," pp. 81, 89–90; Duffy, *A History of Public Health in New York City, 1866–1966*, pp. 125–26; "The Military Element in Colonel Waring's Career," pp. 544–47.

form first and foremost because his message was clear: waste is a menace to health and to palatable living conditions and can be eradicated only through the coordination of municipal authorities and civic action. Waring's varied career and his ebullient personality gave him the necessary tools to promote his message. He was a skilled publicizer and promoter who took to heart a famous punch line from an old joke: ". . . but first you have to get [their] attention." Although he exhibited an unbridled faith in elite rule, he nonetheless realized the importance of seeking a congenial public forum to promote his reforms. He was not simply a publicizer and promoter, however; he was a man of action with an uncompromising belief in the art of the possible. He was not an ideologue, nor was he an ecologist in the broadest sense of the term. He recognized the interrelationships among myriad health and sanitation problems, but he did not perceive the city in a broad, organic sense. For good or for bad he accepted the city on its own terms, never questioning its form or structure, the nature of its growth, or its economic activity. He was primarily concerned with the quality of human life, which certainly made him an environmentalist of a specialized type. "Pragmatic environmentalism" best describes the thrust of Waring's sanitary programs. Publicizing the department's activities and mustering all available human and material resources, Waring proved that change was possible without elaborate facilities and without blind adherence to a technological panacea. Waring was naïve about the possible achievements of environmental sanitation in promoting health, but his instincts about acting upon obvious problems and his tenacity in promoting community involvement in sanitation paid rich dividends. Unfortunately, future generations of reformers would sometimes lose sight of the pragmatic approach the colonel took in New York City.

Waring also came to be recognized as the leader in his field because his timing was perfect. He spoke the language of the progressive reformers, who sought to bring some order out of chaos created by the emergence of a new industrial society. Industrialization and urbanization challenged the values, way of life, and state of mind of Americans throughout the country. After the Panic of 1893 reformers began to realize that Americans must reconcile their old ways to the new and accommodate themselves to the many changes a modern industrial-urban culture would bring. The fervent optimism at the heart of progressivism grew out of the belief that, given the proper physical, social, economic, and moral environment, Americans would overcome their problems.

Waring's nascent environmentalism, with its emphasis on improving the quality of urban life, coincided well with mainstream progressive thought. His goal to place public welfare above private gain mirrored progressive support for various civic improvements. Waring was also quick to declare his optimism about the prospects for change, and he exhibited a familiar faith in the inherent good of "the people." In characteristic pose he recoiled in moral outrage at the physical and social degradations of city life and, much like a Jacob Riis or a Lincoln Steffens, envisioned himself as a noble crusader against the forces of evil. Like other progressive reformers, Waring was an elitist whose faith in "the people" was tempered by the belief that leadership in reform must come from those best suited to the task. This belief accounts for Waring's support of sanitation reform through municipal channels—at least those channels freed from machine dominance. In a real sense, therefore, Waring was a product of his time. He had harsh words for the old order that was still clinging to power, but he provided hope and enthusiasm for the wide-eyed reformers, who were confident that they could find solutions to the pressing problems of the day.

Refuse management was never the same after Colonel Waring. The "apostle of cleanliness" demonstrated that cities could move beyond the primitive and haphazard practices of the nineteenth century. A controversial figure to the end, he nonetheless pointed the way to modern refuse management and helped encourage an urban environmental consciousness which would produce some positive results in the twentieth century.

3

Refuse as an Engineering Problem: Sanitary Engineers and Municipal Reform

In a 1906 issue of *Charities and the Commons* (later called the *Survey*), the editor proclaimed the rise of sanitary engineering as "a new social profession." This profession, he stated, "is neither that of physician, nor engineer, nor educator, but smacks of all three. It levies on autocratic powers, kin to those of ancient tyrants, but at the same time depends upon the sheerest democracy of information and co-operation to give its work effect."[1] Sanitary engineers were the twentieth-century heirs of Colonel Waring and his sanitary reforms. In one sense they were highly trained (or experienced) specialists in the increasingly complex field of public works. They were the experts upon whom reform politicians depended to solve the pressing problems of advancing industrialization. In a larger sense, however, sanitary engineers were generalists when it came to broad questions concerning the maintenance of a viable physical environment. In the years before the appearance of professionally trained and academically educated ecologists, sanitary engineers were among the small minority of technocrats who possessed a comprehensive knowledge of the urban ecosystem.[2] It is no wonder that they came to dominate refuse reform in the early twentieth century. Their efforts to measure more scientifically the extent of the refuse problem, to devise modern collection and disposal methods and technologies, and to implement business efficiency in administering public works departments went a long way in giving credence to

[1] "The Sanitary Engineer—A New Social Profession," *Charities and the Commons (Survey)* 16 (2 June 1906): 286.

[2] See Stanley K. Schultz and Clay McShane, "To Engineer the Metropolis: Sewers, Sanitation, and City Planning in Late-Nineteenth-Century America," *Journal of American History* 65 (September 1978): 389–411. Schultz and McShane primarily emphasize the role of the engineer as technical expert and administrator, rather than as an environmental generalist.

Colonel Waring's claim that refuse was more than a simple nuisance—that it was a serious environmental problem.

In the early twentieth century sanitary engineers superseded health officers and sanitarians as the leaders of refuse reform in the United States. They accomplished this feat as much by default as by their training or their environmental vision. In the wake of the bacteriological revolution of the late nineteenth century, many in the health field came to regard environmental sanitation as inconsequential as a means of combating disease and virtually abandoned it. They placed their faith in the germ theory of disease transmittal, which led to the establishment of bacteriological laboratories and the widespread use of inoculation and immunization as the means of eradicating communicable diseases. Dr. Fred B. Welch, commissioner of health of Janesville, Wisconsin, noted that the science of bacteriology and parasitology had "completely changed man's concept of environmental sanitation."[3] Doctors and health officials recognized the advantages of eradicating filth and cleaning the physical surroundings, but they had been frustrated for years by their inability to prevent communicable diseases through sanitary measures alone. As medical historian John Duffy wrote, "The discovery of specific pathogenic organisms enabled public health workers to understand for the first time precisely what they were fighting."[4]

The transition from the widely accepted miasmic theory to the germ theory was not a simple one. Through the mid-1880s anitcontagionists offered strong resistance to the germ theory. Most people were unable to comprehend that something unseen or unfelt could be the cause of disease. In 1878 even *Scientific American* chided the advocates of the new theory for accepting such a farfetched notion. Impressive reductions in the mortality rate between 1860 and 1880, attributable in some measure to good sanitation practices, further weakened the case for bacteriology. The death rate in most cities fell from twenty-five to forty persons per thousand in 1860 to sixteen to twenty-six per thousand in 1880. Rates were especially low in cities with sound sanitary practices. Nonetheless, the tenacity of the germ-theory advocates and the inconsistent results of environmental sanitation perpetuated the controversy. Not until the turn of the century did the contagionists successfully topple the miasmic theory. The verifiable suc-

---

[3] Fred B. Welch, "History of Sanitation" (Paper read at the First General Meeting of the "Wisconsin Section" of the National Association of Sanitarians, Inc., Milwaukee, Wis., December 1944), p. 45.

[4] John Duffy, *A History of Public Health in New York City, 1866–1966*, p. 91.

cesses of immunization and inoculation and the advances credited to the bacteriological laboratories far exceeded the erratic record of "municipal housecleaning" and other sanitation practices.[5]

The contagionists' victory over the anticontagionists was only a qualified success. Adherents of the germ theory too easily accepted bacteriology as offering the means of preventing disease and too quickly dismissed environmental sanitation as a valuable practice in disease prevention. In the eyes of many in the health field the emphasis on the "environment" as a root cause of disease had been misplaced, or at least exaggerated. The scientific base of environmental sanitation had been seriously flawed, but its goal—removing potential breeding cultures of disease from the range of human senses—had validity. Too often in the zeal to promote new ideas much is lost in abandoning the old. That is what happened when health officers relinquished their leadership in promoting and providing environmental sanitation in the cities.[6]

The demise of the filth theory led to a critical appraisal of environmental sanitation as a function of health departments. With respect to the refuse problem several public-health officials questioned the necessity for health workers to supervise or direct the collection and disposal of waste. They recognized that refuse was in some respects a health problem, but few believed that its solution required the active involvement of municipal health departments. The views of Dr. Charles V. Chapin, superintendent of health of Providence, Rhode Island, and one of the pioneers in the American public-health movement, typified the contagionists' beliefs:

Though abandoning the time honored [filth] theory which was taught him, the writer has not abandoned the fight against filth. Filth is a nuisance, and is usually an evidence of some one's carelessness of his neighbor's comfort. The state or city should certainly protect its citizens against such nuisances. Good sewerage, well swept streets, promp scavenging, public baths, clean tenements, are all parts, desirable and essential parts, of our civilization. They would be worth what they cost

[5] Howard D. Kramer, "The Germ Theory and the Public Health Program in the United States," *Bulletin of the History of Medicine* 22 (May–June 1948): 233–47. See also James H. Cassedy, *Charles V. Chapin and the Public Health Movement*, pp. 39–45, 96, 141; Barbara G. Rosenkrantz, *Public Health and the State: Changing Views in Massachusetts, 1842–1936*, pp. 75, 103, 177–82; George Rosen, *A History of Public Health*, pp. 233–50.

[6] Kramer, like other historians of public health and medicine, assumed that the shift away from environmental sanitation by health workers was a good sign: "Many municipal matters that had concerned earlier sanitarians, such as street cleaning, had gravitated into other hands, where they really belonged." See Kramer, "The Germ Theory and the Public Health Program in the United States," p. 246.

even if they had no relation to health; but the proper disposal of excreta and cleanliness of person doubtless do have much to do with the prevention of the spread of many communicable diseases. Much is to be gained by promoting cleanliness, but nothing by fostering false notions of the dangers of filth.[7]

Chapin's observations led him to conclude that the "filth nuisance" should not be a health-department responsibility. The health officer, he asserted, "should be free to devote more energy to those things which he alone can do. He should not waste his time arguing with the owners of pig-sties or compelling landlords to empty their cesspools."[8]

Chapin recognized the need to employ health experts with the highest possible levels of training and skill. In many ways, however, his opinions suggested a return to the nineteenth-century view of filth as simply a nuisance. While paying respect to the value of municipal cleanliness, he underrated the problem of waste as an environmental threat and underrated the importance of health-department supervision of refuse collection and disposal. His views were by no means the most extreme. Others in the health field were quick to abandon the old theories and were strident in their criticism of environmental sanitation.

At the 1912 meeting of the APHA in Washington, D.C., a very lively session focused on the relationship between public health and municipal waste. Dr. P. M. Hall, Minneapolis commissioner of health, provoked an emotional debate when he contended that, although "unsanitary conditions of the home and unclean surroundings do not cause or originate infectious disease, . . . they do have a great influence upon the severity of the attack, and consequently have a direct bearing upon . . . mortality." He added that the origin of infectious disease was not "a closed book" and that the "teachings of centuries" should not be automatically abandoned but should be taught in conjunction with newer theories. "Why should we ignore the surroundings?" he concluded.[9] Hall's comments brought forth a flurry of rejoinders. M. N. Baker, an eminent sanitarian, flatly stated, "I do not think you can find any proof whatever that garbage collection and disposal has

[7]Charles V. Chapin, "The End of the Filth Theory of Disease," *Popular Science Monthly* 60 (January 1902): 239.

[8]Charles V. Chapin, "Sanitation in Providence," in *Proceedings of the Providence, Rhode Island, Conference for Good Government and the Thirteenth Annual Meeting of the National Municipal League*, p. 326.

[9]P. M. Hall, "The Collection and Disposal of City Waste and the Public Health," *American Journal of Public Health* 3 (April 1913): 314–15.

any material relation to health." Army Colonel J. R. Keane concurred: "There is no relation between garbage removal and public health." The sentiments of these men and others in attendance ran strongly against health-department responsibility for collection and disposal of waste. A Dr. Gillett, of Colorado Springs, agreed that boards of health should not take up the question of removal of garbage, but, he asked, "if they do not, who will?"[10]

For those who continued to support the control of refuse collection and disposal by health departments or boards of health, Dr. Gillett's question was of central importance. By abandoning environmental sanitation, would health departments actually free themselves to combat communicable diseases more effectively? Would municipal cleanliness suffer under new supervision? It appears that those who adhered to the germ theory and were disenchanted with the results of environmental sanitation may not have given serious thought to who should or would be responsible for sanitation measures. Some of the advocates of health-department responsibility feared that the progress that had been made in providing sanitary service to the city would be lost as private contractors once again assumed major control and direction of municipal sanitation. At the 1917 meeting of the APHA, Edward D. Rich, state sanitary engineer of Lansing, Michigan, suggested that health-department supervision over collection and disposal of municipal waste would justify itself "if it did no more than to protect the municipalities from the unscrupulous vendor or untried or worthless devices."[11]

Irrespective of the controversy over responsibility, the trend in the early twentieth century was decidedly away from health-department control.[12] A survey of eighty-six cities, conducted by the American Child Health Association and published in 1925, showed that in forty-seven cities operating their own collection service only nine (or 19 percent) gave the

[10] Ibid., pp. 316–17. See also "Control of Garbage Disposal," *Municipal Journal and Engineer* 30 (3 May 1911): 633.

[11] Edward D. Rich, "State Health Departments and Municipal Refuse Disposal," *American Journal of Public Health* 8 (February 1918): 135–36. See also "Disposal of Garbage," *City Government* 5 (August 1898): 66; Benjamin Lee, "Preventive Medicine in Pennsylvania," *Sanitarian* 40 (February 1898): 99–100; William Hay McLain, "A Sanitary Method of Garbage Collection," *American City* 8 (April 1913): 402–403; C. E. Terry, "The Public Dump and the Public Health," *American Journal of Public Health* 3 (April 1913): 341.

[12] See Wilson G. Smillie, *Public Health Administration in the United States*, pp. 4, 255; Wilson G. Smillie, *Public Health: Its Promise for the Future*, pp. 351–52.

responsibility to departments of health (that figure represents only 10.5 percent of all cities surveyed).[13] In most cities where health departments did not oversee collection and disposal, they did have enforcement power over nuisances and in some instances supervisory power over the selection of contractors. Such compromises, however, often led to jurisdictional disputes among municipal departments and failed to resolve the question whether health departments should retain full or at least partial control. The outcome of the trend away from health-department responsibility was that health officers lost much of their influence over defining and controlling waste.

The engineer was the obvious choice to assume responsibility for sanitation problems. The growing assumption that environmental sanitation was a task primarily requiring effective administrative and technical expertise, supplemented by some basic medical and scientific knowledge, pointed directly to the engineering profession. Professionally trained engineers were products of the industrial age, and, as Edwin T. Layton, Jr., suggests, they were to be the "stewards of technology."[14] In an increasingly mechanized and technically advanced world, engineers were recognized as the agents of material progress. In the words of David F. Noble, "As he strove to create a professional identity for himself, the engineer commonly tried to present himself to the public as 'technology' itself, the great motive force of modern civilization."[15]

By 1900 engineering was the second-largest profession in the United States, following close behind teaching. In that year there were about 45,000 engineers in the United States. By 1930 their ranks had swelled to 230,000. The vitality of the profession was apparent not only in the increasing numbers of engineers but also in the diversity of its activities, which reflected the impact of technology. Civil engineers were the first professional engineers. They emerged in the great canal- and railroad-building era of the early nineteenth century. By 1900 professional civil engineers had been joined by professionally trained mining, mechanical, electrical, and chemical engineers. As early as 1852 civil engineers had established their own professional organization, the American Society of Civil Engi-

[13] American Child Health Association, Research Division, *A Health Survey of 86 Cities*, p. 214.

[14] Edwin T. Layton, Jr., *The Revolt of the Engineers: Social Responsibility and the American Engineering Profession*, pp. viii, 53–69.

[15] David F. Noble, *America by Design: Science, Technology, and the Rise of Corporate Capitalism*, p. 44.

neers. This group was soon followed by the American Institute of Mining and Metallurgical Engineers (1871), the American Society of Mechanical Engineers (1880), the American Institute of Electrical Engineers (1884), the American Institute of Chemical Engineers (1908), and others.[16]

Inevitably large numbers of engineers looked to the cities as their primary arenas of enterprise and opportunity. Rampant urban growth created massive physical problems which engineers were often best trained to address. By the late nineteenth century engineers were playing major roles in American cities as consultants to city officials or as administrators and employees of various municipal departments. Some became widely known for their accomplishments. Colonel Waring, who had built a lucrative business as an itinerant consultant before accepting the street-cleaning position in New York, was by no means the only municipal engineer with a national reputation. Rudolph Hering, the "dean of sanitary engineering," was equally prominent but less flamboyant. His experience ranged from park surveys to bridge building, from sewer construction to water supplies. Among his best-known projects (all carried out in the late nineteenth century) were the extension of Fairmont Park in Philadelphia and the construction of sewerage systems for Washington, D.C.; Mexico City; and Santos, Brazil. He also sat on the important Drainage and Water Supply Commission of Chicago between 1885 and 1887. Probably his most important contribution to sanitary engineering was his supervision of many investigations of water supplies, sewerage systems, and refuse collection and disposal practices. These investigations took him throughout the country and the world. His investigation of water supplies alone resulted in reports on more than 150 cities. He became an active or honorary member of almost every major organization in his field, and his expertise and public recognition led to his election as president of the APHA in 1913. In 1953 the APHA honored Hering by naming him the "Father of American Sanitary Engineering."[17]

Other important leaders in municipal engineering during the period were Ellis Sylvester Chesbrough, George Soper, William R. Morse, and William Mulholland. Chesbrough was the first city engineer of Boston (1851–55), but he was best known as the engineer of Chicago's Sewerage

[16]Ibid., p. 35–36. See also Layton, *The Revolt of the Engineers*, pp. 3–6, 53–74.

[17]*A Biographical Dictionary of American Civil Engineers* (New York: American Society of Civil Engineers, 1972), pp. 58–59; Neal FitzSimons, "Pollution Fighters: Rudolph Hering," *Civil Engineering–ASCE* (October 1971): 100; Jacqueline Wilkie, "Rudolph Hering," *APWA Reporter* 48 (April 1981): 4–5.

Commission (1855–79). Under his guidance Chicago became the first city to implement a systematic sewerage plan, which included raising the level of the streets so that sewage flowed off into Lake Michigan. He also developed a system whereby the city water supply flowed through pipes under the lake and into the city.[18]

An expert in sanitary science and water purification, Soper was responsible for the sanitary rehabilitation of Galveston, Texas, after the disastrous hurricane and flood of 1900, which took six to ten thousand lives and destroyed $20 million in property. He spent most of his career, however, in New York, attempting to eradicate communicable diseases. He gained a reputation as an autocrat—he was known to burn down infected houses and seize schools for makeshift hospitals—but he also was regarded as a dedicated and successful sanitary reformer.[19]

Colonel Morse, today probably the least-known sanitary engineer of the era, gained a significant reputation as a designer of modern incineration systems and as a prolific writer on the subject of refuse collection and disposal. Not unlike several of his colleagues, including Colonel Waring, Morse was sometimes accused of conflict of interest, especially with respect to his design and marketing of garbage crematories. Yet he made some of the most thorough examinations of collection and disposal techniques carried out at the time, which helped cities select sanitation systems more intelligently.[20]

Mulholland, like Chesbrough, was a major figure in the development of municipal water supplies. According to his biographer, for fifty years Mulholland "led development of water supply systems that enabled [Los Angeles] to become a great municipality." Born in Ireland in 1855, he emigrated to the United States in 1874. A self-taught engineer of the old school, he rose through the ranks of the Los Angeles City Water Company, a private firm which supplied the city with water. When the city assumed control of the system in 1902, Mulholland was retained as chief engineer, a position he held until his retirement in 1928. A major proponent of the fa-

---

[18] *A Biographical Dictionary of American Civil Engineers*, pp. 23–24. See also Louis P. Cain, "Raising and Watering a City: Ellis Sylvester Chesbrough and Chicago's First Sanitation System," *Technology and Culture* 13 (July 1972): 353–72.

[19] "The Sanitary Engineer—A New Social Profession," pp. 286–87.

[20] "A Veteran in Garbage Disposal," *Municipal Journal and Engineer* 19 (September 1905): 124–25; "The Disposal of Municipal Waste," *Municipal Journal and Engineer* 20 (31 January 1906): 102.

mous Los Angeles Aqueduct, he was embroiled in the controversy over building the aqueduct from Owens Lake to Los Angeles. During the campaign for its construction he was asked to predict the consequences of relying on the existing supplies. He bluntly answered, "Well if you don't get it now you'll never need it!"[21]

Legions of less-well-known municipal engineers assumed leadership in established departments of streets, street cleaning, and public works or were responsible for spearheading the establishment of "engineering departments" with a wide range of duties. Soon sanitary and other engineers were entrenched groups in several municipal governments throughout the country. According to historians Stanley Schultz and Clay McShane: "Labeling themselves neutral experts, engineers professed to work above the din of local politics. Usually they tried to isolate themselves from partisan wrangles, and often succeeded. In the creation of administrative bureaucracies, engineers apparently were the earliest municipal officials to achieve anything like job security."[22]

As the growing concentration of people in the central cities in the nineteenth century strained the meager city services, and as suburban residents clamored for the extension of these services to their communities, municipal authorities called on engineers to improve existing conditions and often deferred to them in the making of policy on these matters. The need for safe water supplies, adequate sewerage, well-ventilated housing, and efficient refuse collection and disposal required the engineer's technical expertise and the public-health officer's knowledge of sanitation. A hybrid profession—sanitary engineering—emerged to try to meet the environmental challenge of the burgeoning industrial cities.

The origins of the new profession were to be found in Europe, not in the United States. During the 1870s the emergence of sanitary engineers, primarily in England and Germany, coincided with the development of the biological sciences and the implementation of water filtration and sewage treatment in London and other major European cities. Edwin Chadwick, the preeminent English sanitarian, was a precursor of the professional sanitary engineers in Europe and the United States. As early as 1842, Chad-

---

[21] Michael Robinson, "William Mulholland," *APWA Reporter* 43 (September 1976): 12–13.

[22] Schultz and McShane, "To Engineer the Metropolis," p. 399. See also "Needed Reforms in the Collection and Disposal of City Refuse," *Engineering News* 59 (23 April 1908): 462–63; Raymond H. Merritt, *Engineering in American Society, 1850–1875*, pp. 157–76.

wick had proposed a unitary sewerage system for London which was designed to remove all water-borne wastes from the city.[23] In the United
States, Hering, Waring, and others had led the way toward the professionalization of sanitary engineering, based on Chadwick's model. By 1890 a
few professionally trained sanitary engineers were graduating from technical schools. By early in the new century leading private schools, such as
the Massachusetts Institute of Technology, Carnegie Technical School,
Harvard, Yale, Cornell, and Columbia, as well as major state universities
of Ohio, Illinois, and Michigan, were offering courses and even whole cur-
ricula in sanitary engineering. Harvard and MIT jointly sponsored a Graduate School of Public Health, which trained students to hold administrative
positions in the health field. Among those allowed to enroll were sanitary
engineers.[24]

Like their European counterparts American sanitary engineers received their first practical education in developing public water supplies and
constructing city-wide sewerage systems. In the post–Civil War years most
large cities were forced to abandon many of their local water sources—
wells, cisterns, and local springs—for less-contaminated and larger-vol-
ume sources usually far from the city limits. By 1896 engineers were helping to provide more than three thousand new water sources, and by 1910
more than 70 percent of cities with populations over thirty thousand were
maintaining their own waterworks.[25] The introduction of running water
into urban residences and business establishments led to tremendous increases in water use. Per capita water consumption increased from about
two to three gallons a day to between fifty and one hundred gallons a day.
The convenience of running water also led to the widespread adoption of
water closets; by 1880 about one-third of all urban households had them.
This sanitary innovation added greatly to the growing consumption of
water. The dramatic increases in water use placed excessive burdens on

[23] Jon A. Peterson, "The Impact of Sanitary Reform upon American Urban Planning,
1840–1890," *Journal of Social History* 13 (Fall 1979): 83–103; R. Winthrop Pratt, "The Industrial Need of Technically Trained Men: Sanitary Engineering," *Scientific American Supplement* 77 (7 March 1914): 150.

[24] Ellen H. Richards, *Conservation by Sanitation*, p. ix; Pratt, "The Industrial Need of
Technically Trained Men: Sanitary Engineering," p. 150.

[25] Stuart Galishoff, "Triumph and Failure: The American Response to the Urban Water
Supply Problem, 1860–1923," in Martin V. Melosi, ed., *Pollution and Reform in American
Cities, 1870–1930*, pp. 35–57; Schultz and McShane, "To Engineer the Metropolis," p. 393.

existing cesspools and privy vaults, since waste water had no place to go but into the soil or into the yards of adjacent houses. The health hazards implicit in this phenomenon and the inconvenience of overflowing water led city officials to support the construction of city-wide waste-water systems.[26] After 1880 most major cities adopted sewerage systems to accompany or combine with their storm-water systems (in the form of underground sewers or sometimes open gutters). Naturally sanitary engineers were given the task of designing and constructing them.[27]

The efforts of the sanitary engineers produced impressive results. In 1860 there were only 136 municipal waterworks in the country; by 1880 there were 598. Increases in sewer lines of all kinds were no less extensive. The miles of sewers increased from 8,199 (in cities of more than ten thousand population) in 1890 to 24,972 (in cities of more than thirty thousand population) in 1909.[28] The central role of the sanitary engineers in the construction of abundant and effective water- and waste-water carriage systems propelled the profession into the forefront of environmental sanitation in the United States. Sanitary engineers seemed to offer the best balance between technical and health expertise in dealing with the water problem.

The widespread recognition of the accomplishments of sanitary engineers and the simultaneous abandonment of environmental sanitation by health departments encouraged municipal officials to look to them to resolve another pressing urban problem—refuse collection and disposal. The growing faith in sanitary engineers as protectors of the urban environment also led to the assumption that solid waste was primarily an engineering problem. Faith in technology fostered the belief that since the water-carriage problem had been solved by technical means refuse could likewise be mastered through the skills of the engineer. An editorial in *Engineering News* commented:

Besides bad politics and general inefficiency in municipal administration, the chief hindrance to putting refuse collection and disposal on a satisfactory basis is the

[26] Joel A. Tarr and Francis Clay McMichael, "Historical Decisions about Wastewater Technology: 1800–1932," *Journal of the Water Resources Planning and Management Division, ASCE* 103 (May 1977): 48–50.

[27] Ibid., pp. 50–61. For more references on water supply and sewerage development see "A Bilbiography of Urban Pollution Problems," in Melosi, ed., *Pollution and Reform in American Cities*, pp. 199–201.

[28] Joel A. Tarr, James McClurley, and Terry F. Yosie, "The Development and Impact of Urban Wastewater Technology: Changing Concepts of Water Quality Control, 1850–1930," in Melosi, ed., *Pollution and Reform in American Cities*, pp. 68–69.

failure of the public and of non-technical city officials to recognize that the most difficult of the problems involved are engineering in character and will never be satisfactorily solved until they are entrusted to engineers.[29]

Confidence in sanitary engineers to find immediate solutions to the refuse problem, resting as it did on a too-optimistic faith in technology, placed a heavy responsibility on their shoulders. Refuse had always been more than an engineering problem. Despite growing adherence to the germ theory, refuse remained a health problem to be reckoned with (it also had serious aesthetic and economic impacts, which will be described later). It presented even more confounding administrative problems than sewerage had raised. If engineers had relied solely on their technical expertise, their contribution to refuse reform would have been minimal. Instead, trained as environmental generalists as well as technical specialists, sanitary engineers, while failing to provide the quick solutions expected of them, did advance refuse management significantly. Having developed a more comprehensive understanding of the refuse problem than had those who grappled with it in the nineteenth century, they capably defined the range of issues associated with refuse collection and disposal. Opportunities for thoughtful solutions, therefore, were greatly improved. Some contemporaries recognized the true nature of the sanitary engineers' skills. In 1901, John H. Emigh, city engineer of North Adams, Massachusetts, addressing a meeting of the American Society for Municipal Improvements, commented on the engineer's role:

It has been said that the problem of garbage disposal is becoming more and more a question of engineering. This is true. If I interpret aright engineering may be defined as a science that manipulates, applies and makes the best use of the laws of nature; and I am sure that every municipal engineer will agree with me that the problems connected with the manipulations of human nature are quite as intricate and difficult as any with which he has to deal. He cannot avoid having his acts modified by the opinions and sentiments of people competent or incompetent, right or wrong. Here, then, rests also his high duty and privilege, namely, that of leading his constituency into right conclusions, however tedious and torturous such pro-

[29] "Needed Reforms in the Collection and Disposal of City Refuse," *Engineering News* 59 (23 April 1908): 462. See also M. N. Baker, "Condition of Garbage Disposal in United States," *Municipal Journal and Engineer* 11 (October 1901): 147; William T. Sedgwick, *Principles of Sanitary Science and the Public Health*, pp. 117–18; Rich, "State Health Departments and Municipal Refuse Disposal," p. 135; Herman G. James, *Municipal Functions*, p. 85; Earl B. Phelps, *The Principles of Public Health Engineering*, p. 236.

cesses may be. The intent of the mass of people and its tendency is to have conditions that are right and best; but it is deplorably unfortunate that so many mistakes are made, and faulty conditions prevail as the result of ignorant or selfish planning.[30]

Other contemporary evaluations of the sanitary engineer reflected an emphasis on the environmental generalist. In 1898, in his *Elements of Sanitary Engineering*, Mansfield Merriman suggested a broad definition of sanitary science: "Sanitary science embraces those principles and methods by which the health of the community is promoted and the spread of disease is prevented. Hygiene properly relates to the individual or to the family, but sanitary science has a wider scope and includes the village, the city, and the community at large."[31] Prevailing wisdom dictated that, to fulfill his assignment as the new protector of the community's health, the sanitary engineer should be broadly trained. William Paul Gerhard, a noted sanitary engineer, asserted: "The mere fact that a man is qualified in a single special branch—for instance, in house drainage or in the plumbing work of buildings—does not entitle him to be regarded as a sanitary engineer." Gerhard suggested that the sanitary engineer should be "a man with the broadest possible general culture. Only a person combining a liberal education with broad views can expect to attain a high position in modern life."[32] Among the subjects Gerhard thought that the sanitary engineer should acquaint himself with, beyond basic engineering, were biology, chemistry, physics, medicine, architecture, law, and the social sciences.[33] Although this broad training suggests the ideal, rather than the actual, training of practicing sanitary engineers, the formalizing of the curriculum at major technical schools, colleges, and universities brought some standards to the profession—standards which required a breadth of training.

The contemporary view of the goals and responsibilities of sanitary engineers also indicates strong emphasis on the development of environmental generalists. According to A. Prescott Folwell, author of *Municipal*

[30] *Proceedings of the American Society for Municipal Improvements, Eighth Annual Convention, Niagara Falls, New York* (October 1901), p. 183 (hereafter cited as *Proceedings of the ASMI*).

[31] Mansfield Merriman, *Elements of Sanitary Engineering*, p. 7.

[32] William Paul Gerhard, *Sanitation and Sanitary Engineering*, p. 56. See also "Place of the Engineer in Public Health," *American Journal of Public Health* 4 (July 1914): 589.

[33] Gerhard, *Sanitation and Sanitary Engineering*, pp. 56–59; Merriman, *Elements of Sanitary Engineering*, p. 8; Richards, *Conservation by Sanitation*, pp. 216–19.

Engineering Practice, one of the most influential early guides to sanitary engineering, no one individual could have an expert's knowledge of all necessary subjects, but "a capable city engineer should have a good general knowledge of the most important; a pretty complete one of the most strictly municipal branches, such as paving and sewers; and sufficient common sense and moral courage to recognize when he needs the assistance of an expert in any line, and to secure it."[34]

Beyond the regular duties of sanitary engineers, some perceived a higher calling: sanitary engineers had to transcend their training and seek larger roles as community leaders in philanthropic and political capacities, especially as members of civic commisions, as municipal administrators, and even as officeholders. As sanitarian Ellen H. Richards stated:

> The sanitary engineer has a treble duty for the next few years of civil awakening. Having the knowledge, he must be a "leader" in developing works and plants for state and municipal improvement, at the same time he is an "expert" in their employ. But he must be more; as a health officer he must be a "teacher" of the people to show them why all these things are to be. The slowness with which practicable betterments have been adopted among the rank and file is, partly at least, due to the separation of functions, of specialization, and partly to the exclusiveness of agents in the work.[35]

Richards coined the phrase "public [or civic] engineer" to describe what she perceived to be the goal of the sanitary engineer in society.[36] Gerhard suggested an almost spiritual calling for the sanitary engineer: "Much of the sanitary engineer's work is necessarily of a missionary character, as the public must be educated to appreciate the benefits of sanitation."[37]

The views of Gerhard and Richards typify the elitist mentality which accompanies professional identity. There is always the danger that a professional will assume that he or she has a monopoly on the answers to so-

---

[34] A. Prescott Folwell, *Municipal Engineering Practice*, pp. 1–2.

[35] Richards, *Conservation by Sanitation*, p. v. See also "The 'Civil Engineer,' " *Engineering Record* 67 (10 May 1913): 509.

[36] Richards, *Conservation by Sanitation*, p. 222. According to Schultz and McShane, "Sanitarians, landscape architects, and engineers formed a troika that tried to pull critics and officials alike from the mire of governmental inaction to the higher ground of municipal planning and administration." Schulz and McShane, "To Engineer the Metropolis," p. 396.

[37] Gerhard, *Sanitation and Sanitary Engineering*, p. 58. In the 1920s sanitary engineering led to the formation of yet another new engineering subdivision—public-health engineering, a combination of sanitary engineering and sanitary inspection. Later the term "environmental engineer" became a popular title for modern engineers with duties similar to those of the sanitary engineer. See Smillie, *Public Health Administration in the United States*, p. 260; Earle B. Phelps, *The Principles of Public Health Engineering*, pp. 236–43.

ciety's ills. And so with the sanitary engineers, who came to view themselves as guardians of the urban physical environment. Yet the growing professionalism of sanitary engineers helped formalize their training as environmental generalists and technical specialists. As they grew in stature as leaders in sanitation reform, this dual role would ensure a relatively sophisticated view of the problem.

Sanitary engineers became a powerful force in municipal affairs not simply because of their apparent suitability for the task but also because of the powerful influence they exerted nationally and internationally through their professional organizations. Involvement in various engineering societies and other professional group activities, plus access to a network of technical publications, such as *Engineering News* and *Municipal Journal and Engineer*, provided suitable media for the communication of new ideas and specifically for the reinforcement of the growing conviction that refuse was an engineering responsibility. One of the first and best-known groups dealing with the refuse problem was APHA's Committee on the Disposal of Garbage and Refuse. It claimed among its members many of the most respected sanitary engineers of the time, including Hering. The committee was appointed in 1887 to inquire into and make recommendations about the waste problem in the United States. In 1897, after a decade of research and the assimilation of thousands of pieces of data, the committee issued its seminal report, certainly the most thorough evaluation of American collection and disposal practices of its time. It incorporated information from approximately 150 cities, including evaluations of collection and disposal methods, costs, and comparisons with European methods. The 1897 report was the first step in developing a consensus on many of the refuse problems of the day and how to deal with them.[38]

The American Society for Municipal Improvements (later the American Society of Municipal Engineers) concentrated much of its effort on the refuse problem. The ASMI was the first national organization to try to unite all municipal engineers into one group. In 1894, Geroge H. Frost, publisher of *Engineering News*; M. J. Murphy, street commissioner of Saint Louis; and a few others brought together more than sixty city officials from sixteen cities at an organizational meeting in Buffalo, New York. In

---

[38]Rudolph Hering, "Report of the Committee on Disposal of Garbage and Refuse." in American Public Health Association, *Public Health: Papers and Reports* 29 (October 1903): 129 (hereafter cited as APHA); APHA, *A Half Century of Public Health*, ed. Mazyck P. Ravenel, pp. 190–91.

1897, the ASMI resisted absorption by the newly formed League of American Municipalities but in so doing lost almost all its mayor and councilman members to the new group. Thereafter ASMI's membership became narrower, and the organization evolved into an engineering society. It devoted much effort to disseminating information about the newest municipal engineering techniques and encouraged professional exchanges and social interaction among its members as a means of forging bonds of cooperation among municipal engineers. The annual convention became the primary medium through which most of the ideas were transmitted, and it was designed to attract the widest representation. To that end meeting places were often selected outside the manufacturing belt of the East, in such cities as Dallas, Texas; Birmingham, Alabama; and even Montreal and Toronto, Canada. Although the ASMI never achieved the numerical strength of other engineering societies, it had a steady growth throughout the early decades of the new century. In 1894 the membership totaled 53; by 1916 it was 552. Fewer than 20 cities were represented at the original Buffalo meeting; 266 cities were represented at the 1916 meeting in Newark, New Jersey.[39]

Other engineering groups with broader interests than those of the ASMI devoted at least some attention to the waste problem. At its conventions the American Society of Civil Engineers (ASCE) usually included sessions on refuse. Periodically the ASCE established ad hoc committees to investigate garbage and related problems. From time to time specialized groups not directly associated with major engineering organizations were formed to meet a specific need or provide a vehicle for the dissemination of information. For instance, in 1915 the Society for Street Cleaning and Refuse Disposal of the United States and Canada was established with the stated aim to "guide the thought and concentrate the effort to secure better conditions in street cleaning and refuse methods." Like other groups it gathered statistics, held conventions, and distributed information about the newest techniques and equipment available to cities.[40]

Since the engineering profession had always had strong ties abroad, it is not surprising that many American sanitary engineers belonged to inter-

---

[39] *Proceedings of the ASMI, Twenty-fourth Annual Convention, Buffalo, New York* (October 1918), pp. 296–313; American Society for Municipal Improvements, *American Society for Municipal Improvements* (hereafter cited as ASMI).

[40] "Society for Street Cleaning and Refuse Disposal of the United States and Canada," *Municipal Journal and Engineer* 41 (23 November 1916): 646–47.

national organizations with shared interests in sanitation. In August, 1900, the International Committee on Street Hygiene was formed as an outgrowth of the important International Congress for Hygiene and Demography. The committee consisted of seventeen members with British engineer H. Alfred Roechling as chairman. The ubiquitous Hering was also a member. The committee met in Brussels in 1902 to outline its aims of the "furtherance of good sanitation" through street construction, repair, cleaning, and planting; public water closets; and proper disposal of waste. In 1904, at the International Congress of Engineers, three sessions were devoted to sanitary engineering, including one on the disposal of refuse. Most significantly, the International Association of Public Works Officials regularly conducted conferences on sanitary matters, including street cleaning.[41] The worldwide ties which many sanitary engineers established helped broaden their perspectives and provide comparative models to judge domestic refuse-management programs.

Possessing a broad environmental consciousness, administrative experience, and technical training, sanitary engineers were better prepared to confront the refuse problem than were the city bureaucrats and politicians who hired them or sought their counsel. Sanitary engineers were not always successful in finding permanent solutions, but they produced the first comprehensive evaluation of the extent, nature, and complexity of the refuse problem, which pointed to a range of potential solutions. Although some of their recommendations were criticized or ignored by municipal leaders in the politically charged atmosphere of city government, they offered realistic alternatives to the primitive methods still being widely practiced. They also provided the first national, and even international, perspective on refuse problems which further helped discredit the shortsighted programs of the past.

Imbued with a penchant for the systematic and the orderly, sanitary engineers understood the importance of gathering and collating data about past and present collection and disposal practices as a necessary prelude to offering possible solutions. The first stage in the evaluation process was to take account of local conditions which affected the waste problem. Hering believed that local conditions had to be observed to "protect health, to avoid nuisance and to require an expenditure that is comfortably within

[41] *Engineering News* 48 (30 November 1902): 359; *Municipal Journal and Engineer* 17 (November 1904): 214–15; International Association of Public Works Officials, *Report of Proceedings—Conference of Street Cleaning Officials* (1919), pp. 5–26.

the available means of the community."[42] To understand a community's problems in context, however, required more than evaluating local conditions. That is where the sanitary engineer's involvement in national and international organizations could pay off handsomely. From the late nineteenth century onward, engineering societies—often in conjunction with other groups interested in sanitation—applied their resources to conducting surveys and collecting data on collection and disposal practices in North America and abroad. As Hering stated:

> The problem of refuse has . . . become more complex than formerly, and this complexity may not yet have reached its limit. In order that correct solutions for the best methods of disposal may be found, both from the standpoint of sanitation and economy, it is necessary to inquire into details far more than formerly, so as to have more definite facts and figures with which to solve the problem. The more accurate information now required is necessary for the varying special conditions existing in different communities. In short, we must have more special data and statistics before we can indicate the best methods for the disposal of a particular town's refuse.[43]

The importance of the surveys often transcended their use as envisioned by Hering. Such surveys ultimately provided a national focus for the refuse problem, allowing investigators to observe trends and patterns not recognizable when the problem was examined from the narrow local perspective. Indeed, much of the information gathered produced a consensus among engineers about the important aspects of the waste issue.

The surveys varied in quality and comprehensiveness. Some were based on extensive statistical samples, while others were less scientific. Despite these problems a veritable reservoir of information became available to city governments. APHA's "Report of the Committee on Garbage" of 1897 was a model upon which many subsequent investigations were based. Although the committee did not actually conduct its own local investigations or experiments, it did collect and collate statistical information, inspect disposal works, and evaluate the evidence and opinions of

[42]Rudolph Hering, "How to Attack the Sewage and Garbage Problems," *American City* 9 (August 1913): 111.

[43]Rudolph Hering, "The Need for More Accurate Data in Refuse Disposal Work," *American Journal of Public Health* 2 (December 1912): 909–10. See also American Public Health Association, Sanitary Engineering Section, "Report of the Committee on Street Cleaning" (Report read before the APHA, Jacksonville, Fla., November–December, 1914); Rudolph Hering, "Report of the Committee on Disposal of Refuse Materials" in APHA, *Public Health: Papers and Reports* 27 (September 1901): 184–85.

others. The committee also examined the contemporary literature on the subject. The report in many ways simply restated the obvious, suggesting that local conditions often dictated collection and disposal practices, but it presented the first panoramic view of the refuse problem in the United States. Unfortunately, because of a shortage of funds, the report was published without the accompanying statistical tabulations. It nonetheless provided encouragement to other groups hoping to refine the study and determine its applicability to their city or region. Between 1900 and 1917 the report inspired many additional studies and special municipal investigations. Cities such as Buffalo, Chicago, Louisville, and Washington, D.C., carried out extensive inquiries.[44] With the flurry of investigations in the early years of the twentieth century, the APHA's garbage committee, realizing the problems inherent in interpreting disparate data from a wide array of sources, devised the "Standard Form for Statistics of Municipal Refuse" in 1913 to bring some order to the collection of data.[45]

Collection of data and investigations of city practices offered a sounder base for evaluating the sanitary needs of communities than the qualitative measures of the nineteenth century had provided. Sanitary engineers were not satisfied simply to collect statistics, however. Implementing new programs or revising old ones was a necessary second step, which required effective administration. Sanitary engineers advised municipalities on ways of placing their public-works departments on a business footing. Sanitary engineers sought uniformity in organizational methods, and several of them, such as the noted Samuel A. Greeley, looked to European practices for guidance:

One who has investigated refuse disposal work abroad, cannot but be impressed with the uniformity of the methods used there, more especially for the house treat-

[44] "Report of the Committee on the Disposal of Garbage and Refuse," in APHA, *Public Health: Papers and Reports* 23 (October 1897): 206–18. See also W. F. Morse, "The Next Step in the Work of Refuse and Garbage Disposal," in APHA, *Papers and Reports* 25 (October–November 1899): 312; APHA, *A Half Century of Public Health*, pp. 190–91; *Proceedings of the ASMI, Seventeenth Annual Convention, Erie, Pennsylvania* (October 1910), p. 67; Rudolph Hering, "Vexed Question of Garbage Disposal," *Engineering Magazine* 13 (June 1897): 392–98; Hering, "Modern Practice in the Disposal of Refuse," *American Journal of Public Health* 1 (December 1911): 910; "Refuse Disposal Investigations," *Municipal Journal and Engineer* 25 (2 December 1908): 787; Rudolph Hering and Samuel A. Greeley, *Collection and Disposal of Municipal Refuse*, pp. 12–20.

[45] "Report of the Committee on Refuse Collection and Disposal," *American Journal of Public Health* 5 (September 1915): 933–34.

ment and collection of refuse, but also for the disposal. German cities are approaching a common standard in this work. Differences in the effectiveness of the service are in large part due to differences in the ability of the department chiefs in charge of the work.[46]

Sanitary engineers vigorously debated the advisability of implementing specific European programs, but they tended to share Greeley's admiration for European organization.

Careful record keeping came to be regarded as one of the best ways to improve municipal refuse management. Itemizing costs, recording the quantity and composition of wastes, and evaluating seasonal variations in collection and disposal practices proved to be effective ways of monitoring a city's sanitation program. For example, determining the amount of moisture and combustible matter in garbage or considering the potential by-products in the wastes helped city officials determine the most efficient and effective methods of disposal. Cities often failed to take such factors into consideration before choosing new disposal methods, with the result that thousands of dollars were squandered on expensive equipment which did not produce the desired results. According to *Engineering Record*:

It is not enough to make a few estimates in the winter and in the summer, but a year's records obtained at least once every month and preferably more often should be secured. Unless this is done, any system of collection and disposal that is adopted is based on guess-work, and every intelligent citizen has had enough opportunity to observe the results of guesswork in municipal affairs to be loathe to encourage anything of that sort.[47]

In the sanitary engineers' recommendations for efficient refuse management was almost universal support for municipal control of sanitation functions. Although commitment to community responsibility in street cleaning and garbage removal was spotty during the 1880s and 1890s, the

[46] Samuel A. Greeley, "A Standard Form for Statistics of Municipal Refuse," *American Jouranl of Public Health* 2 (June 1912): 403. See also Louis L. Tribus, "Refuse and Garbage Disposal—A General Survey," *American Journal of Public Health* 6 (December 1916): 1307–14.

[47] "Refuse Disposal in America," *Engineering News* 58 (25 July 1908): 85. See also S. Whinery, "Recent Progress in Methods and Character of Street Cleaning," *American Journal of Public Health* 4 (August 1914): 680; S. Whinery, "How to Keep the Streets Clean," *American City* 10 (January 1914): 23–24; Baker, "Condition of Garbage Disposal in United States," p. 147; F. C. Bamman, "Analysis of Cost Keeping as Applied to Municipal Management of Street Cleaning," *American Journal of Public Health* 4 (August 1914): 674–78; P. M. Hall, "Methods of Accounting in the Collection of City Waste," *American Journal of Public Health* 2 (June 1912): 399–402; Hering, "How to Attack the Sewage and Garbage Problems," p. 111.

increasing emphasis on "home rule" in the larger cities and the subsequent expansion of municipal bureaucracies made municipal control of sanitation seem more practicable. At first glance it might seem that a large portion of the engineering community would disapprove of municipal control, especially since many sanitary engineers made their livings as itinerant consultants, selling their advice and expertise to city officials throughout the country. Also, some engineers, like Colonel Morse, channeled their engineering expertise into entrepreneurial ventures, such as manufacturing and marketing collection and disposal equipment. Yet the itinerant consultant and the engineering entrepreneur had vested interests in municipal control of sanitation. After all, municipal control provided a greater degree of permanence than contracted services. New sanitation programs required a large investment as well as considerable time to produce the complex management system required, especially in the large cities. Furthermore, city-provided sanitation services ensured jobs for sanitary engineers, jobs which afforded them substantial responsibility, authority, and power. The sense of permanence and stability which municipal control implied offered the best atmosphere for the sanitary engineer to promote his career and the necessary reforms required to produce a well-organized program of sanitation. In their influential book *Collection and Disposal of Municipal Refuse*, Hering and Greeley stated bluntly, "The collection of public refuse is a public utility."[48]

If any support for the contract system existed among sanitary engineers, it was qualified to provide more rigorous municipal supervision of contracted work. Not everyone accepted consulting engineer Louis L. Tribus's matter-of-fact conclusion that "unsightliness and uncleanliness have gone hand in hand with private collection," but many tended to agree.[49] M. N. Baker condemned what was considered the greatest abuse of the contract system, the short-term (annual or biannual) contract. According to Baker, the contract was "one important cause for the unsatisfactory condition of garbage disposal in the United States." The short-term contract came under attack not primarily because it granted exclusive responsibility to the private sector but because it provided little long-range planning for the city. Baker repeated an oft-stated conclusion that contracts were granted for political reasons, which made them suspect. He also strongly emphasized that the duration of such contracts was too short to

---

[48] Hering and Greeley, *Collection and Disposal of Municipal Refuse*, p. 4.
[49] Tribus, "Refuse and Garbage Disposal—A General Survey," p. 1311

allow for the adoption of new disposal methods, which required extensive coordination and planning, not to mention heavy costs.[50] Unlike political reformers who spoke about the contractor's indifference and lack of commitment to civic betterment, the sanitary engineer tended to emphasize the technical and administrative problems associated with the contract system.

Surveys conducted from the 1890s to the outbreak of World War I indicate a substantial shift away from the contract system and toward increased municipal responsibility in street cleaning and garbage collection and disposal. By 1880 a significant number of American cities (approximately 70 percent) had made important strides in the municipal control of street cleaning, and a survey of 150 cities taken in 1914 indicated that about 90 percent of the cities had assumed responsibility for street cleaning.[51] In collection and disposal, which had traditionally lagged far behind street cleaning, surveys from the 1890s onward indicated a steady rise in municipal responsibility. By World War I at least 50 percent of American cities had some form of municipal collection system, as compared with only 24 percent in 1880.[52] Whether the sanitary engineers influenced this trend is difficult to determine, but there is little question that municipal control of sanitation provided them with a solid base of operations in municipal government.

Once sanitary engineers began exploring the magnitude and complexities of the refuse problem, they came to realize, more than any other group had before them, that tinkering with the existing programs would be insufficient. Consequently they advocated centralization of refuse management through municipal departments operating under the newest managerial techniques. Their administrative and organizational programs borrowed heavily from private industry as well as from successful water- and waste-water-carriage programs. While the administrative methods and or-

---

[50] Baker, "Condition of Garbage Disposal in United States," p. 148. See also James, *Municipal Functions*, pp. 234–44; League of American Municipalities, *Proceedings of the Fifth Annual Convention, Jamestown, New York* (August 1901), p. 21; *Proceedings of the ASMI, Sixth Annual Convention, Toronto* (October 1899), pp. 232–35; "Municipal Ownership of Refuse Plants," *Municipal Journal and Engineer 32 (27 June 1912): 987.*

[51] Gleaned from "Statistics of Cities," in *U.S. Department of Labor, Bulletin no. 36* (September 1901): 880–85; *Municipal Journal and Engineer 37* (10 December 1914): 836–44.

[52] Gleaned from "Refuse Collection and Disposal," *Municipal Journal and Engineer 39* (11 November 1915): 723–27; B. F. Miller, "Garbage Collection and Disposal," in *Proceedings of the ASMI, Twenty-second Annual Convention, Dayton, Ohio* (October 1915), pp. 10–11.

ganizational techniques of these bodies had validity for refuse management, solutions to the problems of collection and disposal required further examination and study. As William T. Sedgwick, a leader in water-pollution control, suggested, "Doubtless one reason why the refuse problem is still so vexing in most communities is because the collections, of necessity, must be intermittent, and yet the system must function smoothly and without interruption."[53] Sedgwick, of course, revealed only the tip of the iceberg, since no single method of collection and disposal could be universally applied.

If sanitary engineers were unable to find the ultimate technological methods of collection and disposal, they did make strides in placing in perspective the relative strengths and weaknesses of primitive methods and the potential applicability of new techniques. With the luxury of hindsight they understood many of the limitations of nineteenth-century methods. They almost universally condemned or at least criticized such practices as land and sea dumping, open burning, and filling with untreated wastes. In an informal discussion at the annual meeting of the American Society of Civil Engineers in 1903, John McGaw Woodbury, the street-cleaning commissioner of New York, asserted, "It is of the utmost importance that dumping at sea be stopped, not simply because it makes the beaches unsanitary and unsightly, but because it is a waste of valuable material."[54]

Woodbury and other critics of primitive methods failed to take into account ecological considerations, but the ever-increasing quantities of refuse convinced sanitary engineers that in the selection of methods more comprehensive criteria had to be devised. As pragmatists, sanitary engineers placed emphasis on the need to examine local conditions thoroughly before advising about appropriate collection and disposal methods for a given community. In planning new systems, they tried to take into consideration not only the types and quantities of wastes but also the quality of local transportation facilities, the composition of the agency in charge of the work, and physical characteristics of the city that might determine the type and location of the disposal system. Engineers also began considering political and social factors that might indicate the receptivity of the local government and citizenry to changes in sanitation practices. The reliance of sanitary engineers on a technological solution to the problem of refuse,

[53] William T. Sedgwick, *Principles of Sanitary Science and the Public Health*, p. 115.

[54] "The Sanitary Disposal of Municipal Refuse," *Transactions of the American Society of Civic Engineers* 50 (1903): 104 (hereafter cited as *Transactions of the ASCE*).

therefore, was increasingly being tempered out of necessity by considerations which were broader in scope and not directly related to refuse as an engineering problem. In a sense, sanitary engineers, as implementers of new systems, began adapting to the complexity of the issue, relying more on their roles as environmental generalists than on their positions as technical specialists.[55]

Because of their low regard for primitive methods of collection and disposal, sanitary engineers focused their attention on newer methods which they hoped would fulfill the sanitary and financial requirements of the various cities. Incineration and reduction were most often discussed as the logical alternatives to the older methods. Each method had its advocates and detractors, but both came under greater scrutiny than they had when they were first introduced in the late nineteenth century. Gone was the naïve view that either method offered the final answer. The maturity of the sanitary-engineering profession and the knowledge gleaned from hasty implementation of poorly tested equipment brought a more measured response to the unqualified advocacy of a single method.

The success of the English destructors abroad had led the APHA's refuse committee to give its provisional endorsement to incineration in 1897 and had also led to the rapid implementation of the method in several cities.[56] As further study of the application of British systems to American needs indicated, however, some municipalities had acted rashly in building untested or inappropriate equipment. Colonel Morse argued that several failures had occurred because of insufficient professional analysis of incineration principles, faulty incinerator designs, overconfidence in the capabilities of the apparatuses, and unskillul management of the crematories.[57] With further study it became clear that British destructors could not be employed without careful adaption to American needs, both financial and technical.[58]

[55] Hering, "Disposal of City Refuse," pp. 398–406; "Report of the Committee on the Disposal of Garbage and Refuse" (1897), p. 207; Harry R. Crohurst, *Municipal Wastes: Their Character, Collection, and Disposal*, pp. 79ff; *Proceedings of the ASMI, Twenty-second Annual Convention* (1916), pp 244–45; Baker, "Condition of Garbage Disposal in the United States," pp. 147–48; "Report of the Committee on Street Cleaning," *American Journal of Public Health* 5 (March 1915): 255–59.

[56] "Report of the Committee on the Disposal of Garbage and Refuse," in APHA, *Public Health: Papers and Reports* 22 (April 1897): 108.

[57] William F. Morse, "The Disposal of Municipal Wastes," *Municipal Journal and Engineer* 22 (6 March 1907): 232–35.

[58] Morse, "The Sanitary Disposal of Municipal Refuse," *ASCE Transactions* 50 (1903):

The reduction process, which appeared in the United States about the same time as incineration, went through a similar evolution: impulsive implementation, severe criticism, and reevaluation. The 1897 report indicated a great deal of interest in the method because of its promise of returning revenue to the city.[59] Experiments by Colonel Waring and others generated considerable interest, but after a period of operation in some cities, several undesirable side effects led to increased criticism of the method. The foul odors emanating from the plant raised loud protests. Memphis Mayor J. J. Williams complained:

The air for miles and miles around [the reduction plants] is so contaminated that the courts and lawmakers have been appealed to, and have, as a rule, given relief to the sufferers by abating the foul, diseasebreeding business. . . . if for no other cause, the laws should prohibit these establishments, because it is degrading and inhuman for human beings to spend their days in such an occupation as assorting the filth of our cities.[60]

In 1916, ASMI's Committee on Refuse Disposal and Street Cleaning recommended a compromise. Reduction was fine for large cities where the revenue derived from it might warrant its use, but for small cities incineration appeared to be more sanitary and less costly.[61] (Incineration and reduction will be discussed more fully in chapter 6.)

The days of haphazard collection and disposal practices appeared to be ending with the rise of sanitary engineers. The careful accumulation of data, the design and evaluation of new equipment, and the organizational structure of public-works departments were the kinds of improvements admired in an increasingly complex—and confounding—age. In the chaos of the newly emerging urban-industrial society, dependence on experts seemed imperative. Not only technical expertise but managerial skills and efficiency were especially prized talents. As Samuel Haber suggested, many Americans were having a love affair with efficiency: ". . . the pro-

114ff; "Refuse Disposal in America," *Engineering Record* 58 (25 July 1908): 85; "Why American Garbage Crematories Fail," *Municipal Journal and Engineer* 13 (November 1902): 234; *Proceedings of the ASMI, Eighteenth Annual Convention* (1911), pp. 8–11.

[59] "Report of the Committee on the Disposal of Garbage and Refuse" (1897), pp. 215–18. See also *Proceedings of the ASMI, Fourth Annual Convention, Nashville, Tenn.* (October 1897), p. 223.

[60] "Garbage Collection and Disposal," *City Government* 7 (September 1899): 50. See also Joseph G. Branch, *Heat and Light from Municipal and Other Waste*, pp. 7–8.

[61] "Report of Committee on Refuse Disposal and Street Cleaning," in *Proceedings of the ASMI, Twenty-second Annual Convention* (1916), p. 245.

gressive era gave rise to an efficiency craze—a secular Great Awakening, an outpouring of ideas and emotions in which a gospel of efficiency was preached without embarrassment to businessmen, workers, doctors, housewives, and teachers, and yes, preached even to preachers."[62]

Yet the impact of sanitary engineers on refuse management depended at least as much on their ability to perceive the totality of the urban environment as on their skill in tinkering with its parts. Had there been greater cooperation between health departments and public-works departments during the period, that perspective might have been broader yet. Nonetheless, sanitary reform came a long way under the guidance of the sanitary engineers. They effectively refined Colonel Waring's rudimentary environmentalism and formalized it through their young profession.

Operating from within the institutional structure of municipal government, sanitary engineers had little occasion (or inclination) to define their responsibilities in terms of popularizing refuse reform or promoting civic involvement in finding solutions. They often failed to grasp that to the nonspecialist and to the layman refuse was primarily an aesthetic problem. Responding to sanitary reform with emotional zeal, early in the twentieth century voluntary citizens' groups—especially women's organizations—added an aesthetic perspective and a social consciousness to the sanitary engineers' technical and organizational reforms. Somewhere between the time of Waring's death and World War I refuse reform found expression in two distinctive, though not totally divergent, groups: one technical and organizational, the other aesthetic and civic-oriented. How civic reformers dealt with the refuse problem is the subject of the next chapter.

[62] Samuel Haber, *Efficiency and Uplift: Scientific Management in the Progressive Era, 1890–1920*, p. ix. The "efficiency" movement was a central feature of reform efforts of the late nineteenth and early twentieth centuries. For a discussion of this issue from various standpoints see Martin J. Schiesl, *The Politics of Efficiency: Municipal Administration and Reform in America: 1880–1920*; Samuel P. Hays, *Conservation and the Gospel of Efficiency: The Progressive Conservation Movement, 1890–1920*; Layton, *The Revolt of the Engineers*; Maury Klein and Harvey A. Kantor, *Prisoners of Progress: American Industrial Cities, 1850–1920*, pp 27–32.

4

Refuse as an Aesthetic Problem: Voluntary Citizens' Organizations and Sanitation

In his widely circulated technical tract *Garbage Crematories in America* (1906), William Mayo Venable commented optimistically on the growing interest in sanitary reform in the early years of the twentieth century:

The reason why the problem of refuse disposal is receiving an ever-increasing amount of attention from engineers, municipal authorities, and from the American public does not lie in the newness of the problem, but rather in an intellectual awakening of the people. The same spirit that leads men to realize the corruption of politics and business, and to attempt to remedy those conditions by adopting new methods of administration and new laws, also leads to a realization of the primitiveness of the methods of waste disposal still employed by many communities, and to a consequent desire for improvement.[1]

The sporadic protests against the "garbage nuisance" in the nineteenth century had made way for better-organized and more comprehensive reform efforts in the twentieth century. Yet, as sanitary reform broadened in scope and appeal, it also splintered into two distinctive though not totally independent factions. The first was dominated by the sanitary engineers, a technical elite who functioned within the municipal infrastructure. The second group, primarily composed of citizens' organizations, operated in the public realm. Seeking the same ends, they approached the refuse problem from different perspectives. Sanitary engineers attempted to identify the problems associated with waste collection and disposal and offered administrative and technical solutions. Although they were in a good position to influence policymaking within the city bureaucracy, their professional allegiances and obligations tended to limit their effectiveness as popularizers

[1] William Mayo Venable, *Garbage Crematories in America*, p. 1.

of their reforms at the grassroots level. Citizens' groups and civic organizations, on the other hand, had to rely on some form of public support or public participation to give their protests moment. These two strains of reform were not at odds; they appealed to different audiences, different constituencies.

The significance of the civic dimension of refuse reform did not lie primarily in efforts to devise new collection and disposal programs or in the writing of new ordinances. The institutionalization and bureaucratization of refuse management placed responsibility for the former directly on the public-works and engineering departments. The writing of new ordinances, although important, simply resulted in updating existing laws or attempting to make them more enforceable. The major impact of civic reform was educational, that is, in publicizing and popularizing a new environmental ethic of cleanliness and efficiency, with the hope of promoting greater civic involvement.

The time was right for public action. Especially after the Panic of 1893, a municipal-reform impulse permeated all facets of urban life. The depression of the 1890s placed in high relief the price which unregulated economic growth exacted from the country, especially in major urban centers dependent on industrial production. Would-be reformers, reflecting on the benefits versus the costs of rapid economic and physical growth, argued that the time had come to consider the priorities of the new industrial society. In 1896, Thomas C. Devlin wrote:

> This magical growth of cities has been the pride of the people. The metropolis of each state is a sort of Mecca for its people. The cities have become a gigantic power in the political and social life of the nation. It is the intellectual force of the American cities which shapes legislation through state and national conventions. Within them are all the allurements and excitements of modern life. . . . This movement is necessarily attended by many evils, and much has been said and written to counteract the crowding of cities. Such efforts are useless. The present population of cities is permanent. The evils which have been incidental to their rapid growth must be eliminated. Living in cities must be desirable.[2]

"Living in cities must be desirable" captures the essence of urban reform in the late nineteenth and early twentieth centuries, especially the

[2] Thomas C. Devlin, *Municipal Reform in the United States*, pp. 39–40. For additional bibliographic references on the emergence of municipal reform in the 1890s and beyond, see William M. Leary, Jr., and Arthur S. Link, eds., *The Progressive Era and the Great War, 1896–1920*, 2d ed.

civic phase. Urbanites began responding to the need for what Roy Lubove called "the creation of a socially integrated and physically beautiful city." [3] The determination to "humanize" the urban environment was not original with reformers of the post-1893 period, nor were their proposed solutions necessarily original. Reforms which had received random local attention in the 1870s and 1880s became national issues in the late 1890s. Only a year after the Panic of 1893 the United States was experiencing the most intense public interest in municipal affairs in its history. In the early months of 1894 there were fewer than 50 urban reform groups; by December the total had risen to well over 180. Every large city and many smaller ones had at least one reform organization by 1896. Enthusiasm for the groups' activities broadened as well, with substantial support coming from academics, city officials, and journalists. In 1909 there were more than one hundred periodicals dealing primarily with urban affairs. [4]

The momentum generated by the municipal-reform groups touched many nagging problems which had befuddled and annoyed city dwellers in the past and brought attention to other problems which had been ignored or had gone undetected. Civic groups confronted issues in areas ranging from education to entertainment, from parks and public buildings to water purification, from smoke abatement to transportation. [5] For the moment at least the mood for reform had no bounds. It was the anarchy of the reformist mood, the boundlessness of zeal, and the depth and breadth of enthusiasm, as much as the substance of the problems themselves, which provided a public forum for many civic issues. And who or what should be responsible for the urban revival? Municipal government, of course. As Devlin wrote:

To protect the lives and property of the people, to care for the morals, health, education, and protection of the community, to foster its interests, to manage its finances judiciously, to demand and secure the best service in every work under its supervision, are all within the purview of city government. Shall these be done well or shall the evils that have followed in the wake of great national progress finally engulf the whole? There is more national patriotism and local pride than ever before, but less civic spirit. This too is being aroused, and the intelligence and energy

[3] Roy Lubove, "The Twentieth Century City: The Progressive as Municipal Reformer," *Mid-America* 41 (October 1959): 200.

[4] Melvin G. Holli, "Urban Reform in the Progressive Era," in Lewis L. Gould, ed., *The Progressive Era*, pp. 133–41; Ernest S. Griffith, *A History of American City Government: The Progressive Years and Their Aftermath, 1900–1920*, pp. 118–19.

[5] See William Howe Tolman, *Municipal Reform Movements in the United States*.

which have accomplished so much in the development of industries and the building of cities will also find good forms of government.[6]

The proliferation of municipal reform organizations had several causes: growing civic pride, intercity rivalries, new interest in community-wide projects and building programs, humanitarian concerns, and physical disasters and epidemics. In other words, the realization of common goals drew citizens closer together. Voluntary citizens' organizations and taxpayers' associations were the first groups to become interested in civic betterment (several of them originated even before the post-1893 reform upsurge). Some of the organizations professed a general interest in municipal reform, taking such names as City Improvement Society, the City Reform Club, and the City Government Club. Others had more specific interests and goals. The Anti-Spoils League of New York, for instance, sought to abolish the patronage practices which had undermined public-service jobs. Another group, the Society for the Prevention of Crime, attempted to make the city a safer place to live.[7]

Municipal officials and bureaucrats also acquired group identities at this time. The professionalization of service departments and the reorganization of city governments through charter revisions or through the adoption of new forms such as the Commission Plan and later the City Manager Plan provided the impetus for these associations.[8] Some formed alliances with citizens' organizations and vied for leadership of reform movements. Among the first organizations of municipal officials were the Municipal Finance Officers Association and the National Association of Port Authorities, both with specialized interests. Most significant, however, was the rise of groups composed of executive officials, such as the Conference of Mayors and the Conference of City Managers. Like the various engineering societies, the executive officials of these organizations sought out their peers to form state and national associations whose interests transcended local problems.[9]

[6] Devlin, *Municipal Reform in the United States*, pp. 14–15.

[7] Tolman, *Municipal Reform Movements in the United States*, pp. 47–136. See also Holli, "Urban Reform in the Progressive Era," pp. 135–36; Griffith, *A History of American City Government: The Progressive Years and Their Aftermath, 1900–1920*, pp. 117–19.

[8] For a discussion of the Commission Plan see Bradley Robert Rice, *Progressive Cities: The Commission Government Movement in America, 1901–1920*; see Rice's bibliography for citations on the City Manager Plan.

[9] Griffith, *A History of American City Government: The Progressive Years and Their Aftermath, 1900–1920*, pp 156–60.

The National Municipal League (NML), an outgrowth of the first National Conference for Good City Government (held in 1894), was the best known of the municipal associations. Herbert Welsh, of the Municipal League of Philadelphia, organized the NML and attracted representatives from New York City, Brooklyn, Chicago, Boston, Baltimore, Minneapolis, Milwaukee, Albany, Buffalo, Columbus, and, of course, Philadelphia. The league began in May, 1894, with 16 affiliated local groups. By the next year the ranks had swelled to 180 branches, and 80 or 90 more were added in 1896. The core of the membership came from the Middle Atlantic states, especially New York and New Jersey.[10] A rival organization, the League of American Municipalities, was founded in 1897. It garnered strength from small and medium-sized cities instead of from the larger metropolises, where the National Municipal League dominated. Despite the emergence of these major associations, state organizations continued to flourish, largely because they concentrated on manageable issues relevant to the regions they served. In 1901 there were only 11 state organizations, but by 1915 their number had increased to at least 29.[11]

In the congenial reform atmosphere of the 1890s and later, environmental problems in general and sanitation problems in particular gained wide interest. Water, smoke, noise, and refuse pollution became important subjects of community protest, since they affected a large cross section of the population. The progressive spirit which dominated the reform milieu of the day was geared to view social problems in an environmental context—human beings, it was believed, would seek "the good" if the physical and social environments were made less hostile. As sanitary engineers borrowed the gospel of efficiency from progressivism, citizens' organizations and their allies borrowed its civic-mindedness, its emphasis on aesthetics, and its moralistic tone. Like Colonel Waring, the citizens' groups spoke the language of progressivism, couching sanitary reform in environmental and moralistic terms. Waste, by polluting the physical surroundings, threatened health and promoted squalor. Primitive collection and disposal practices were signs of backwardness and barbarity; civilized societies were well-kept and sanitary. One could hardly expect citizens to seek moral and material progress in a despoiled habitat polluted by litter

---

[10]Clifford Patton, *Battle for Municipal Reform: Mobilization and Attack, 1875–1900*, pp. 34–35.

[11]Griffith, *A History of American City Government: The Progressive Years and Their Aftermath, 1900–1920*, pp. 159–60.

and disease-breeding refuse. In the broadest sense filth bred chaos, while cleanliness promoted order. Civic pride and responsibility, therefore, were necessary attributes of urbanites committed to municipal improvement.[12]

Historian Melvin Holli has argued that most urban reforms of the late 1890s were "basically refinements of older concepts."[13] That is certainly true of sanitation reform. Civic groups continued to emphasize that waste was a health problem much in the vein of the protests of the Ladies' Health Protective Association in the 1880s. The rhetoric of progressivism, however, changed the tone of sanitation reform, and national publicity secured for it a larger and more diverse audience. The latter was accomplished largely through its association with the "City Beautiful" movement, which swept the nation in the 1890s. At the Columbian Exposition in Chicago in 1893, which marked the four hundredth anniversary of the discovery of America, citizens were treated to the spectacle of the White City:

In contrast to the sprawling, ugly industrial cities that were becoming common at that time, the classical buildings rising from blue lagoons, with their white plaster-of-Paris facades gleaming in the sun, seemed to be a vision of a lost utopia. Observers called it the White City, and it epitomized cleanliness, grandeur, beauty, and order. The lush green lawns and the frequent display of statuary combined with the architecture to impart a classical flavor to the entire exposition.[14]

The visual impressions of the exposition provided dramatic impetus for an aesthetic revival in American cities. "The city no longer need be perceived as an ugly, ungainly giant, but rather as a beautiful, graceful physical creation of human beings. The entire city could be downtown."[15] Almost overnight many projects for city beautification were begun, and major redevelopment plans were designed for Washington, D.C., and Chicago.[16]

The link between City Beautiful, with its grandiose objectives, and sanitary reform, with its more modest goals, might seem tenuous at first glance. The connection was natural and complementary, however. In a perceptive article historian Jon A. Peterson has effectively demonstrated the importance of the civic-improvement idea as a pillar of City Beautiful. Unlike those who claimed that City Beautiful was primarily an effort to promote Classic and Renaissance architecture and monumental planning, Pe-

[12]See Martin V. Melosi, ed., *Pollution and Reform in American Cities, 1870–1930.*
[13]Holli, "Urban Reform in the Progressive Era," p. 133.
[14]David R. Goldfield and Blaine A. Brownell, *Urban America: From Downtown to No Town,* p. 214. See also David F. Burg, *Chicago's White City of 1893.*
[15]Goldfield and Brownell, *Urban America,* p. 214.
[16]Ibid., pp. 214–17.

terson argued that the movement "had other meanings and origins and that their recovery enables us to recognize the phenomenon as a complex cultural movement involving more than the building arts and urban design." Three distinct concepts helped to launch City Beautiful: municipal (or decorative) art, outdoor art (city park development and landscape architecture), and civic improvement. Only after 1901 did City Beautiful appear to shift toward urban planning in the most traditional sense.[17]

The civic improvement legacy, according to Peterson, began as a "laymen's cause" primarily in small and medium-sized cities, especially through village improvement societies. These groups appeared as early as the mid-nineteenth century. Civic improvement achieved national attention through the National League of Improvement Associations (NLIA), established in 1900. Because of the close relationship between the goals of civic improvement—order, cleanliness, moral uplift—and the roles of women as mothers and housewives, women reformers dominated many of the local groups. In 1901 and 1902, the NLIA, renamed the American League for Civic Improvement, defined its goals as promoting outdoor art, public beauty, and town, village, and neighborhood improvement. It emphasized "civic improvement" over the narrower village improvement concept of the past. Through this maneuver "the League aligned itself with the reform ethos of the era," that is progressivism. Its thrust, like City Beautiful itself, was strongly aesthetic. For many people City Beautiful was "the aesthetic expression of turn-of-the-century urban reform."[18]

The emphasis on aesthetics was the major contribution of City Beautiful to sanitary reform. Although there was an indirect connection between sanitary improvement and the architectural and landscape modes of City Beautiful, there was a direct relationship between the cleansing of the physical surroundings and civic improvement. For example, the Civic League of Saint Louis sponsored programs such as a "Keep Our City Clean" campaign, as well as helping secure the appointment of a woman sanitary inspector.[19] Aesthetic considerations had often played a role in the pre-1893 sanitation protests, but City Beautiful institutionalized reform for aesthetics' sake on a national scale.

[17] Jon A. Peterson, "The City Beautiful Movement: Forgotten Origins and Lost Meanings," *Journal of Urban History* 2 (August 1976): 416–28.

[18] Ibid., pp. 421–30.

[19] Ibid., p. 424. See also "Clean Streets and Smokeless Chimneys Demanded," *California Municipalities* 5 (November 1901): 114; Civic League of Saint Louis, *Yearbook* (1907), pp. 9–11, 16–17, 36–37; Saint Louis, Civic Improvement League, *Keep Our City Clean*.

By promoting sanitary reform primarily as an aesthetic and civic issue, citizens' organizations tended to underrate other important considerations. This meant emphasizing health and comfort, moral uplift, and city beautification and downplaying scientific management and efficient administration of public works. Laymen's approach to sanitary reform was broad enough to encompass a wide range of issues which the populace could identify as improving the urban quality of life. In other words, reformers equated City Beautiful with city cleanliness. Caroline Bartlett Crane, a well-known health expert, noted: "We gladly hear much to-day of the movement for civic art; but it is well to remember that civic art without civic cleanliness is a diamond ring on dirty hands. The adornments of a dirty city do but emphasize its dirtiness, while cleanliness has not only a virtue but a beauty of its own."[20] Some reformers carried the argument a bit too far, however. The Friday Conversational Club of Monongahela, Pennsylvania, published the following:

DID YOU EVER STOP TO THINK THAT:

> A clean town means a sanitary and healthful town.
> A clean town means a more beautiful town.
> A clean town means an increase in the value of our property.
> A clean town brings business to our merchants.
> A clean town induces a better class of people to locate here.[21]

The fusing of the aesthetic appeal of City Beautiful with the more traditional health argument did much to broaden the impact of sanitary reform in the public realm without fundamentally changing its purpose and goals. In an atmosphere of civic-mindedness, neighborhood protests with only local significance became city-wide crusades with state and even national ramifications. Periodicals and published proceedings of civic groups were filled with stories describing the refuse problems of various cities and towns and the need for immediate solutions.[22] Demands for municipal management of collection and disposal were greater than ever before. Most reformers accepted the idea that city taxes should provide decent living and working conditions, not simply protect lives and property. This

[20] Caroline Bartlett Crane, "The Work for Clean Streets," in New York City, Women's Municipal League, *Bulletin* 5 (August 1906): 1.

[21] Civic Club of Philadelphia, *Civic Club Bulletin* 5 (October 1911): 15.

[22] See such periodicals as *City Government; Pacific Municipalities; City Hall: Bulletin of the League of American Municipalities: and American Municipalities*. See also bulletins of local civic groups and proceedings of national civic organizations.

An unsanitary open dump in Richmond, Virginia, before the city's 1914 cleanup ordinance was enacted. From *American City*

Dumping ashes and rubbish from barges at Sandy Hook outside New York Harbor about 1900. The material often washed up on the shores of Long Island and New Jersey. From *Scribner's Magazine*

Hand-sorting of refuse in New York City (1903). From *Scribner's Magazine*

Immigrants sorting various grades of paper (1916). From *Scientific American*

This traveling garbage burner meandered through the alleys of Chicago in 1893. It operated at a total cost of about twenty dollars a day. From *Scientific American*

Hydraulic press room in the reduction plant on Barren Island, New York (1903). Steam-treated garbage was pressed to separate reusable by-products. From *Scribner's Magazine*

George E. Waring, Jr., "The Apostle of Cleanliness." Courtesy Public Works Historical Society

The annual parade of Colonel Waring's White Wings in 1897. The sweepers earned fifty dollars a month their first year. From *McClure's Magazine*

One of New York City's White Wings shows off his can carrier in 1905. Each sweeper was supplied with three or four cans. From *Municipal Journal and Engineer*

Headquarters for New York's Juvenile Street Cleaning Leagues (1910). Reuben S. Simons, blind supervisor of the leagues, is on the right. From *American City*

The Alley "L" Club in Chicago pitches in to clean the streets (1911). From *American City*

Edith Pierce awards a badge to one of her Junior Sanitary Leaguers of Philadelphia in 1916. From *Literary Digest*

Little Women Civic League of P.S. No. 4, Manhattan, one of the seventy-one leagues in New York City in 1910. From *American City*

Clean City Campaign—April 26 to May 1

**Everybody
Get Behind
THE BRUSH**

Members are urged to assist in this effort to promote civic pride, healthfulness and fire prevention.

Poster promoting a cleanup campaign in Reading, Pennsylvania, in 1916. Pushing the broom are, left to right, characters representing city departments, fathers, women's clubs, housewives, boy scouts, commercial organizations, painters, paint dealers, and "everybody else." From *American City*

Flushing the streets in Saint Louis (1905). From *Municipal Journal and Engineer*

Dumping garbage from a horse cart into railroad cars in Saint Louis about 1916. The garbage was usually carried away on barges, but at this particular time the Mississippi was frozen over. From *Municipal Journal and Engineer*

The incinerator at Montgomery, Alabama, 1911. The cart on the ramp at the left is approaching the unloading floor. From *American City*

The clinkering process at the Montgomery, Alabama, incinerator (1911). From *American City*

Milwaukee's motor-driven squeegee truck used rubber blades on a roller to scrape the streets clean (1916). It replaced six horse-drawn machines. From *Scientific American*

Flushing streets by trolley car in 1916. The nozzle was mounted on a swinging arm to reach across wide streets. From *American City*

THE "AUSTIN" STREET SWEEPER

For over 25 years has been the *standard of excellence* in leading cities.

Its mechanical parts are simple and strong. Its operating devices are accessible and easily controlled by the driver.

Its construction has no equal in material and workmanship.

The Austin Street Sprinklers

Made in 16 Designs and Sizes

We ship them in carloads and trainloads to governments and large cities; and single machines to small villages and road contractors.

All Unite in Pronouncing Them the Best

Write for list of users—the best proof of SUPERIORITY. We also manufacture Road Plows, Drag and Wheeled Scrapers, Road and Elevating Graders, Dump Wagons, Gyratory and Jaw Rock Crushers, Road Rollers, Scarifiers, etc.

THE AUSTIN-WESTERN CO., Ltd.

50 Church St., NEW YORK   910 S. Michigan Ave., CHICAGO

New York; San Francisco, Cal.; Los Angeles, Cal.; Syracuse, N. Y.; Memphis Tenn.; Salt Lake City, Utah; Atlanta, Ga.; Dallas, Tex.; St. Paul, Minn.

Advertisement for horse-drawn street-cleaning machines (1912). From *Municipal Journal and Engineer*

Springfield, Ohio, became one of the first cities to experiment with completely motorized street-cleaning equipment in 1914. These are two of its garbage dump trucks. From *Municipal Journal and Engineer*

Picking up rubbish. Motorized collection trucks like this one were coming into increased use by 1916. From *American City*

Garbage cans and bags were exchanged from this truck in Fredericksburg, Virginia, about 1960. Courtesy *Public Works Magazine*

A garbage-compactor truck of the type brought into common use by the late 1950's. Courtesy *Public Works Magazine*

The "Godzilla" system. Ninety- to three-hundred-gallon containers are emptied into the truck's hopper by a mechanical loading arm. This truck is in Phoenix, Arizona. Courtesy American Public Works Association, *APWA Reporter*

A modern incinerator in Belmont, Massachusetts (1959), showing its vertical spray tower and stack dust collector. Courtesy *Public Works Magazine*

A sanitary landfill site near Albuquerque, New Mexico (1958). Courtesy *Public Works Magazine*

A community recyling project. Courtesy *Library of Congress*

Source separation and recycling center, Wabash, Indiana. Courtesy Public Works Historical Society

Courtesy American Public Works Association, *APWA Reporter*

view substantially broadened the perceived role of municipal government in citizens' lives.

The private contract, as might be expected, became the most obvious symbol of corruption and inefficiency. Reformers claimed that the contract system of collection and disposal was an unworkable compromise between personal responsibility and municipal authority. In a speech delivered at the annual convention of the League of American Municipalities in 1903, one staunch advocate of municipal responsibility stated a widely accepted view of urban reform:

> When the proposition is finally accepted that municipal governments are incapable of doing every class of public work cheaper and better than it can be done by letting the work to private contractors, then the failure of municipal government is conceded, and the inability of the people to govern themselves finally established.[23]

The fear of private monopoly, not uncommon among reformers of all kinds in that period, lent support to the anticontract sentiment. Many environmental reformers in particular feared that privately controlled water supplies or privately controlled energy supplies (particularly coal) threatened a vulnerable urban society. Public ownership, whatever weaknesses it had, was a better gamble than contract systems.[24] A private monopoly in garbage collection hardly posed the same potential danger as a privately controlled water supply, but the principle was the same: public works were meant for the benefit of all the citizens; they should not be the means of private gain. For civic reformers the question of municipal responsibility transcended questions of efficiency; municipal responsibility was a safeguard against damage to the public welfare.

Increasingly in the early twentieth century reformers demanded the termination or alteration of contracted collection and disposal systems. In 1898 the Philadelphia Municipal Association sent a message to the city council strenuously opposing the awarding of garbage contracts to the

[23] "The Advantages of Municipal Construction over the Contract System," *Proceedings of the League of American Municipalities* (1903), p. 21. See also City Club of Philadelphia, *City Club Bulletin* 5 (13 May 1912): 199–200; "Street Cleaning Without Contract," *City Government* 6 (January 1899): 16.

[24] "The Advantages of Municipal Construction over the Contract System," pp. 21ff. The Cleveland Board of Control offered a unique alternative to the contract and the municipal systems. In 1900 it adopted a resolution stating that if a citizen took charge of his own street cleaning the city would turn over to him from the street fund the amount allocated to the particular street. See "Cleveland Citizens Keep Streets Clean," *City Government* 9 (July 1900): 19.

same combination of bidders who always won them. Charging favoritism and declaring that the bidding process was "a cunning scheme for robbing the city," the association complained that there was an effort afoot to keep large contracts of that kind out of competitive bidding. In Saint Louis in 1912 members of the Civic League promoted the move to municipal collection of ashes and rubbish by distributing circulars to civic groups throughout the city. They also lobbied for appropriations to implement a plan for municipal disposal which the city council had passed two years earlier. Efforts like these stirred up public dissatisfaction with the contract system and the handling of refuse in several cities.[25]

Despite their unwavering support of municipal control of public works, civic groups did not assume that all the problems of the past could be rectified by a simple stroke of the pen. They hoped that greater municipal commitment to such services as garbage removal and street cleaning would mean a greater sensitivity of government to the needs and demands of the people as a whole. Believing that they were constituted spokesmen for the public at large, civic groups hoped that their activities would give them permanent access to the sources of political and administrative power.

In the area of garbage collection and disposal civic organizations tried various methods of entering the decision-making process. Usually they were concerned with bringing the refuse problem to public attention. They wrote, printed, and disseminated thousands of pamphlets and handouts and also initiated or supported city-wide investigations. The Citizen's Research Council of Michigan sponsored an extensive investigation of street-cleaning practices in Detroit. The report, completed in 1917, was intended to "indicate conditions and problems, and suggest solutions which have proven successful in communities of similar size and conditions." The council relied on experts inside and outside the city to prepare the study. They selected Raymond W. Parlin, deputy commissioner of street cleaning in New York City, and H. S. Morse, of the Detroit Bureau of Government Research, as chief investigators. The report made a number of recommendations and suggestions, including the complete reorganization of the Detroit

[25] "Garbage Contracts," *City and State* 4 (20 January 1898): 259; Civic League of Saint Louis, *Yearbook* (1912), p. 5; "The Collection and Disposal of Rubbish and Ashes," Saint Louis, Civic League, *Civic Bulletin* 2 (8 January 1912): 2–4. See also Frederick C. Wilkes, "Should the City Remove Rubbish?" *City Hall* 4 (October 1905): 134–36; "Wants No Garbage Contract," *City Government* 6 (March 1899): 57; New York American, Public Welfare Department, *Considerably More Than Too Much!* pp. 3–9; Pittsburgh, Civic Club of Allegheny County, *Fifty Years of Civic History, 1896–1954*, comp. H. Marie Dermitt, pp. 7–8.

Street-Cleaning and Sanitation Department. It also recommended extending service to areas not previously included, updating the methods used to clean the streets, and offering greater incentives to sanitation workers.[26]

Significant investigations sometimes grew out of smaller or more specific projects, as in the City Club of Chicago conference called in 1911 on the city's mosquito problem. The club's Committee on Public Health sponsored a local conference to consider the mosquito nuisance as it related to public-health problems. At the conference a special committee was established to continue the investigation. Later its functions were expanded to include a wide range of problems related to household pests, which inevitably led to greater attention to municipal cleaning practices.[27] Through the initiation of investigations civic groups often provided momentum for city-wide action.

Some organizations chose to employ more direct action, with varying degrees of success. The Citizen's Health Committee of San Francisco, like many similar groups throughout the country, had applied public pressure to force local scavengers to improve their collection practices. In 1909 the committee members took some of the responsibility into their own hands and distributed three thousand garbage cans among the poor to keep the refuse from attracting rats. They also urged those who could afford it to purchase cans with tight lids. The garbage-can drive ultimately led to an ordinance in San Francisco making the use of receptacles compulsory.[28] In another important campaign the Civic League of Saint Louis relentlessly sought a comprehensive plan for refuse collection and disposal in the city. In 1906 the Public Sanitation Committee of the league published a report recommending source separation, increased numbers of collections, improved transportation of wastes, recycling programs, and the construction of a reduction plant and a rubbish destructor. The committee had been investigating practices in Saint Louis since 1903 and had rejected several piecemeal solutions offered by the municipal authorities. In 1908 the league announced that officials had accepted a comprehensive plan based on the

---

[26] Michigan, Citizen's Research Council, *Report on Street Cleaning and Refuse Collecting, Department of Public Works, City of Detroit.*

[27] City Club of Chicago, "Household Pests and Their Relation to Public Health," *City Club Bulletin* 4 (1 May 1911): 77.

[28] San Francisco, Citizen's Health Committee, *Eradicating Plague from San Francisco,* prepared by Frank Morton Todd, pp. 122–25. For information about other civic lobbying for better conditions in San Francisco, see "San Francisco Street-cleaning Department Assailed," *Engineering Record* 69 (28 March 1914): 368.

league's recommendations. The plan called for a cooperative venture between municipal government and private enterprise: the city would collect garbage, rubbish, and ashes, and the Standard Reduction and Chemical Company would be given a contract to turn the garbage into salable by-products at a relatively low cost. The second part of the plan was implemented in 1909, but the first part was snarled in red tape. Nonetheless, the league kept up the pressure and continued to lobby for its program.[29]

Civic organizations worked for improvements in street cleaning as well. Municipal control of street cleaning, which was almost universal by the turn of the century, had not proved to be a solution to uncleanliness in many cities. Complaints of patronage, squandering of city funds, administrative bungling, poor cleaning practices, and citizens' neglect were typical. These complaints were often followed by rounds of indirect and direct civic-group action—investigations, demands for updated ordinances, publicity campaigns, and efforts to secure modern cleaning methods. A national street-cleaning conference held during the period indicated nationwide interest in the problem.[30]

With more intensity that they had attacked the garbage problem, civic groups appealed for citizen action in the battle against dirty streets. After all, the streets were a truly community utility; if the streets, especially the major thoroughfares, were full of litter and garbage, everyone was affected. Aesthetic and even moral outrage pervaded the demands for clean streets. As Frederick C. Wilkes concluded in an article on Pittsburgh's street problem:

Is there not presented in this matter a topic well worthy of the most serious consideration from every business man, and every citizen having in his heart the least degree of interest in his home and the welfare of this community? It is well estab-

[29] Saint Louis, Civic Improvement League, Public Sanitation Committee, *Disposal of Municipal Waste*, pp. 1–19; Saint Louis, Civic League, *Yearbook* (1907), pp. 36–37; *Yearbook* (1908), p. 12; *Yearbook* (1909), pp. 39–40; Saint Louis, Civic League, *Civic Bulletin* 1 (6 March 1911): 2.

[30] See Saint Louis, City Improvement League, *Keep Our City Clean*, pp. 2–3; Philadelphia, Civic Club, *Annual Report* (1911), p. 56; "Street Cleaning," *City Hall* 4 (September 1905): 61–62; Merchants Association of San Francisco, *Street Cleaning Problem in San Francisco*, pp. 10–11, 28–29; "Street Cleaning," *City Hall* 8 (July 1907): 55–58; Douglas Sutherland, *Fifty Years on the Civic Front: A History of the Civic Federation's Dynamic Activities*, pp. 16–17; Henry G. Selfridge, *Suggestions on the Problem of Cleaning the Streets of Chicago*; Carol Aronovici, "Municipal Street Cleaning and Its Problems, *National Municipal Review* 1 (April 1912): 225.

lished as an immutable law, that environment is what makes the character of men. Cleanliness of man makes a good man. Cleanliness of a city makes a good city. It elevates its moral atmosphere, and tends to encourage all that is good in humanity.[31]

Many civic reformers concluded that citizens must not only assume the responsibility for paying someone to clean their streets but also take a personal role in assuring by good habits that the streets would remain clean.

The activities of the citizens' groups in their pursuit of sanitary reform points to their dual approach to achieving cleaner cities. On the one hand they sought to influence city officials by supporting municipally directed programs. On the other hand they sought to educate the public to the need for a personal commitment to civic cleanliness. The influence that citizens' groups enjoyed with city officials was inconsistent at best; more often they had to rely on public education and public arousal to achieve their goals. Citizens had to be convinced that sanitary reform should have priority over other issues competing for municipal dollars. It was the public that voted officials into office—and out again if they did not live up to expectations. Therefore, it is not surprising that citizens' organizations spent a great deal of time appealing to the officials' constituencies through publicity programs and programs of direct action.

It is also not surprising that women came to dominate the civic phase of sanitary reform. They were the most convincing speakers for such a cause, especially because they were perceived as having the greatest personal interest in it. In their roles as homemakers and mothers women seemed to be the logical group to promote a clean and healthful environment. Writing about the period from 1890 to 1920, Lois W. Banner suggested that never before or since have "so many women belonged to so many women's organizations; not until the 1960s was feminism so vigorous." By World War I the primary focus of the women's movement was suffrage, but before that time most organized women were "social feminists" who displayed great sympathy for the disadvantaged, devoted considerable time to civic improvement, and hoped to obtain social justice for their sex. Social feminism was an outgrowth of several important factors. Like male reformers women were caught up in the reformist mood of the day, confronting the excesses of rapid industrialization. Because of grow-

[31]Frederick C. Wilkes, "Cleanliness and Economy: How Pittsburgh Might Be Cleaned," *City Hall* 4 (November 1905): 154. See also "Citizen Co-operation in Street Cleaning," *Municipal Journal and Engineer* 29 (30 November 1910): 746.

ing educational and professional opportunities, as well as expanded rights under the law, women took the opportunity to speak out on issues affecting themselves and the citizenry at large. Furthermore, women came to see in their own plight circumstances which they had in common with other groups, such as children, the disadvantaged, and the poor, all of whom were subject to the whims of society.[32]

By the mid-1890s women's organizations and clubs had become bastions of many social reforms, such as child welfare, education, housing, health, and city beautification. Their commitment to civic improvement in all its forms made women's groups major supporters of environmental reforms. Women played a vital role in all phases of environmental reform— noise and smoke abatement, sewage reform, pure-water campaigns, and refuse reform. For example, Julia Barnett Rice, a New York physician, became the driving force behind the Society for the Suppression of Unnecessary Noise, the largest and best-known antinoise organization of the period.[33] In 1892 the Ladies' Health Association of Pittsburgh helped gain passage of a major antismoke ordinance; similar campaigns were waged in Saint Louis; Cincinnati; Salt Lake City, Utah; Chicago; Baltimore; Youngstown, Ohio, and elsewhere. In Chicago, Mrs. Charles Sergel was elected president of the city's Anti-Smoke League.[34] The efforts of women's groups in sanitation reform were also well known through such organizations as the Ladies' Health Protective Association of New York.[35]

By the early years of the twentieth century the association of women with city-improvement projects was so common that the term "municipal housekeeping" became synonymous with sanitation reform. Mildred Chadsey, commissioner of housing and sanitation of Cleveland, Ohio, defined "municipal housekeeping" succinctly: "Housekeeping is the art of making the home clean, healthy, comfortable and attractive. Municipal housekeeping is the science of making the city clean, healthy, comfortable and attractive."[36] Caroline Bartlett Crane used the term to impress upon women their

[32] Lois W. Banner, *Women in Modern America: A Brief History*, pp. 87–89. See also Zane L. Miller, *The Urbanization of Modern America: A Brief History*, pp. 104–105.

[33] Raymond W. Smilor, "Toward an Environmental Perspective: The Anti-Noise Campaign, 1893–1932," in Melosi, ed., *Pollution and Reform in American Cities, 1870–1930*, pp. 141–46.

[34] R. Dale Grinder, "The Battle for Clean Air: The Smoke Problem in Post–Civil War America," in ibid., p. 89.

[35] See chap. 2.

[36] Mildred Chadsey, "Municipal Housekeeping," *Journal of Home Economics* 7 (February 1915): 53.

responsibility in civic cleanliness: "Municipal housekeeping! That is a word I want, to make women feel their share of responsibility for the cleanliness of their city. We say, when on a journey, 'Grand Rapids,' or 'Kalamazoo,' or 'Coldwater' is my home. And is not one's city in truth the extension of one's home?"[37]

The identification of municipal housekeeping with sanitation reform fit well with the strong aesthetic, moral, and civic cast of the women's organizations (there were, of course, other women's reform efforts during the period which did not fit this image). At the same time, however, municipal housekeeping imposed limits on the work of these groups, because it lacked the precision and comprehensiveness needed for a well-developed program of sanitary reform. For all its clarity of image, municipal housekeeping was little more than a layman's perception of a complex environmental problem.

Municipal housekeeping also circumscribed the role of women as sanitary reformers. Since it so directly paralleled their domestic responsibilities, municipal housekeeping seemed a logical avenue of reform for women. In an article written in 1897, Edith Parker Thomson bemoaned the limitations of the reform model as it applied to women, especially in the public-health field. She was astonished to discover how little the public knew about the significant role of women in public health during the late nineteenth century. She concluded:

. . . every attempt on the part of women to benefit the public is necessarily somewhat indirect. They do not hold the ballot, nor sit in legislative halls. Their only course is either to arouse public opinion or to present their cause to the public officials. Their part in public reforms is chiefly suggestive or cooperative. They can seldom of themselves carry anything to completion, as a Board of Health or a Street-Cleaning Department can do. Hence their work is frequently unmentioned in the public record.[38]

Although women's impact on sanitary reform would be much greater and better publicized in the twentieth century, Thomson pointed to important limits imposed on social feminists in the public-health and sanitation fields. One reason for these limits was that most women reformers came from one economic stratum in the United States, the middle class, and

---

[37] Caroline Bartlett Crane, "The Work for Clean Streets," New York City, Women's Municipal League, *Bulletin* 5 (August 1906): 2.

[38] Edith Parker Thomson, "What Women Have Done for the Public Health," *Forum* 24 (September 1897): 54–55.

most of the women were housewives. As Suellen M. Hoy noted, "Many of [the women reformers] were middle-aged, had children in school, and often hired servants to clean their homes."[39] To this middle-class base were added some upper-class and upper-middle-class women, many of whom were holdovers from the days when women's groups were primarily exclusive social clubs. Nonetheless, the women involved in sanitary reform were strongly imprinted with their "proper" role in society. Banner suggested that for women "of every class, ethnic group, and region, [life] was governed by the simple statistic that the overwhelming majority would marry and become housewives and mothers." In the twentieth century approximately 90 percent of all American women had been married at some point in their lives. In 1900 only 5 percent of all married women in the country worked outside the home; ten years later, only 11 percent. "Thus for almost all women," Banner concluded, "marriage was a natural goal of life."[40] This was especially true of middle-class women. It is no wonder that municipal housekeeping garnered such immediate support from both women and men; it did not undermine the status quo. Men who reeled in horror at the mention of woman suffrage or more radical reform, such as Margaret Sanger's birth-control movement, saw little in sanitary reform which threatened the sanctity of the family or undermined the domestic role of women. The noted sanitarian Samuel Greeley was typical of male reformers who spoke with high praise of the activities of women in city-cleaning projects. He also accepted the premise that women were particularly well suited to the work:

It is unfortunately true that cleanliness and efficiency in the house treatment of refuse are sometimes defeated by careless and infrequent collection service or by improperly conducted disposal works. This condition must be very trying to the careful housekeeper, and is, perhaps, one reason why women have taken an active interest in promoting the efficiency of the larger phases of the work.[41]

While the times imposed limitations on the "legitimate" role of women in pursuing social changes, and despite the narrowness of municipal housekeeping as a reform goal, the efforts of women and women's groups to improve the quality of urban life were valuable and helped raise

[39] Suellen M. Hoy, " 'Municipal Housekeeping': The Role of Women in Improving Urban Sanitation Practices, 1880–1917," in Melosi, ed., *Pollution and Reform in American Cities*, p. 174.

[40] Banner, *Women in Modern America*, p. 47.

[41] Samuel A. Greeley, "The Work of Women in City Cleaning," *American City* 6 (June 1912): 874.

public consciousness of the need for sanitary improvements. Municipal housekeeping took many forms, from the superficial to the substantial. Women's organizations, especially those in smaller cities, launched antilittering campaigns. The Woman's Club of Dayton, Ohio, distributed leaflets to every household decrying the practice of throwing wastepaper into the streets. The Civic Club of Huntington, Tennessee, and the Woman's Club of Green Cove Springs, Florida, provided trash cans for their towns. The Green Cove Springs Club even decorated the cans and emblazoned amusing rhymes on them:

> My name is Empty Barrel,
> I'm hungry for a meal.
> Pray fill me full, kind stranger,
> With trash and orange peel.

According to one observer, the "jolly cans so appealed to the public that refuse upon the streets became an unheard-of thing, and Green Cove Springs was known as the Parlor City of the South."[42] Other women's groups attacked the tin can problem, initiated civic rallies, and lobbied for ordinances prohibiting spitting in the streets or indiscriminantly dumping rubbish.[43]

Gains were made in some of the largest cities, where women's organizations often acquired substantial influence in municipal affairs. In Boston the Woman's Municipal League organized a traveling exhibit to educate the citizens about sanitation. The exhibit consisted of models contrasting dirty and clean meat markets, dairies, and tenements and provided information about the prevention and cure of tuberculosis. In cooperation with a Boston settlement house, the league paid the salary of a woman inspector for the Board of Health. The Indianapolis Sanitary Association also publicized good sanitation practices. The first women's group in the city's history to venture into municipal affairs, the Sanitary Association held neighborhood meetings to instruct citizens on health matters, lobbied for improved garbage collection, and surveyed street-cleaning practices. In Louisville the Women's Civic Association was most effective in its publicity campaigns. It organized an exhibit, published pamphlets, and even produced a motion picture through the cooperation of the Board of Trade,

[42] Imogen B. Oakley, "The More Civic Work, the Less Need of Philanthropy," *American City* 6 (June 1912): 807–808.

[43] Ibid., pp. 808–11; Mrs C. G. Wagner, "What the Women Are Doing for Civic Cleanliness," *Municipal Journal and Engineer* 11 (July 1901): 35.

the Rotary Club, the Men's Federation, and the Jefferson County Medical Association. The film, *The Invisible Peril*, depicted "the travels of a discarded hat, and the disease which can be spread thru the open can, open wagon, open dump system of waste disposal." More than twenty thousand persons saw the film. In direct and effective action the Waste Committee of the Woman's City Club of Chicago brought pressure on the city to secure a scientific report and plan for garbage collection and disposal. The committee was also responsible for the decision by the Chicago City Council to establish a City Waste Commission, on which two club members served.[44]

Probably the best known of the activist women's groups was the Woman's Municipal League of New York City, which played as important a role in the early twentieth century as the Ladies' Health Protective Association had played in the late nineteenth century. The Woman's Municipal League appealed to "the intelligent women of New York for their co-operation in the present struggle for a morally and physically clean city."[45] An enemy of Tammany Hall, the league advocated improved methods of collection and disposal, including night disposal of wastes, and fought to increase benefits and improve working conditions for city sanitation workers. It also sponsored the Waring Medal, which was awarded to workers with the best performance records.[46] The league was most effective as a civic watchdog, monitoring the activities of the Street-Cleaning Department and evaluating its work. Lest anyone believe that the league played merely a ceremonial role in New York City's sanitary affairs, it should be noted that in 1907 it forced the resignation of MacDonough Craven, the street-cleaning commissioner. After investigating the department that year, the league charged Craven with incompetence, and after a strike by sanitation drivers

[44] "Cleaning Up American Cities," *Survey* 25 (October 1910): 85; Oakley, "The More Civic Work, the Less Need of Philanthropy," pp. 810–11; Mrs. Lee Bernheim, "A Campaign for Sanitary Collection and Disposal of Garbage," *American City* 15 (August 1916): 135–36; Hester M. McClung, "Women's Work in Indianapolis," *Municipal Affairs* 2 (September 1898): 523–24; Mary Ritter Beard, *Women's Work in Municipalities*, pp. 89–90. See also Tolman, *Municipal Reform Movements in the United States, pp. 167–82.*

[45] New York City, *Woman's Municipal League, Campaign Bulletin*, November 1903, p. 12.

[46] See the following publications by New York City, Woman's Municipal League: *Bulletin* 5 (April 1907): 8–9; 5 (June 1907): 3–4; 6 (June 1908): 7–8; *Yearbook* (1911), pp. 45–50; *Yearbook* (1912), pp. 26–46; *Yearbook* (1913), pp. 24–25; *Yearbook* (1914), pp. 22–25. See also William H. Edwards, "Four Kinds of Cooperation Needed by Street Cleaning Departments," *American City* 9 (July 1913): 65; Mrs. Julius Henry Cohen, *What We Should All Know about Our Streets*.

aggravated the deteriorating condition of the department, Craven was allowed to resign.[47]

The flurry of projects initiated by women's groups throughout the nation produced several leaders who became synonymous with sanitation reform. The Reverend Caroline Bartlett Crane, of Kalamazoo, Michigan, was one of the most highly respected of these leaders. After graduating from Carthage College in Kenosha, Wisconsin, in 1879, she taught school and also worked briefly as a newspaperwoman. Her primary interest was theology, and in 1886 she was ordained in the Unitarian church. In October, 1889, she was installed as pastor of the First Unitarian Church of Kalamazoo. Seven years later she married Dr. Augustus Warren Crane. Caroline Bartlett Crane had a strong inclination for the social, as well as the spiritual, improvement of her flock, and she plunged into projects ranging from education to police and fire protection. By the turn of the century she was deeply engrossed in sanitation problems and had become a leading proponent of municipal housekeeping. In 1904 she founded the Women's Civic Improvement League of Kalamazoo, and by 1907 she had achieved national attention for her work in street-cleaning reform. She was constantly sought after as a lecturer, conducted many sanitary inspections throughout the country, and drew wide attention to sanitation problems with her incisive reports.[48]

Mary McDowell, of Chicago, also gained repute as a sanitary reformer. Like Caroline Bartlett Crane, she had strong religious ties. McDowell taught classes in religion for young people and became a devoted follower of Frances Willard, founder of the Women's Christian Temperance Union. She also was committed to social service, later joining Jane Addams at Chicago's Hull-House in 1890. In 1894 she was asked to direct a new settlement, Packingtown, a project of the University of Chicago. Packingtown was in a desolate location, and she quickly became aware of its primitive facilities and physical blight and gained an appreciation for proper sanitation measures. From her experience at Packingtown, she acquired an interest in city-wide sanitation reform and sought to attract popu-

---

[47] New York City, Woman's Municipal League, *Bulletin* 5 (July–August 1907): 1.

[48] Hoy, "'Municipal Housekeeping,'" pp. 181–88; "Cleaning Up American Cities," pp. 83–84; Beard, *Woman's Work in Municipalities*, pp. 86–87; Crane, "The Work for Clean Streets," pp. 1–10; Suellen M. Hoy, "Caroline Bartlett Crane," *APWA Reporter* 45 (June 1978): 4–5.

lar support. She persuaded several Chicago women's groups to establish waste committees, and she chaired the City Waste Committee of the Women's City Club. Through her leadership the women's groups were instrumental in the establishment in 1913 of the Chicago City Waste Commission, which became influential in refuse reform. The "Garbage Lady," as she became known, was recognized as a major force in the improvement of Chicago's massive waste disposal problems and a national figure in environmental reform.[49]

Interestingly, some of history's best-known women in other fields of endeavor also contributed greatly to sanitary reform. Jane Addams, the founder of Hull-House and a pioneer in the development of social welfare as a profession, was also a sanitary reformer. Among her many acitivites Addams regularly brought pressure to bear on the Chicago City Council to improve collection service. A colleague of Mary McDowell's in the Women's City Club, Addams lectured on sanitary reform and was named garbage inspector for her ward.[50] Ellen Swallow Richards, instructor in sanitary chemistry at MIT, a pioneer in the field of ecology, and a leader of the home-economics movement, also wrote and lectured on the importance of municipal housekeeping.[51] Through the leadership of women's organizations and the emergence of nationally recognized women reformers, by World War I sanitary reform (indeed, much of environmental reform in general) was being identified with social feminism.

Among their environmental projects social feminists spearheaded health education among urban children and enlisted droves of youngsters in sanitation activities. Several times the women drew on the efforts of Colonel Waring and his Juvenile Street Cleaning League. On a broader plane the beginnings of civic involvement among children are to be found in the rise of progressive education during these years. As historian Lawrence A. Cremin noted:

Progressive education began as part of a vast humanitarian effort to apply the promise of American life—the ideal of government by, of, and for the people—to the puzzling new urban-industrial civilization that came into being during the latter

[49] Hoy, " 'Municipal Housekeeping,' " pp. 188–93; Beard, *Woman's Work in Municipalities*, pp.88–89; "Chicago's Struggle for Scientific Garbage Collection and Disposal," *Survey* 31 (21 March 1914): 776–77.

[50] Hoy, " 'Municipal Housekeeping,' " p. 190; Beard, *Woman's Work in Municipalities*, p. 88; Jane Addams, *Twenty Years at Hull-House*, pp. 200–205.

[51] See Robert Clarke, *Ellen Swallow: The Woman Who Founded Ecology*.

half of the nineteenth century. The word "progressive" provides the clue to what it really was: the education phase of American Progressivism writ large.[52]

Cremin went on to suggest that Progressives sought, among other things, to use the schools to improve the lives of individuals, which meant broadening the function of the schools to incorporate concern for the quality of life, health, civic-mindedness, and vocational training. This approach was complementary to the environmental view of Progressives, which emphasized that, to improve human beings, the moral and physical environment must first be improved. Progressive education, however, was not elitist; instead it attempted to appeal to children of all economic classes and ethnic backgrounds. In part, at least, Progressive education was seen as an important tool for assimilating the children of the foreign-born into American society. Of course, the assumption was that assimilation was a worthy goal and that American values and culture were superior to those of immigrants from southern and eastern Europe.

An important thrust of progressive education was to provide children with training that was practical and immediately useful.[53] Thus emerged a strong commitment to "civic education," that is, the teaching of the structure and functions of government and its legal system and the instilling of "citizenship." In 1904, expert on municipal government and publisher of Detroit's *Civil News* Delos F. Wilcox declared what he believed to be the value of civic education in the urban setting:

In cities human nature comes to the parting of the ways; allowed to drift along the lines of least resistance, it develops intense selfishness of the future, and those other characteristics of degeneration found in highly civilized society; but, properly trained, human nature in cities develops a wider social consciousness, a heartier spirit of cooperation, a more refined appreciation of the arts of life, a keener sense of responsibility to the future, and all those other characteristics of progress that are the hope of evolution and the justification of social effort. It is the character of civic education that will determine in the long run whether or not democracy can succeed in cities.[54]

Wilcox and many others perceived of civic education as a goal for all citizens but for practical reasons focused their attention on the young. "It is

[52] Lawrence A. Cremin, *The Transformation of the School: Progressivism in American Education, 1876-1957*, pp. viii–ix.

[53] See Raymond E. Callahan, *Education and the Cult of Efficiency: A Study of the Social Forms that Have Shaped the Administration of the Public Schools*, pp. 5–6.

[54] Delos F. Wilcox, *The American City: A Problem in Democracy*, p. 91.

one of the paradoxes of reform," Wilcox said, "that no absolute social salvation can be brought about unless the children can be reached, while the only possible way to reach the children is through the grown people."[55] Responsibility for training the young, therefore, had to fall to the "enlightened" reformers who understood society's needs. The schools were the most expedient institution for reaching the greatest number of children. Within the schools the most direct way to incorporate civic studies was through curricular additions or modifications. Manual training became a popular way to introduce practical skills to children; in the realm of civic education the civics class became the most widely accepted method of inculcating citizenship. Civic classes appeared as early as grammar school and were carried over into high school. Student-government programs were established as extracurricular activities to provide practical experience in government organization and decision making.[56] Outside the schools but working in close concert with them were citizenship organizations for children, usually managed by local civic organizations and women's groups. For instance, the Newport, Rhode Island, Civic League established a League of Good Citizenship with ten divisions in the public schools. In Jeanette, Pennsylvania, junior civic leagues planted trees and beautified stretches along railroad tracks. In Cleveland, Ohio, Hiram House Social Settlement set up "Progress City," a play city operated by the local children which included a city council, a court, a newspaper, and all the other trappings of a real municipality—without the graft and corruption, crime, violence, and unsanitary conditions of life in the "real" city.[57]

Inculcating civic pride and civic responsibility naturally led to attempts to give children a broad appreciation of their surroundings, including city cleanliness and beautification. The leap from the broader goals of civic education to a concern about sanitation needs was not great; indeed it was an integral part of the process. A citizen was just as responsible for

---

[55] Ibid., p. 92. See also "Junior Improvements," *American City* 3 (October 1910): 196; "The Junior Civic Leagues of Binghamton, N.Y.," *American City* 5 (November 1911): 297; Charles Dwight Willard, *City Government for Young People*; Julia Richman and Isabel Richman Wallach, *Good Citizenship*; Mrs. Julius Henry Cohen, *What We Should All Know about Our Streets*.

[56] Cremin, *The Transformation of the School*, pp. 58–61; Callahan, *Education and the Cult of Efficiency*, pp. 8ff.; Wilcox, *The American City*, pp. 102–20; Samuel H. Ziegler, "Practical Citizenship Taught to High School Boys," *American City* 11 (July 1914): 20–23.

[57] "The Children's Responsibility," *American City* 5 (July 1911): 41; William H. Allen, "Teaching Civics by Giving Pupils Civic Work to Do," *American City* 14 (February 1916): 154–55; Ethel Rogers, "Playing at Citizenship," *American City* 9 (November 1913): 445–48.

obeying a garbage ordinance as for obeying any other law. City cleanliness was as much a mark of civilized society as was an honest and efficient government—or so it was argued. An observer noted:

To "chuck" our fruit skins, wrappers, cigar stumps, sputum, everything, in fact, that no longer has value to us, is as natural as life when we are in public places, while in our homes those of us who are "civilized" and "cultured" would never think of such a thing. How deep is a culture that will keep rubbish and garbage off the floors of the private home and cast it at random upon the floors of the community home? Not very deep, nor very consistent, nor very valuable, we all know when we come to think of it.[58]

Civic pride through city cleanliness was an important ingredient of the various civic education programs for children. It was so important that it became the basis for many children's organizations, usually initiated and sustained by women reformers. Juvenile sanitation organizations were therefore a very significant element in the sanitation-reform movement.

Colonel Waring's Juvenile Street Cleaning League was an archetype. What had been a unique experiment in 1896 became widespread a decade or so later. In the summer of 1889 there were seventy-five leagues in operation with some 5,000 participants. After Waring's resignation the league lost its vitality and was disbanded in 1900. In 1909 it was reestablished with fifty leagues under the leadership of Reuben S. Simons, who had helped organize the original league. The new league operated through the schools—the result of the impact of civic education—largely under the guidance of women teachers. The activities of the new league were essentially the same as the first. The children inspected streets and alleys, reported litterers, held meetings, and, of course, conducted parades. The 1910 outing included more than 15,000 children from thirty-one leagues; the next year more than 25,000 children took part from the seventy-one leagues in operation.[59]

At the zenith of the league's popularity other juvenile groups sprouted up throughout the country. In Philadelpha, Mrs. Edith W. Pierce, a nurse

---

[58] "Junior Improvements," p. 196.

[59] Rueben S. Simons, "The Juvenile Street Cleaning Leagues of New York," pt. 1, *American City* 3 (October 1910): 163–66; pt. 2, *American City* 3 (November 1910): 239–43; "New York Street Cleaning," *Municipal Journal and Engineer* 39 (13 July 1910): 49. During the years between the termination of the league and its reestablishment, the Woman's Municipal League of New York kept the idea alive with the Juvenile City League. See *Bulletin of the Woman's Municipal League* 2 (October 1903): 3–4; 2 (December 1903): 5; 2 (February 1904): 3–4; 3 (September 1904): 4; 3 (October 1904): 3; 3 (December 1904): 4; 5 (November 1906): 1–3; 5 (June 1907):4.

and the city's first woman street-cleaning inspector, organized a Junior Sanitation League with over 10,000 members. Every child wore a button bearing the seal of the city and emblazoned with the motto "For Clean Philadelphia Streets." The children were also furnished with instructions for volunteer inspectors. Pierce gained the cooperation of the city's teachers for her project, and occasionally the teachers required the children to write compositions about the league and their ideas about what a good citizen was. Leagues were organized in several other cities and towns throughout the country. The organizer of the Binghamton, New York, Junior Civic League, a Mrs. Johnson, echoed the sentiments of others involved in civic education when she wrote: "We must picture to the children how each one of us has pride in his home, and wants it to be as perfect as possible, and how that feeling extends to its surroundings, to the lawns and streets in the vicinity. Then in a broader way we think of the city as our home." In Kenosha, Wisconsin, the Department of Education and the Department of Health organized Junior Health Leagues to produce "health missionaries." In San Diego, California, the city health officer organized a group of junior deputy sanitary inspectors to assist in a fly-prevention campaign. Other cities experimented with variations on these themes.[60]

Enlisting children was a logical step for sanitary reformers who sought to generate public support for their programs. A whole generation of urban Americans could be educated through the public schools to "reprogram" their habits of personal cleanliness and to become sensitive to their physical surroundings. Many reformers also believed that children, especially those from immigrant families, could transmit their experiences and knowledge to their parents and affect their behavior as well (substantial bigotry was attached to the notion that immigrants needed this education more than native-born Americans did). Beyond their educational value the juvenile leagues were also outstanding avenues of publicity. The novelty of

[60] "A Street Cleaning Nurse," *Literary Digest* 52 (18 March 1916): 709–10; "The Junior Civic Leagues of Binghamton, N.Y.," pp. 297–98; "Health Leagues in the Schools," *American City* 17 (August 1917): 152–53; William W. B. Seymour, "Junior Deputy Sanitary Inspectors," *American City* 15 (December 1916): 696–98; "Young Boosters for a Chicago Beautiful," *American City* 4 (June 1911): 290; "Anti-Litter League," *American City* 15 (July 1916): 67; Bernheim, "A Campaign for Sanitary Collection and Disposal of Garbage," p. 136; "Street Cleaning," *City Hall* 8 (July 1907): 55–56; Oakley, "The More Civic Work, the Less Need of Philanthropy," p. 811; St. Louis, Civic League, *Civic Bulletin* 1 (12 December 1910): 4; Cleveland, Department of Public Service, Subdivision of Street Cleaning, *Annual Report* (1914), p. 3: Philadelphia, Department of Public Works, Bureau of Highways and Street Cleaning, *Annual Report* (1913), p. 53.

the organizations and the large number of participants assured that sanitation problems would get widespread public notice. The novelty would wear off sooner or later, but the civic programs were likely to continue.[61]

In raising public consciousness about sanitation, no program, not even the junior leagues, captured as much attention or enjoyed as much publicity as city cleanup campaigns. The earliest such campaigns were generally held for one or two days in the spring to encourage citizens to get rid of rubbish accumulated during the winter months. Drawing on the concept of municipal housekeeping, reformers promoted cleanup campaigns as city-wide spring cleanings. Eventually the campaigns became community projects, lasting a week or longer and emphasizing good sanitation practices, fire prevention, fly and mosquito extermination, home and neighborhood beautification, and many other programs. In their more elaborate forms the cleanup campaigns relied on the cooperation of all segments of the community and brought together all groups concerned with sanitary reform, including civic and women's organizations, children's groups, social clubs, municipal authorities, and the press. Cleanup campaigns reached the proportions of a movement in the 1910s, spreading so rapidly that almost every city and town conducted at least one spring campaign. Some projects instituted during the cleanups were maintained year round.[62]

The cleanup campaigns took many forms and varied in degree of success. Some had very limited goals. For instance, the Civics Committee of the State Federation of Pennsylvania Women sponsored a "Municipal Housecleaning Day."[63] In many other cities the cleanup drives were designed to promote overall civic-mindedness. This was particularly true in smaller cities and towns, where the sense of community was strong. In Kirksville, Missouri, the Civic League and the Elks Lodge joined forces to produce a bulletin *For a Cleaner and More Beautiful Kirksville* which was placed in every home in the city. Several businesses set up displays in their windows demonstrating the proper tools for cleaning up and posted placards with catchy inscriptions. School children were asked to sign cards certifying that their yards at home had been thoroughly cleaned. Pastors of

[61] For a good example of the effort to "civilize" the immigrants, see David Willard, "The Juvenile Street-Cleaning Leagues," in George E. Waring, Jr., *Street Cleaning and the Disposal of a City's Wastes: Methods and Results and the Effects upon Public Health, Public Morals, and Municipal Prosperity*, pp. 177–86.

[62] William Parr Capes and Jeanne Daniels Carpenter, *Municipal Housecleaning*, pp. 213–14.

[63] Beard, *Woman's Work in Municipalities*, p. 85.

various churches preached sermons about the virtues of cleanliness. The league distributed flowers and vines to citizens who wanted to hide unsightly fences or other structures. For two years the league also had the direct responsibility for cleaning the streets.[64]

Some of the campaigns produced substantial and long-lasting results, especially the initiation of new and more effective sanitation ordinances. Those responsible for the campaign in Richmond, Virginia, realized that "the habit of littering streets, alleys and yards appeared to have been so thoroughly grounded in Richmond that the educational effect of the clean-up campaigns was not sufficient to eradicate it." As a result the Society for the Betterment of Housing and Living Conditions recommended to the city authorities a more comprehensive ordinance to improve collection and disposal methods. The new law went into effect in February, 1914. In Sherman, Texas, the women of the Civic League launched a cleanup campaign which resulted in an ordinance requiring the city to sponsor four annual four-day cleanup periods. The first cleanup campaign was received with such enthusiasm that it lasted ten days. The Women's Civic League of Baltimore received high commendation from Chief Engineer August Emrich of the Fire Department for its cleanup "crusade" in 1912. According to Emrich, fire losses in that year were the lowest in thirty-four years, and he credited the cleanup campaign with having achieved this record through the removal of rubbish and other inflammable materials from homes and business establishments.[65]

As with other sanitation activities, civic organizations made great efforts to incorporate children into the cleanup efforts. In almost all the cities which sponsored campaigns, children were the object of its appeal, an integral part of the campaign, or both. According to *American City*, "No other movement for civic betterment has made better use of the ability and energy of children than have the clean-up campaigns." In 1915 chil-

[64]Mrs. C. J. Baxter, "A Women's League That Keeps the Streets Clean," *American City* 6 (June 1912): 898–99, 901. See also Mrs. George E. Bird, "The Parade Inaugurated a Village Clean-up Campaign," *American City* 14 (February 1916): 162–64; "Recognizing the Work of the Children," *American City* 3 (July 1910): 42. See also Capes and Carpenter, *Municipal Housecleaning*, pp. 214–32; Baltimore, Department of Street Cleaning, *Annual Report* (1912), pp 4–5; *Annual Report* (1915), pp. 6–7.

[65]Gustavus A. Weber, "A 'Clean-up' Campaign Which Resulted in a 'Keep-Clean' Ordinance," *American City* 10 (March 1914): 231–34; Ewing Galloway, "How Sherman Cleans Up," *American City* 9 (July 1913): 40–41; Beard, *Woman's Work in Municipalities*, p. 84.

dren played important roles in some five thousand local cleanup and paint-up campaigns under the auspices of the National "Clean Up and Paint Up" Bureau—the only national organization of its kind. Children were employed in the campaigns in every possible way. Thousands of children marched in parades promoting the cleanup activities, distributed pamphlets, organized cleanup brigades and wrote essays extolling the virtues of cleanliness. They also memorized appropriate pledges:

I will not throw any paper into the streets, because I
   want our streets to be clean.
I will take my own drinking cup to school with me.
I will not bite anyone else's apple or chew anyone else's
   gum, because I do not want anyone else to bite my apple
   or chew my gum.[66]

Cleanup campaigns thus became crash courses in hygiene, sanitation, and civic education.[67]

Philadelphia's week-long cleanup campaign of 1913 was the biggest of them all. It incorporated all the elements of successful campaigns throughout the country but on a larger scale. Ultimately the annual campaign became such an integral part of the life of the city that the municipal government assumed leadership of it and made it a major civic event akin to a festival. In 1913 the city distributed 3,400 personal letters, 750,000 gummed labels, 260,000 bulletins, 20,000 colored display posters, 750 streamers, 1,000,000 cardboard folders, 300,000 badges, 300,000 blotters, 350,000 circulars, and various other promotional materials. All segments of the city participated. In 1914, during the second annual cleanup week, participants collected 140,000 cubic yards of rubbish. Special teams of cleaners scoured five hundred vacant lots, municipal buildings received thorough cleanings, and crews splashed paint on everything. The Second Annual Clean-Up Week for a "Spick and Span" Philadelphia was a huge success.[68]

The cleanup campaign epitomized the public phase of sanitary reform. It preached the City Beautiful civic-improvement idea, and it pro-

[66] "Children in City Clean-up Work," *American City* 14 (February 1916): 156–61.

[67] See R. P. Crawford, "Training the Young in Civic Duties," *American City* 16 (April 1917): 359–61; *American City* (March 1911): 146; "A Plan for Interesting Children in Civic Betterment," *American City* 8 (April 1913): 415.

[68] "Philadelphi's Second Annual Clean-up Week," *Municipal Journal and Engineer* 37 (10 September 1914): 348–49; "Annual Municipal Clean-up Week in Philadelphia," *Engineering News* 73 (1 April 1915): 620–21; R. Robinson Barett, "Philadelphia's Second Annual

moted good public-health practices. It also brought together the various groups who had been most responsible for the popularization of sanitary reform: civic organizations, women's groups, children, sympathetic journalists, and city officials. Its greatest contribution was in mustering citizen participation in cleaning the surroundings and in raising public consciousness about environmental problems. As a publicity device it had dramatic appeal.

The cleanup campaign had serious shortcomings, however, and drew some criticism. When Charles Zueblin argued that "annual clean-up days are unnecessary in well-regulated cities,"[69] he addressed the flaw in the idea, namely, that cleanup campaigns in and of themselves were cosmetic activities, short-term substitutes for effectively enforced ordinances and efficiently conducted collection and disposal practices. They gave citizens a sense of accomplishment, but they pointed to sanitary problems which could not be resolved in a burst of activity one week a year.

The cleanup campaigns also pointed up the constraints on the civic phase of sanitary reform. At their best, civic organizations promoted cleanliness and helped improve collection and disposal methods through publicity and direct pressure on city officials. Though often effective in raising public awareness about sanitation problems, the civic groups could not bring about policy changes. Municipal governments are moved to action for many reasons; public pressure alone cannot ensure results. Sanitary reform was not simply a question of implementation. Imbedded in the reformist effort were other inherent weaknesses. Foremost among them was that technical reformers (sanitary engineers) and civic reformers (citizen's groups) never joined in a single, broadly based movement. Each group possessed powerful reform tools, and each had links to important constituencies, but the gap between them was never bridged. The male-dominated elitist, efficiency-oriented technical reformers operated independently of the primarily female-dominated aesthetics- and health-oriented civic groups. Nor were the gaps bridged among the myriad groups interested in various phases of environmental reform. Lacking a sufficiently broad environmental perspective, antismoke groups, noise-abate-

Clean-up Week," *American City* 12 (April 1915): 299–304; "Get the Habit," *American City* 16 (February 1917): 154–55. See also Philadelphia, Department of Public Works, Bureau of Highways and Street Cleaning, *Annual Report* (1914), pp. 63–75; *Annual Report* (1915), pp. 32–35; Philadelphia Bureau of Street Cleaning, *Annual Report* (1917), pp. 9–12.

[69] Charles Zueblin, *American Municipal Progress*, p. 78.

ment groups, and sanitary-reform groups pressed their specific causes independently, failing to coordinate their efforts. Groups concerning themselves with the broader issues of environmental quality and the collective effects of pollution had not yet appeared.[70]

To say that sanitary reform had its limitations, however, is not to demean the efforts of those who grappled with the waste problem or to apply today's standards to their achievements. The early-day sanitary reformers, both technical and civic, were ahead of their time in seeking workable solutions to perplexing problems. In their refusal to accept untended waste as an inevitable by-product of industrialization and urbanization, they pointed the way for the reformers of the future.

Chapters 5 and 6 examine the manner in which environmental consciousness, engineering expertise, public pressure, and government action in the early twentieth century brought the refuse problem under control in American cities.

[70] For a detailed discussion of environmental reform efforts in the late nineteenth and early twentieth centuries, see Melosi, ed., *Pollution and Reform in American Cities.*

5

Street-Cleaning Practices in the Early Twentieth Century

THOSE persons committed to ending the refuse problem—from engineers to journalists, from municipal authorities to civic leaders—looked optimistically toward a time when cities would be uniformly clean and free of pollution and disease. The flurry of reform activity and the abundance of rhetoric heightened the anticipation. As with any attempt at change, however, there was a gap between expectations and achievements. Strides were made in street cleaning and in the collection and disposal of solid wastes, but vestiges of the "out of sight, out of mind" mentality persisted. Partial solutions and incomplete victories were the best that reformers could reasonably expect, especially since the improvements they demanded required major institutional, as well as attitudinal, adjustments by American city dwellers. The actual accomplishments of refuse reform in the years before World War I, stripped of the reformers' hyperbole, is the subject of this chapter and the next.

At the turn of the century several informed contemporaries, while recognizing the improvements achieved since the 1890s, also realized that quick solutions to refuse problems were too much to expect. In 1905 a writer commented in the *Municipal Journal and Engineer*:

> The whole question of economical and efficient methods of municipal waste disposal is just at this time in a changing, unsettled state; the tendency is consequently to "go slow" and not to commit the city to the adoption of schemes and plans that have not been thoroughly tested by practical uses or that cannot be recommended by the endorsement of those competent to report upon the particular conditions governing each individual case.[1]

[1] "Disposition of Municipal Refuse," *Municipal Journal and Engineer* 19 (October 1905): 169. See also *Proceedings of the American Society for Municipal Improvements,*

To "go slow" was not simply to be deliberate, as the quotation implies. There was a hesitancy among city officials to give priority to refuse management over other important city services and programs, such as police and fire protection, municipal building projects, park construction, and transportation. Reformers faced the unenviable task of trying to convince municipal leaders of the need to invest great amounts of time and money in the improvement of refuse management because of its intrinsic importance. Although government leaders may have been sympathetic to the reformers' case, they tended to react to immediate, as opposed to long-range, sanitary needs. Their lack of foresight and neglect of planning were largely responsible for the delays in implementation of effective programs.

Textbooks on sanitation written in this period echoed the reformers' concerns about the state of management. In evaluating past and present methods of street cleaning and refuse collection and disposal, they bemoaned the primitiveness of nineteenth-century practices but also criticized highly publicized newer methods, such as incineration and reduction. In 1906, William Mayo Venable, in his book on garbage crematories, leveled a devastating broadside at the methods of refuse disposal practiced in American cities:

. . . the crudity of the methods of refuse disposal in most of our American cities is almost incredible to an intelligent person when his attention is first directed to observe such matters, the disposal of garbage being in many cities less intelligently managed than among savages, and the disposal of litter, tin cans, waste paper, etc., a class of waste with which savages do not have to deal, being conducted in so slovenly a manner as to excite disgust in any person who realized the facts.[2]

The textbooks also criticized the intransigence or disinterest of municipal governments that failed to take an active part in resolving refuse problems. According to M. N. Baker:

In the removal and disposal of city wastes we are far behind our attainments in providing municipal supplies. Only a small portion of the communities which enjoy public water supplies have the benefit of sewerage systems, and most of the latter discharge their sewage into the nearest body of water without regard to consequences. Garbage collection is strangely neglected in the majority of cities and

---

Twenty-first Annual Convention, Boston, (1914), pp. 1–3, 49–58 (hereafter cited as *Proceedings of the ASMI*); Rudolph Hering, "Disposal of Municipal Refuse; Review of General Practice," *Transactions of the American Society of Civil Engineers* 54 (1904): (pt. E), pp. 265–66 (hereafter cited as *Transactions of the ASCE*).

[2] William Mayo Venable, *Garbage Crematories in America,* p. 2.

towns, and its final disposal is one of the greatest blots upon American municipal administration.[3]

In the two major problem areas, street cleaning and refuse collection and disposal, street-cleaning practices made the greater overall strides. Civic reformers brought the problem to the attention of the public and city officials, while technical reformers instituted efficiency programs in public-works departments. Most important was the impact of technology. First, improved paving made city streets more essential as transportation arteries and generated a greater demand for clean, unobstructed streets. Second, smooth pavement could accommodate a vast array of mechanical sweeping and flushing devices that significantly altered cleaning practices in both large and small cities.

The demand for more and better-paved streets which had become widespread in the late nineteenth century continued unabated in the early twentieth century. Althoug major federal support for a municipal highway system did not emerge until 1916, most major cities and many of the smaller ones were interlaced with elaborate street systems by that time, at least in central-city areas. Dr. Carol Aronovici, a leading sanitarian, was among those who recognized the earlier important role of streets in the lives of urbanites:

> Until recently a street, from the standpoint of municipal government, was considered a thoroughfare, or a means of reaching various parts of the community without regard to the surrounding property, be that of a business or residential character. A closer observation, however, makes it clear that the street is essentially the means of approaching a home and of serving its conveniences. It is the hallway which connects the school and the church, the factory and the office with the home. From the standpoint of the tenement dweller, the street is the nursery and playground of the young, the social center and meeting place of the adult, the free market place for the transaction of business, and the display and distribution of the food supply. Not infrequently during hot weather the street is the common bedroom of the dweller in the congested, ill-ventilated and over-heated tenement house district. With such broad functions it is clear that the construction and care of streets implies more than the requirements of accessibility, easy grade and safety.[4]

---

[3]M. N. Baker, *Municipal Engineering and Sanitation*, pp. 5–6; see also pp. 151–56; Harry R. Crohurst, *Municipal Wastes; Their Character, Collection, Disposal*, U.S. Public Health Service Bulletin no. 107 (October 1920), pp. 7–8; William F. Morse, *The Collection and Disposal of Municipal Waste*, pp. 1–95.

[4]Carol Aronovici, "Municipal Street Cleaning and Its Problems," *National Municipal Review* 1 (April 1912): 218–19. See also Edward T. Hartman, "The Social Significance of Clean Streets," *American City* 3 (October 1910): 173.

The construction of elaborate street systems, however, produced a significant change in the role of streets in urban life. Use of the streets as marketplaces, social gathering places, and even extensions of homes was fading by the turn of the century. Indeed, as noted in chapter 1, by 1900 city streets had lost much of their importance as areas of neighborhood and family social life. According to historian Clay McShane, "By 1900 many, possibly most, urban residents saw streets as arteries for transportation since house yards and porches in the new streetcar suburbs assumed the traditional social and recreational functions of streets." He added that "urban bureaucrats, who by 1900 controlled paving in most cities, had completely lost sight of the traditional functions of streets." Municipal engineers planned pavement to cope with the increase in traffic or to provide easier means of removing wastes from the cities. These changes predated the widespread use of the automobile. Asphalt, the paving material usually associated with the rise of private motorized transportation, had been used to pave nearly one-third of city streets by 1909, the year Henry Ford introduced the Model T. The impact of the automobile on urban street construction and transportation patterns was not significant until about 1914.[5]

In deemphasizing the neighborhood functions of streets and accentuating their transportation functions, municipal officials acknowledged that extensive paving programs were vital to the economic interests of the city. As a result street cleaning took on new significance. A clean, unobstructed street not only was healthful and aesthetically pleasing but also aided the flow of traffic. By World War I most cities of more than 30,000 population had adopted a street-cleaning system, and, whereas 70 percent of the cities surveyed in the 1880 census had assumed responsibility for street cleaning, by around 1917 about 90 to 95 percent of American cities had municipally operated programs.[6]

By the 1920s the contract system of street cleaning was being discarded in almost every major city. San Francisco, Indianapolis, and Wash-

[5] Clay McShane, "Transforming the Use of Urban Space: A Look at the Revolution in Street Pavements, 1880–1924," *Journal of Urban History* 5 (May 1979): 279–307. See also "Street Cleaning Standards," *Municipal Journal and Engineer* 35 (11 December 1913): 794–96; "Street Cleaning and Pavement Economy," *Municipal Journal and Engineer* 40 (6 January 1916): 8–9; Charles A. Beard, *American City Government: A Survey of Newer Tendencies*, pp. 242–48.

[6] See "Tables of Street Cleaning Statistics," *Municipal Journal and Engineer* 37 (10 December 1914): 833–44; William Parr Capes and Jeanne Daniels Carpenter, *Municipal Housecleaning*, pp. 64–65.

ington, D.C., abandoned the contract system in 1903, 1905, and 1911, respectively. Philadelphia, one of the last major cities to maintain the contract system, finally abandoned it in 1921.[7] Critics of street cleaning by contract charged that it was less efficient than municipally run programs and rarely provided adequate service for the money. The most serious problem was enforcement. Speaking before the Sanitary Engineering Section of the American Public Health Association in 1913, J. W. Paxton stated:

> Street cleaning is probably the most difficult work to inspect of any which could be let under contract. No street is ever perfectly clean, only relatively so, depending on the accumulation of dirt and the amount of efficient cleaning. It is impracticable to specify that the contractor shall furnish clean streets or even clean streets at certain periods, but each detail of the required operation of street cleaning must be specified, inspected to see that each detail is carried out, and the city then must be satisfied with [the] results.[8]

Many sanitation reformers and some city officials believed that the termination of street-cleaning contracts and the establishment of municipally operated programs would assure improved service. This assumption was not always borne out. Municipally operated systems had to contend with serious problems in establishing effective street-cleaning programs.[9]

[7] See L. M. King, "Street Cleaning in San Francisco," *Engineering News* 50 (20 August 1903): 169; "Indianapolis Discards Contract Street Cleaning," *Municipal Journal and Engineer* 18 (June 1905): 31; "Street Cleaning without Contractors in Washington, D.C.," *Engineering News* 70 (2 October 1913): 681–82; J. W. Paxton, "Municipal versus Contract Street Cleaning in Washington, D.C.," *American Journal of Public Health* 4 (November 1914): 1032–34; "Philadelphia Street Cleaning by Contract," *Engineering News* 74 (1 July 1915): 6; Philadelphia, Bureau of Municipal Research, *Municipal Street Cleaning in Philadelphia*, p. 9.

[8] Paxton, "Municipal versus Contract Street Cleaning in Washington, D.C.," p. 1033. See also Philadelphia, Bureau of Municipal Research, *Municipal Street Cleaning in Philadelphia*, pp. 10–12.

[9] An important exception to anticontract sentiment caused a change in policy in New York City. Until 1909 the city force had been completely responsible for street cleaning. In that year the governor of New York signed a bill giving the city the authority to enter into five-year contracts for machine street cleaning and sprinkling. The city did not abandon its sweeping patrols but added machine sweeping by contract to its operations. The argument in favor of this move was two-fold: (1) municipal operation was more successful in service branches with small numbers of employees than in large departments where politics influenced decisions, and (2) mechanical substitutes for hand sweeping had come of age and should be substituted for brooms for some tasks. The example of New York City was not followed by many other cities, however. Only 1 or 2 percent of the cities surveyed in this period combined muni-

For instance, few cities cleaned all the streets uniformly. Because city officials associated streets with the vitality of the local economy, major thoroughfares in central business districts had the highest priorities. Streets in outlying areas and in working-class and immigrant neighborhoods had much lower priorities and received less frequent service—and no service at all if the streets were unpaved.[10] Moreover, street cleaning remained vulnerable to political influence, graft, and corruption. Even municipally operated street cleaning provided many opportunities for conferring political favors, exacting votes from grateful employees, and pilfering appropriations. Some officials lived by the axiom of the colorful Tammany ward boss and layman philosopher George Washington Plunkitt: "I seen my opportunities and I took 'em."[11] Thus municipal street-cleaning systems were not without their shortcomings in a period when under the best of circumstances services could not keep pace with the growing cities. George A. Soper, author of *Modern Methods of Street Cleaning* (1909), summed it up well when he wrote that street cleaning had "not yet emerged from the state of a nondescript kind of emergency undertaking to the position of an effective art."[12]

Nonetheless, a municipally operated street-cleaning program was generally regarded as the best means of ensuring effective service. In an attempt to improve the administrative structure of street-cleaning programs, several cities adopted Colonel Waring's organizational reforms as well as the new cost- and record-keeping methods which reformers were introducing into city management. Some officials cribbed directly from the master himself. Street Commissioner William A. Larkins of Baltimore acquired a reputation as a leading sanitarian by reorganizing his staff, upgrading the equipment, and improving service city wide. His men were dressed in "spotless white and brown uniforms," and he initiated an annual parade of workers. He even had the street-cleaning carts painted in "re-

---

cipal and contract operations. See "Street Cleaning by Contract or Day Labor," *Municipal Journal and Engineer* 26 (26 May 1909): 931. See also note 6 above.

[10] In 1916 the following comment was made about street cleaning in suburban Philadelphia: "Another advance in the department [of street cleaning] was the provision for cleaning suburban streets and country roads. Prior to 1915 street cleaning work covered only the paved streets. Now a force of uniformed men are at work on the suburban roads, resulting in a great improvement in appearance at a slight cost." See "Street Cleaning in Philadelphia," *Municipal Journal and Engineer* 40 (29 June 1916): 898.

[11] William L. Riordan, *Plunkitt of Tammany Hall*, p. 6.

[12] George A. Soper, *Modern Methods of Street Cleaning*, p. 11.

splendent colors."[13] The Philadelphia Bureau of Highways and Street Cleaning also adopted some of the trappings of the colonel's program: uniformed cleaners, street-cleaning parades, source separation, public-education programs, and cleanup campaigns.[14] Street Commissioner J. F. Fetherston of New York City, seeking to resurrect Waring's spirit, initiated some significant reforms in the Department of Street Cleaning, which had fallen into disarray under Tammany Hall domination. Chief among his reforms was the establishment of a "model district," in which street cleaning was conducted "along the most improved and modern lines by the use of the highest developments in street cleaning and refuse removal apparatus."[15]

The reformers' enthusiasm for scientific management and efficiency programs manifested itself in the application of cost- and record-keeping techniques to city services, including street-cleaning and public-works departments. In a paper read before the Sanitary Engineering Section of the American Public Health Association in 1913, consulting engineer S. Whinery stated:

> Perhaps the most promising and fruitful advance that has been made in recent years is the greater attention given to the study of the details of street cleaning and the keeping and analysis of more complete and itemized accounts. The older accounts and reports of street-cleaning departments were so barren in details that they were generally of little or no value to either the student or the practical man.[16]

Whinery believed that efficiency and economy in street-cleaning departments, rather than new machinery or new cleaning methods, were largely responsible for the noticeable improvement in street appearance. Although he acknowledged the importance of technical advances in street-cleaning devices in the first decade of the new century, he perceived "no radical or particularly notable advancement" in machinery or methods. "The flood of patents issued for street cleaning devices continues unabated," he ar-

[13] Stuart Stevens Scott, "The Street Cleaning Department of Baltimore," *American City* 9 (December 1913): 546–48.

[14] Philadelphia, Department of Public Works, Bureau of Highways and Street Cleaning, *Annual Report* (1914), pp. 49–53.

[15] "New York City Will Try Innovation in Modern Street Cleaning," *Better Roads and Streets* (July 1915): 30.

[16] S. Whinery, "Recent Progress in Methods and Character of Street Cleaning," *American Journal of Public Health* 4 (August 1914): 680.

gued, "but these patents relate largely to details and disclose little of value for practical use. This is somewhat surprising in this land of inventors."[17]

The results produced by the introduction of cost- and record-keeping methods in some of the major cities seemed to bear out Whinery's claims. The best example was Washington, D.C. In 1911 Congress passed a law terminating the street-cleaning contract for the capital city and turned over responsibility to the commissioners of the District of Columbia. One of the direct results of this change was the establishment of a modern cost-keeping system. After two years in operation the new system had made some important gains, especially in helping determine labor efficiency and operating costs. The improvements under the "Washington system" were modest, but the initiators of the program had implemented it with deliberation, hoping to improve it over time. Instead of hiring an efficiency expert to develop a system in a few weeks or months, they charged a permanent employee with the task of developing and monitoring the system. As a spokesman for the new program noted:

The Washington system, as a whole, will probably fit no other department in Washington nor the Street Cleaning Department of any other city. Cost keeping is necessarily a process of first, evolution, and second, elimination. This department has gone through the first and the question now is can we do without this detail or how may we obtain it with less effort?[18]

Advancement in cost- and record-keeping and departmental reorganization, important as they were, did not attract the widespread attention that mechanization and motorization of street-cleaning equipment achieved. While these technological changes did not resolve all the problems associated with street cleaning, they did promote significant alterations in methods and in the variety of tasks which street crews could perform. New street designs and new paving materials led many American and European cities to employ machine sweepers. Between 1899 and 1905 about 85 percent of American cities with populations of more than 25,000 were using mechanical sweeping devices as supplements to or replacements for hand

[17] Ibid., p. 679.

[18] F. C. Bamman, "Analysis of Cost Keeping as Applied to Municipal Management of Street Cleaning," *American Journal of Public Health* 4 (August 1914): 677–78. See also J. W. Paxton, "Street Cleaning Methods and Costs at Washington, D.C., *Engineering News* 72 (9 July 1914): 58–66.

sweeping.[19] Soon more than 55 percent of the smaller cities and towns had followed the larger cities' lead.[20]

The advantages of machine sweeping were manifold. The advent of smooth pavement made machine sweeping practicable, and advocates of the mechanical devices claimed that they were well suited for the new surfaces, offering efficient and economical service for every city in the nation and eliminating dust, the bane of urban dwellers. As Whinery noted:

It is coming to be generally recognized that from both the sanitary and business point of view the most objectionable part of street dirt is the fine dust produced by the drying out and pulverization of the animal excreta and other matter that finds its way to the surface of the streets. The fresh, raw and usually damp excreta and rubbish are objectionable mainly to the sight, but when dried and ground dust floats in the air when disturbed, and disease germs contained in it are breathed into the nose, mouth and lungs of those exposed to it, where it may develop specific diseases. This dust, carried by the winds, enters residences and business houses to the injury of delicate goods or furnishings, and by reagitation may thence be carried into the human system. Any system of street cleaning that does not provide for the prevention or allaying of street dust cannot therefore be regarded as satisfactory.[21]

Advocates of machine sweeping also claimed that the army of laborers once needed to ensure street cleanliness could be eliminated or employed in other tasks. A reduction in the labor force would cut costs, as well as eliminate many worker-employer conflicts (this was an especially attractive argument for antiunion management).[22]

[19] Statistics gleaned from U.S. Department of Labor, Bulletin no. 24 (September 1899), pp. 662–64; Bulletin no. 30 (September 1900), pp. 958–62; Bulletin no. 36 (September 1901), pp. 880–84; Bulletin no. 42 (September 1902), pp. 958–62; U.S. Bureau of Census, *Statistics of Cities Having a Population of over 25,000: 1902–1903* Bulletin no. 20 (1905), pp. 121–29; U.S. Department of Commerce and Labor, Bureau of the Census, *Statistics of Having a Population of over 3,000: 1905*, Special Reports (1907), pp 338–40. According to the 1905 census, sweeping machines were used by all surveyed cities with populations of 100,000 or more, by 90 percent of cities with populations of 50,000 to 100,000, and by 75 percent of cities with populations of 30,000 to 50,000.

[20] U.S. Bureau of the Census, *Statistics of Cities Having a Population of 8,000 to 25,000: 1903*, Bulletin no. 45 (1906), pp. 92–97. For statistics on regional variations in cleaning methods, see "Street Cleaning Methods," *Municipal Journal and Engineer* 26 (24 March 1909): 485–89.

[21] S. Whinery, "How to Keep the Streets Clean," *American City* 10 (January 1914): 21.

[22] "Hand vs. Machine Street Cleaning," *Municipal Journal and Engineer* 17 (August 1904): 95; "Street Cleaning Here and Abroad," *Outlook* 107 (1 August 1914): 774–75; Gerhard, *Sanitary Engineering*, pp. 58–59; Soper, "Modern Methods of Street Cleaning," pp. 2–3; Frank Hagerdorn, "Sweeping City Streets by Machine," *American City* 12 (February 1915): 147–48; "Some Notes on the Development of Street Methods," *Engineering and*

The fascination of Americans with machinery was nowhere more evident than in the promotion of mechanical cleaning devices. Private companies sprang up across the country, hawking all manner of devices to make the job of the city sanitarian easier, as well as to turn tidy profits for themselves. General Motors Truck Company promoted the Modern Flusher for Progressive Municipalities. The Sanitary (Automatic) Street Flushing Machine, manufactured by a Saint Louis company, "flushes —not merely wets—but scrubs, washes, scours, cleans, *rids the street of all health menacing unsanitary conditions*" with "no complicated mechanism. No skilled labor required." The Matchless Street Cleaner Company of New York sold a "simple, common sense machine" that did away with "all unnecessary work" and would clean 50 percent more surface than any other machine. The Austin-Western Company, Ltd., claimed that "All Unite in Pronouncing [their sprinklers] the best." General Vehicle Company exhorted its patrons to "Tow Your Street Cleaning Apparatus with Electricity."[23]

There were machines for every purpose, every street material, every climate, every city size. There were mechanical brooms for general sweeping, squeegee cleaners that sprinkled and scraped the pavements, vacuum cleaners that sucked dirt into large canisters or bags, machines that swept and disinfected the streets simultaneously, and flushers that washed dirt into gutters and sewers.[24] R. N. Stevens invented an ingenious machine which passed over the street and subjected it to temperatures up to 1,000° F., presumably to bake or burn up germs and dirt.[25] Needless to say, many of the mechanical devices were variations on a few basic themes, and their claims of effectiveness and efficiency were proved only by trial and error—sometimes expensive trial and substantial error. Cities, however, kept several of the companies in business by continuing to seek new solutions to their street-cleaning problems.

Contracting 42 (21 October 1914): 394–96; Edward D. Very, "Modern Methods of Street Cleaning," *American City* 7 (November 1912): 435–39.

[23] See *Municipal Engineering* 50 (January 1916): 26, 44; *Municipal Journal and Engineer* 33 (4 July 1912): 2, 9, 14.

[24] "The Street Cleaning Problem," *California [Pacific] Municipalities* 8 (May 1903): 109–10; "A New Street Cleaning and Disinfecting Method," *Public Improvements* 1 (1 July 1899): 85; "Vacuum Street-Cleanings," *Literary Digest* 48 (14 March 1914): 548; William H. Connell, "Organization and Method of Street Cleaning Departments," *Canadian Engineer* 26 (26 March 1914): 503–505; "Street Sweeping," *Pacific (formerly California) Municipalities* 9 (December 1903): 164–68.

[25] "A New Street Cleaning and Disinfecting Method," p. 85.

The practice of flushing streets gained many adherents. It promised not only to clean the streets of dust and disease-breeding filth but also to cool the pavement in the summer months. The machines were used on practically all surfaces—asphalt, brick, concrete, granite block, macadam, cobblestone, and even wood. The number of flushings a week varied with the importance of the streets. Streets were flushed daily in New Orleans; in Los Angeles the major business streets were flushed three times a week; other streets might be flushed once every two weeks. Denver streets were flushed daily in the summer, but sweepers were used in the winter months. Most of the cities using the flushing method continued hand sweeping or mechanical sweeping as a supplement.[26]

Although mechanical sweepers and flushers promised to revolutionize street cleaning, they did not always produce expected results. Several city officials and municipal engineers questioned their effectiveness and challenged the claim that machine sweeping was cheaper than hand sweeping. For example, in June 1907, Mayor George B. McClellan of New York appointed a commission to recommend a more effective system of street cleaning and waste disposal. The commission, whose members included the notable Rudolph Hering, conducted a thorough investigation. Its findings were critical of machine cleaning and sprinkling to settle dust. According to the report, sprinkling paved streets did not clean them but merely converted the dust into mud. It added that if the streets were properly swept sprinkling would be unnecessary, and sprinkling costs—borne by private citizens—need not be incurred. The commission ranked flushing, hand sweeping, and machine sweeping in descending order of effectiveness. In terms of cost, flushing appeared to be the most expensive method. Hose flushing with fire hoses attached to hydrants cost about the same as machine sweeping, but machine flushing was more than twice as expensive as machine sweeping. Flushing, especially hose flushing,

[26] "Street Flushing Practice in American Cities," *American City* 16 (February 1917): 117–21; Raymond W. Parlin, "Flushing and Street Cleaning," *American Municipalities* 33 (May 1917): 49–53; Raymond W. Parlin, "Hand Flushing—Its Place in the Street Cleaning Field," *American City* 14 (May 1916): 441–48; "Sanitary Street Flushing," *Municipal Journal and Engineer* 18 (June 1905): 295; "Sanitary Street Flushing Machine," *Municipal Journal and Engineer* 19 (July 1905): 46; "Street Cleaning," *Municipal Journal and Engineer* 29 (23 November 1910): 713–14; Gus H. Hanna, "Economy in Street Cleaning," *American City* 14 (January 1916): 22; "Street Cleaning Methods and Costs in Several Ohio Cities," *Engineering and Contracting* 38 (18 September 1912): 319; "Methods and Costs of Street Cleaning at Washington, D.C., During 1911–1912," *Engineering and Contracting* 38 (18 December 1912): 684.

wasted huge quantities of water needed for other purposes. With access to water becoming more difficult for major cities, this fact was a prime consideration in the decision whether or not to use the flushing technique. The commission concluded that, taking into account the strengths and weaknesses of the various methods, flushing combined with hand sweeping was the best solution. This method could properly clean the streets at a reasonable cost and with less water than would be required in a system totally dependent on flushing.[27]

Some cities resisted the temptation to commit themselves to machine-sweeping systems. Reservations about their effectiveness and unwillingness to invest huge sums in the equipment were the usual reasons. Some city officials were reluctant to reduce the rolls of public employees, for obvious political reasons.[28] Many cities, nonetheless, caught up in the promise of a quick solution, adopted machine sweeping as the sole method of street cleaning or as a supplement to other methods. The promoters' claims of greater efficiency, lower costs, and the elimination of a cumbersome labor force often overrode the critics' apprehension.

Another technological advance which significantly altered street-cleaning practices in the United States was motorization of transportation and cleaning equipment. Horses were rapidly being replaced by motorized trucks. Economy and efficiency were most often cited as the primary reasons for the change, and street-cleaning departments were merely keeping pace with the transportation trends of the day.[29] Street-cleaning departments also were coming to realize that the trend toward motorization of private as well as public vehicles would make their jobs easier. The limitations of animal labor—a short productive life, feeding and grooming requirements, and manure—could be overcome with efficient and (seeming-

---

[27] "Street Cleaning and Refuse Disposal in New York," *Engineering Record* 57 (22 February 1908): 208; New York City, Department of Street Cleaning, *Report of the Commission on Street Cleaning and Waste Disposal, 1907*, p. 138. See also Parlin, "Hand Flushing—Its Place in the Street Cleaning Field," pp. 491ff.; Whinery, "How to Keep the Streets Clean," pp. 22–23.

[28] For example, see Edward D. Very, "Modern Methods of Street Cleaning," *American City* 7 (November 1912): 435–36.

[29] "Motor-driven Squeegees in Street Cleaning Service," *Scientific American* 115 (15 July 1916): 66, 68; "Motor Wagons for Municipal Work," *Municipal Journal and Engineer* 16 (February 1904): 81; Thomas Finegan, "The Comparative Cost of Sweeping Pavements by Horse-drawn Sweepers and by Motor Sweepers," *American City* 12 (February 1915): 148–49; "Street Cleaning by Motor Apparatus," *Municipal Journal and Engineer* (14 January 1915): 33–34.

ly) pollution-free motorized vehicles. Interest groups associated with the rising automobile industry, such as the Automobile Chamber of Commerce, painted glowing pictures of the potential benefits of the internal-combustion engine. H. W. Perry, secretary of the chamber, outlined four areas in which motor power could be beneficial in street cleaning: (1) the substitution of motor vehicles for horse-drawn vehicles would reduce the cost of street cleaning, lessen the wear on street pavements, and help decrease the death rate of the population; (2) the use of motor trucks by street-cleaning departments would reduce the costs of cleaning and of waste disposal; (3) the elimination of the horse would lessen wear and tear on street pavements; and (4) the replacement of macadam pavement with permanent pavement to provide easier travel for motor vehicles would ultimately lower street-cleaning and maintenance costs. Perry calculated that Chicago could save $1 million on street cleaning alone if businesses and private citizens would substitute trucks and automobiles for the 80,000 horses used for transportation in the city.[30] Street cleaners around the world heralded the arrival of the truck and the automobile. Few foresaw the long-term environmental impact of the automobile age.

Although mechanization and motorization held out great hopes for improvements in street cleaning, these technolgical achievements could not change citizens' patterns of behavior. Sweepers and flushers may have helped improve the gathering of street debris, but they could not curtail littering. As Joseph J. Norton, supervisor of street cleaning and oiling service in Boston, noted, "The greatest deterrent to clean streets in any community, particularly a cosmopolitan one, is the constant, unrestrained and promiscuous throwing of rubbish and waste materials into the streets."[31] No matter how efficient a street-cleaning crew was, it could not keep up with the litter. Edward D. Very, a New York City sanitary engineer, calculated that cleaning up litter took about 20 percent of a sweeper's time in Manhattan and about 10 percent of a sweeper's time in the other boroughs.[32]

Almost all cities had antilittering ordinances, but they were largely ignored, unenforced, or unenforceable. The Citizens' Research Council of

[30] "Clean Streets and Motor Traffic," *Literary Digest* 49 (5 September 1914): 413–14.

[31] Joseph J. Norton, "The Public and Clean Streets," *American Municipalities* 28 (January 1915): 136.

[32] Edward D. Very, "Street Cleaning Methods and Results," *Munitipal Engineering* 47 (September 1914): 176.

Michigan contended that, although Detroit police and judges had adequate power to stop the littering of streets and alleys, the ordinances prohibiting littering and street obstructions continued to be "violated to an unusual extent."[33] In an address at the First New England Conference on Street Cleaning in 1910, one speaker argued that enforcement of antilitter ordinances was often lax because the police, who had jurisdiction over the ordinances, were independent of the street-cleaning forces and had very little sympathy with their objectives or appreciation of the importance of their work.[34]

Some cities intensified their efforts to bring littering under control. Reformers joined in the cause with cleanup campaigns and other publicity efforts. Some municipal authorities experimented with various new programs. In Washington, D.C., the police were instructed to intensify their efforts to enforce littering ordinances. For a while arrests of violators increased, and the fine for littering was raised from one dollar to five dollars. The mayor of New Haven, Connecticut, admonished the police and the public-works crews to help reduce litter. He offered prizes to school children for the best essays on the importance of maintaining a clean urban environment. Boston and other cities tried to curb littering by installing more trash barrels in the public parks and on street corners and doubled their efforts to educate the public about the evils of littering. No ready solutions were forthcoming, however.[35]

Any evaluation of the improvement in street cleaning in American cities has to take into consideration disparities in service. Local conditions—political, economic, geographic, and climatic—largely determined the quality of street cleaning. Often the question was not whether effective programs, utilizing available organizational and technological tools, could be initiated but whether city governments were willing to finance them. Under

[33] Michigan, Citizens' Research Council, *Report on Street Cleaning and Refuse Collection, Department of Public Works, City of Detroit*, pp. 74–75.

[34] Guy C. Emerson, "Individual Responsibility for Clean Streets," *New Boston*, August 1910, p. 2.

[35] "Street Cleaning in Washington," *City Hall: Bulletin of the Leaue of American Municipalities* 10 (May 1909): 385; "New Haven Fights Street Littering," *Municipal Journal and Engineer* 40 (13 January 1916): 37–38; "To Prevent Littering Parks," *Municipal Journal and Engineer* 39 (1 July 1915): 8; "Street Cleaning and Pavement Economy," *Municipal Journal and Engineer* 40 (6 January 1916): 7–9. See also "Street Cleaning in New York," *Municipal Journal and Engineer* 35 (11 December 1913): 789; New York City, Department of Street Cleaning, *Unsightly Streets and Careless People: Control of the Loose Paper Nuisance*; "Street Cleaning," *Municipal Journal and Engineer* 29 (23 November 1910): 713.

the restrictions imposed by local circumstances, it was very difficult for municipalities to determine what constituted adequate funding for street cleaning.

Expenditures varied widely in the early twentieth century. For example, according to a report issued in 1906, New York City spent more than $5.5 million on street cleaning in that year, while Philadelphia, the city with the second-highest expenditure, spent approximately $688,000.[36] Comparisons of cities' total annual expenditures were not very useful. Comparative and relative costs more effectively indicated disparities in service among cities. A report published in 1915 in the *Municipal Journal* indicated that, in thirty-one major cities surveyed, the average annual cost of street cleaning per thousand square yards was $0.355; however, costs ranged from $0.14 to $1.53. The annual report of the Baltimore Department of Street Cleaning for 1900 showed the disparity among four major cities. The per capita cost in Baltimore was $0.73, as compared with $1.76 in Boston, $1.36 in New York, and $0.96 in Philadelphia. One important conclusion drawn from several investigations was that per capita costs were greater in cities with populations over 300,000. In other words, the financial burden of maintaining the streets was much heavier for residents of larger cities.[37]

Labor costs accounted for much of the expense of street cleaning. In 1909 more than 22,000 people were employed in street cleaning in cities with populations of 30,000 or more. Table 4 gives a breakdown of number of employees by size of city population. Table 5 shows the average number of workers employed in several cities in 1913.

Although the use of machine sweeping was increasing in the early twentieth century, human labor continued to be the mainstay of most large street-cleaning departments. Because of the magnitude of the street-cleaning task the numbers of employees remained high. Good labor relations were vital to the efficiency and effectiveness of street-cleaning programs. Although Colonel Waring had encouraged superintendents not to take their work forces for granted, when machines began to do some of the jobs for-

[36] "Amount and Cost of Street Cleaning," *Municipal Engineering* 30 (April 1906): 280. See also "Comparative Cost of Street Cleaning," *Municipal Journal and Engineer* 12 (April 1902): 160.

[37] Capes and Carpenter, *Municipal Housecleaning*, p. 39; Baltimore, Department of Street Cleaning, *Annual Report* (1900), p. 6. See also Paul Iglehart, "Street Cleaning in Baltimore," *Municipal Journal and Engineering* 10 (March 1901): 89; "Amount and Cost of Street Cleaning," p. 280.

TABLE 4

Total Number of Street-cleaning Employees in American Cities, 1907 and 1909
(by Population)

Size of Cities (by Population)	1907	1909
Over 300,000	14,176	13,963
100,000 to 300,000	3,702	4,052
50,000 to 100,000	2,500	3,072
30,000 to 50,000	1,460	1,473
Totals	21,838	22,560

SOURCE: U. S. Department of Commerce and Labor, Bureau of the Census, *Statistics of Cities Having a Population of over 30,000: 1907*, (Washington, D.C., 1910), p. 474; U.S. Department of Commerce, Bureau of the Census, *General Statistics of Cities: 1909* (Washington, D.C., 1913), p. 133.

merly carried out by human labor, many cities continued to recruit their employees from easily exploitable groups—transients, the chronically unemployed, and newly arrived immigrants. Even in New York City, where the colonel's program had emphasized improved working conditions and labor relations, street cleaners had lost most of their gains. Salaries in 1917 were only $2.50 a day, an increase of only about $0.02 a year since 1895, when Waring was appointed street-cleaning commissioner. Street cleaning continued to be hazardous. In 1917, according to Dr. S. I. Rainforth, chief physician of the New York Department of Street Cleaning, eight out of ten White Wings were physically disabled from job-related causes—a total of 5,484 cases of disability. Accidents, pneumonia, sunstroke, intestinal disorders, neuralgia, and other impairments related to weather conditions and poor sanitation were pervasive. Although New York City provided free medical care for its employees and required annual physical examinations, the hazards of the job, combined with low pay and other grievances, caused instability in street-cleaning departments. Efforts to improve working conditions, increase pay, provide pensions, and establish outlets for worker grievances were slow in coming. Strikes and other demonstrations of discontent, such as frequent absence from work and poor performance, disrupted department operations.[38]

[38] "Some Hazards of City Housecleaning," *Survey* 38 (14 April 1917): 42; "Strike of New York Street Cleaners," *Survey* 27 (25 November 1911): 1243–49; "Street Cleaning and

TABLE 5

Average Number of Street-cleaning Workers in Selected American Cities, 1913

City	Average Number of Employees
Albany, N.Y.	60
Baltimore, Md.	310
Boston, Mass.	590
Chicago, Ill.	1,220
Cincinnati, Ohio	175
Cleveland, Ohio	450
Columbus, Ohio	123
Detroit, Mich.	300
Grand Rapids, Mich.	75
Indianapolis, Ind.	275
Kansas City, Mo.	225
Milwaukee, Wis.	250
Minneapolis, Minn.	425
New Orleans, La.	340
New York City, N.Y.	
Richmond Borough	96
Queens Borough	196
Bronx Borough	930
Manhattan Borough	2,800
Omaha, Nebr.	42
Philadelphia, Pa.	1,115
Providence, R.I.	190
Portland, Oreg.	225
Rochester, N.Y.	125
San Francisco, Calif.	170
St. Joseph, Mo.	24
Toledo, Ohio	45
Washington, D.C.	400

SOURCE: Chicago, Civil Service Commission, *Reports on the Bureau of Streets, Department of Public Works, City of Chicago* (21 April and 15 October, 1913), p. 65.

The obstacles to good street-cleaning service were legion: unfavorable local conditions, lack of adequate funds, lukewarm government support, and serious organizational and technical problems. Nonetheless, sig-

Refuse Collection Methods," *Municipal Journal and Engineer* 42 (17 May 1917): 688; William H. Edwards, "The Work of the Street Cleaning Department of New York City," City Club of Philadelphia, *City Club Bulletin* 2 (24 March 1910): 111.

TABLE 6
Frequency of Street Cleaning in Cities, 1909

Size of Cities (by Population)	Percentage of Paved Streets Cleaned	Average Number of Cleanings per Week
Over 300,000	49.5	4.8
100,000 to 300,000	36.8	5.0
50,000 to 100,000	42.7	5.0
30,000 to 50,000	28.6	4.4
Average	43.5	4.9

SOURCE: U.S. Department of Commerce, Bureau of the Census, *General Statistics of Cities: 1909*, (Washington, D.C., 1913), pp. 124–32.

nificant improvements were made in the early twentieth century. Technological innovations in street paving, the advent of motorized vehicles, and improvements in sweeping machines changed the methods of street cleaning. Cost- and record-keeping techniques offered means of monitoring expenditures and evaluating the effectiveness of programs. Most important was the establishment nationwide of permanent municipal street-cleaning programs. Regularity of service was another important measure of the effectiveness of the progrms. Table 6, compiled from a statistical survey made in 1909, indicates how regular the service had become. Statistics on frequency of service or levels of expenditures do not, of course, tell the whole story. The quality of the service provided was a subjective matter, not easily expressed in statistics. By the measures available, however, it appeared that street cleaning as a municipal function had come of age.

6

Collection and Disposal Practices in the Early Twentieth Century

IN 1908 refuse-disposal expert William F. Morse hypothesized that, as society became increasingly urbanized and as cities grew in size and number, methods for dealing with waste remained unchanged. Primitive methods sufficient for individual or family needs were simply applied to the new circumstances with little thought to the difference in context.[1] In an elementary way Morse's perception was accurate—at least until the late nineteenth century. Colonel Waring made some progress after 1895 by convincing city officials that refuse was more than a personal inconvenience. As with street cleaning, increased public awareness of the physical environment and the activities of reformers had positive effects. Unlike street cleaning refuse collection and disposal were not so easily improved by technological innovations. The complexity of the tasks was only beginning to be addressed by World War I.

The naïveté of late-nineteenth-century reformers, who saw in Waring's programs quick solutions to the waste problem, was tempered by trial-and-error experimentation in the first two decades of the new century. Those willing to accept partial victories as signs of progress expressed guarded optimism about attempts to improve collection and disposal practices. Rudolph Hering and Samuel Greeley contended that impressive results had been achieved in "collating data of experience" about the quantity and quality of refuse. Some observers noted with approval the increasing number of municipal investigations being conducted to evaluate local needs and uncover the shortcomings of refuse-management programs already in operation. *Engineering News* reported: "It is gratifying to ob-

---

[1]William F. Morse, *The Collection and Disposal of Municipal Waste*, p. 1.

serve the general attention now being paid to the disposal of refuse and garbage in American cities. While it cannot be said that any large amount of definite progess is to be recorded, the subject is now receiving the attention of the public, which should long ago have been paid to it."[2]

Other commentators and experts, exasperated by the snail's pace at which municipal officials responded to the refuse problem, could not hide their pessimism. As noted in chapter 5, M. N. Baker criticized the neglect of garbage collection in most cities and towns as a blot on American municipal administration. In another article he asserted that in no branch of municipal service had "so little progress been made in the United States as in the disposal of garbage."[3] Some individuals criticized the widespread public indifference and apathy, while others questioned the sophistication of available methods. Luther E. Lovejoy, secretary of the Detroit Housing Commission, fatalistically concluded, "The accumulation of garbage and rubbish is one of the penalties human society inevitably pays for the luxury of civilization."[4]

Despite the cynicism of some experts, statistics indicate a relatively rapid increase in municipal responsibility for collection and disposal of refuse. As stated earlier, 24 percent of the cities surveyed in the 1880 census had municipally operated garbage-collection systems, and 19 percent contracted with private firms for the service. This meant that only 43 percent of the cities provided for some sort of collection. By the turn of the cen-

[2] Rudolph Hering and Samuel A. Greeley, *Collection and Disposal of Municipal Refuse*, p. 3; Samuel A. Greeley, "Refuse Disposal and Street Cleaning," *Engineering Record* 69 (3 January 1914): 15; "Report of Committee on Refuse Collection and Disposal," *American Journal of Public Health* 7 (April 1917): 412–13; "Refuse Disposal in America," *Engineering Record* 58 (25 July 1908): 85. See also M. L. Davis, "The Disposal of Garbage," *Journal of the American Medical Association* 31 (2 July 1898): 23–26; "Street Cleaning and Refuse Disposal," *Municipal Journal and Engineer* 30 (4 January 1911): 15; *Proceedings of the American Society for Municipal Improvements*, Seventeenth Annual Meeting, Erie, Pa. (1910), pp. 57–58 (hereafter cited as *Proceedings of the ASMI*).

[3] M. N. Baker, *Municipal Engineering and Sanitation*, pp. 5–6; M. N. Baker, "Condition of Garbage Disposal in United States," *Municipal Journal and Engineer* 11 (October 1901): 147.

[4] Luther E. Lovejoy, "Garbage and Rubbish," *Proceedings of the Academy of Political Science* 2 (1911–12): 300; "Need of Sanitary Garbage Disposal," *Municipal Journal and Engineer* 18 (April 1905): 173–74; John H. Simon, "Municipal Waste," *Municipal Journal and Engineer* 18 (January 1905): 10; William P. Munn, "Collection and Disposal of Garbage," *City Government* 2 (January 1897): 6; "The Unsatisfactory Condition of Refuse Disposal in America," *Sanitary Record* 21 (11 February 1898): 146; *Proceedings of the ASMI* Eighth Annual Meeting, Niagara Falls, N.Y. (1901), p. 183; "The Unsatisfactory Condition of Garbage Disposal in America," *Sanitarian* 40 (January 1898): 20.

TABLE 7

Responsibility for Garbage Collection in Cities, Selected Years

Form of Responsibility	Year of Survey. (Percentage and Number of Cities)									
	1880	1899	1901	1902	1913	1915	1915	1918	1918*	1924
City	24.0% (48)	32% (12)	39% (11)	33.5% (54)	57.0% (16)	55.0% (31)	50% (84)	46% (48)	54% (7)	63% (60)
Contract	19.0% (38)	46% (17)	43% (12)	30.0% (48)	39.5% (11)	36.0% (20)	39% (66)	34% (36)	38% (5)	25% (24)
Private	30.0% (59)	3% (1)	11% (3)	25.5% (41)	3.5% (1)	3.5% (2)	1% (2)			10% (10)
Combined or other	1.5% (3)	6% (2)				5.5% (3)	6% (9)	20% (21)	8% (1)	
No data or no system	0.5% (1)	13% (5)	7% (2)	11.0% (18)			4% (7)			2% (2)
Total cities	149	37	28	161	28	56	168	105	13	96

*Cities with 247,000 or more population.

SOURCE: U.S. Department of Interior, Census Office, *Report on the Social Statistics of Cities, Tenth Census, 1880* (Washington, D.C., 1886); "Garbage Collection and Disposal," *Engineering News* 42 (28 September, 1899): 214; "Methods of Garbage Disposal," *Municipal Journal and Engineer* 11 (September 1901): 123–124; William F. Morse, "The Disposal of Municipal Waste," *Municipal Journal and Engineer* 20 (7 February, 1906): 114; Rudolph Hering and Samuel A. Greeley, *Collection and Disposal of Municipal Refuse* (New York: McGraw-Hill Book Co., 1921), p. 106; *American Society for Municipal Improvements, Proceedings of the Twenty-second Annual Convention, (1915)*, pp. 10–11; "Refuse Collection and Disposal," *Municipal Journal and Engineer* 39 (11 November, 1915): 725–27; William Parr Capes and Jeanne Daniels Carpenter, *Municipal Housecleaning* (New York: E. P. Dutton and Co., 1918), table vi; Pittsburgh, Commission on Garbage and Rubbish Collection and Disposal, *Report on Methods of Garbage and Rubbish Collection and Disposal in American Cities* (1918), pp. 14–15; "Garbage Collection and Disposal: A Compilation from Questionnaires Returned by 101 City Manager Cities in the U.S. and Canada," *City Manager Magazine* (July 1924): 12–14.

tury, however, more than 65 percent of the cities surveyed had some form of municipally sponsored collection, and in the period from 1910 to 1920 it rose to 89 percent or even higher. In 1915, for example, 50 percent had municipally operated collection systems, and 39 percent utilized some form of contract work (see Table 7).

The growing trend toward municipal ownership of utilities and control of services led several cities to abandon the contract system because traditional arrangements were proving inadequate to meet the needs of the growing and more complex industrial cities. Contract terms varied greatly, but most were of short duration, running about three to five years. Renegotiation was a continual process and a mixed blessing. Frequent renewals gave cities the opportunity to reevaluate the provisions of the contracts and review contractors' performance, but they were also very time-consuming, entangled in bureaucratic red tape, and, in the long run, clearly disadvantageous to the cities. Contractors, uncertain of their long-term relationships with the cities, were unwilling to devise cleaning systems which required large capital outlays, such as for constructing expensive incinerators, reduction plants, or other permanent structures. Attempting to hold down costs, they often employed poorly trained workers, who received minimal benefits.[5]

Short-term contracts were abused in other ways. For example, city officials in Philadelphia took bids for the ensuing year in late November or early December. Because the period between the reception of the bids and the beginning of actual work was so short, a company lacking extensive resources and a well-developed program could not compete with the existing contractor. Thus one contractor could maintain a long-standing monopoly built upon the yearly bidding system and the short-term contract. In Philadelphia and other cities charges of political favoritism and even bribery were common.[6] As with street cleaning, however, those critical of the contract system too readily assumed that municipal responsibility would assure better service and the elimination of corruption.[7]

[5] See Hering and Greeley, *Collection and Disposal of Municipal Refuse*, pp. 155–56.

[6] Baker, "Condition of Garbage Disposal in United States," p. 148. See also "Garbage Collection and Disposal of Philadelphia," *Engineering News* 45 (17 January 1901): 41; Philadelphia, Bureau of Health, *Annual Report* (1898), p. xix.

[7] In *Collection and Disposal of Municipal Refuse*, p. 156, Hering and Greeley enumerated the advantages and disadvantages of the contract system. Among the advantages they listed a more effective application of business principles, the elimination of politics from the operations, a simplification of the work of cities and especially of small towns, a fixed expen-

Determining responsibility was only the first of many crucial decisions which city officials faced in establishing practical refuse-management systems. In the 1890s, Colonel Waring offered what seemed to be an ingenious solution: primary separation. As explained earlier, the method promised to combine simplicity of collection with a means of recycling usable materials. Waring argued that the sale of salvageable materials would reduce the cost of service as well as return revenue to the city coffers.[8]

Investigations of collection practices throughout the country indicated that no single method was practicable in all cities. As early as 1890 the Garbage Committee of the American Public Health Association (APHA) began a survey of refuse collection. From time to time in the first two decades of the twentieth century other surveys compared primary separation with available alternatives. Municipal engineers and other informed individuals came to the important if not startling conclusion that no single "best" method of collection existed. The choice of system had to depend on the special conditions of the city, the method of disposal in use, and, with the separation system, the availability and dependability of markets for the by-products. Simply to copy methods used in other cities or to accept uncritically the claims of those with financial interests in collection equipment was an irresponsible way to establish a proper system.[9]

In practice, cities had a choice between primary separation and com-

---

diture for service, and limitations in capital expenses for the city. This enumeration assumes an institutional vulnerability of public but not private service; however, Hering and Greeley were not myopic in their evaluation of the contract system. They recognized that contractors were motivated by profit, could ignore contract provisions that were not spelled out clearly, kept inadequate records (at least for municipal consumption), and bore no direct responsibility to the citizenry. See also I. S. Osborn, *Disposal of Garbage in the District of Columbia*, U.S. Congress, House, 64th Cong., 1st sess., 1915, Doc. 661; "How Not to Award a Contract," *Municipal Journal and Engineer* 11 (August 1901): 69–70; Boston, Special Commissions on Collection and Disposal of Refuse, *Reports of the First and Second Special Commissions to Investigate the Subject of the Collection and Disposal of Refuse in the City of Boston*, pp. 24–25; Washington, D.C., Department of Street Cleaning, *Report of the Superintendent* (1899), p. 550; *Engineering News* 46 (24 October 1901): 308; Cleveland, Board of Public Service, Division of Engineering, *Annual Report* (1906), pp. 93–95; J. W. Paxton, "Collection and Disposal of City Refuse, Washington, D.C.," *Engineering News* 72 (1 October 1914): 671–74; "The Latest Garbage-Disposal Contract of Los Angeles," *Engineering News* 70 (28 August 1913): 422.

[8] See chap. 2.

[9] Hering and Greeley, *Collection and Disposal of Municipal Refuse*, pp. 104–105; H. de B. Parsons, *The Disposal of Municipal Refuse*, p. 43.

bined-refuse collection. Advocates of primary, or source, separation echoed the colonel's arguments and were most persuasive in cities in which the reduction process was a major means of disposal. Their main argument was that primary separation promoted cleanliness. The most objectionable organic waste could be easily separated out and disposed of more frequently, since it represented only a small portion (approximately 10 to 12 percent) of the total waste. Advocates further asserted that primary separation not only permitted the recovery of by-products but also allowed for greater latitude in selecting methods of final dispositon.[10]

On the other side of the issue, critics of universal application of the primary-separation method argued that combined collection was much easier for the householder, less complicated for the collection teams, and cheaper for the city. They insisted that the combined system was actually cleaner because objectionable garbage was mixed with other kinds of refuse. Cities relying primarily on incineration were more likely to employ the combined- or single-colleciton method. Indeed, combined collection was on the rise in Europe at that time because of the widespread adoption of incineration.[11]

It is worth noting that American cities rarely employed a single means of disposal. Primary separation might be used in some neighborhoods or under certain conditions but not throughout the city. Surveys conducted between 1902 and 1924 show that 59 to 83 percent of the cities practiced some form of separation, segregating only garbage, rubbish, or ashes. In less than half the cities with separation programs were all wastes separated along the lines of the Waring system.[12]

[10] Morse, *The Collection and Disposal of Municipal Waste*, p. 36; John H. Gregory, "Collection of Municipal Refuse," *American Journal of Public Health* 2 (December 1912): 919; Saint Louis, Civic League, *Civic Bulletin* 2 (8 January 1912): 2; "Refuse Disposal in Ohio," *Municipal Journal and Engineer* 25 (2 December 1908): 776. See also William F. Morse, "The Collection of Municipal Waste," *American Journal of Public Health* 4 (July 1914): 564–69.

[11] Robert H. Wyld, "Modern Methods of Municipal Refuse Disposal," *American City* 5 (October 1911): 205–207; Parsons, *The Disposal of Municipal Refuse*, p. 44. For a discussion of the controversy over separation in New Orleans, see *Engineering News* 39 (10 March 1898): 160.

[12] See C. E. A. Winslow and P. Hansen, "Some Statistics of Garbage Disposal for the Large American Cities in 1902," American Public Health Association, *Public Health: Papers and Reports* 29 (October 1903): 141–52 (hereafter cited as APHA); *Proceedings of the ASMI* (1915), pp. 10–11; "Refuse Collection and Disposal," *Municipal Journal and Engineer* 39 (11 November 1915): 723–25; Pittsburgh, Commission on Garbage and Rubbish Collection and Disposal, *Report on Methods of Garbage and Rubbish Collection and Disposal in American*

No matter which method was chosen, collection was a difficult municipal problem because it was the phase of refuse management which directly affected the greatest number of people. It was also the costliest phase. As Table 8 indicates, the cost of collection was two to eight times as expensive as disposal. One reason for the high cost of collection during this period was the increase in frequency of service. According to a study conducted at MIT in 1902, 79 percent of the cities surveyed (127 of 161) collected garbage on a regular basis.[13] Several factors determined the frequency of collection: the amount and nature of the wastes, population density, the physical layout of the city, climatic and seasonal variations, the financial resources of the municipal government, and the form of transportation used.[14] Not surprisingly, collections were most frequent in the business districts, followed by those at central-city residences. Collections were least frequent in outlying areas. Almost half the cities surveyed between 1909 and 1918 collected garbage from businesses six times a week (the other half collected one to four times a week). In residential areas it was most common to collect garbage at least two or three times a week; in outlying areas, one to three times a week. Of course, suburbs occupied by people in the upper socioeconomic classes might receive preferential treatment. Some cities, for example, might divert some of their collection teams from inner-city routes to upper- and middle-class suburbs.[15]

Cities, pp. 14–15; William Parr Capes and Jeanne Daniels Carpenter, *Municipal Housecleaning*, table vi; "Garbage Collection and Disposal: A Compilation from Questionnaires Returned by 101 City Manager Cities in the U.S. and Canada," *City Manager Magazine* (July 1924): 12–14.

[13] Winslow and Hansen, "Some Statistics of Garbage Disposal for the Larger American Cities in 1902," pp. 141–53.

[14] Collection and disposal vehicles were rapidly being motorized in the early twentieth century. Baltimore was the first city to use motorized garbage trucks. Some cities, including Chicago, New Orleans, and Cleveland, experimented with railway transport of refuse. Not until the 1920s, however, did horse-drawn vehicles relinquish their role in collection and disposal. In fact, horses were preferred to motorized vehicles for certain tasks, especially household pickups. See B. F. Miller, Jr., "Horse or Motor for Collecting City Garbage," *Engineering News* 76 (23 November 1916): 1006–1007; Baltimore, Department of Street Cleaning, *Annual Report* (1913), pp. 6–7; "Collection of Refuse and Disposal in Chicago," *Engineering Record* 69 (11 April 1914): 424–25; Samuel A. Greeley, "Motor Trucks for Refuse Collection," *American City* 14 (March 1916): 239–43; "Garbage Collection Studies in Chicago Justify Continued Use of Horses," *Engineering Record* 72 (10 July 1915): 52–53.

[15] These figures are primarily for summer months; collections were less frequent in the winter months, especially in northern cities. Collections for ashes and rubbish or combined waste with garbage were also less frequent. See "Disposal of Municipal Refuse," *Municipal*

TABLE 8

Comparative Cost of Collection and Disposal in Selected American Cities

City	Year	Material	Collection (Cost per Ton)	Disposal (Cost per Ton)
Albany, N.Y.	Estimated	Mixed refuse	$1.81	$0.41
Richmond Borough New York, N.Y.	1911	Mixed refuse	1.64	0.54*
Seattle, Wash.	Estimated	Mixed refuse	1.30	0.62
Boston, Mass.	1910	All refuse	1.41	0.43
Buffalo, N.Y.	1907	Garbage	2.19	
Chicago, Ill.	1911	Garbage	3.42	0.38
Cleveland, Ohio	1911	Garbage	2.83	1.04†
Columbus, Ohio	1911	Garbage	1.88	0.77†
Milwaukee, Wis.	1910	Garbage	2.85	0.90
Minneapolis, Minn.	1910	Garbage and ashes	1.32	0.92‡
Buffalo, N.Y.	1907	Rubbish	4.90	0.04§
Averages			$2.42	$0.60

*Estimated from cost per cubic yard.
†Profit.
‡Cost of garbage disposal only.
§Cost after deducting profit from rubbish sorting plant.
SOURCE: Rudolph Hering and Samuel A. Greeley, *Collection and Disposal of Municipal Refuse*, (New York: McGraw-Hill Book Co., 1921), p. 106.

The efficiency of refuse collection largely depended on the volume of waste which the city had to remove. Amounts and composition varied widely from city to city, but some trends were obvious. By world standards the United States produced exceptionally large quantities of waste. Although consumption of goods varied widely according to economic status, the amounts of wastes were staggering overall. Between 1888 and 1913 the annual per capita weight of mixed refuse for fourteen American cities was 860 pounds (many other surveys indicated even higher figures for American cities through 1917). Comparisons with several European cities re-

Journal and Engineer 35 (6 November 1913): 632–33; "Uniform Statistics of Refuse Collection and Disposal," *Engineering News* 70 (2 October 1913): 678; "Refuse Disposal and Street Cleaning," *Municipal Journal and Engineer* 36 (12 March 1914): 361; "Refuse Collection and Disposal," *Municipal Journal and Engineer* 39 (11 November 1915): 725–27; Pittsburgh, Commission on Garbage and Rubbish Collection and Disposal, *Report*, pp. 14–15; Capes and Carpenter, *Municipal Housecleaning*, table vi; "Garbage Collection and Disposal," pp. 12–13.

vealed that eight English cities generated 450 pounds per capita and that seventy-seven German cities produced 319 pounds per capita. This meant that the English cities surveyed produced only 52 percent of the garbage produced by their American counterparts and the German cities produced only 37 percent.[16]

Examining the production of refuse by type also revealed some interesting trends. Between 1903 and 1918 the per capita production of garbage in American cities ranged from 100 to 300 pounds; rubbish, 25 to 125 pounds; and ashes, 300 to 1,500 pounds. Total per capita refuse ranged from one-half to one ton a year.[17] Furthermore, some kinds of waste, especially garbage, were increasing at an alarming rate. Between 1903 and 1907, Pittsburgh's garbage increased from 47,000 to 82,498 tons, or 43 percent. Other cities experiencing substantial increases in the same period included Milwaukee, 30,441 to 40,012 tons (24 percent); Cincinnati, 21,600 to 31,255 tons (31 percent); Washington, D.C., 33,664 to 44,309 tons (24 percent); and Newark, 15,152 to 21,018 tons (28 percent). Population growth, greater consumption of goods, and more efficient collection accounted for most of these increases. Obviously not all cities experienced such rapid increases as those listed above. In Cleveland and Saint Louis, for instance, the volume of garbage actually declined over the same period.

[16] Hering and Greeley, *Collection and Disposal of Municipal Refuse*, p. 70.

[17] Rudolph Hering, "Disposal of Municipal Refuse; Review of General Practice," *Transactions of the American Society of Civil Engineers* 54 (1904): 278–79 (hereafter cited as *Transactions of the ASCE*); U.S. Department of Commerce and Labor, Bureau of the Census, *Statistics of Cities Having a Population of over 30,000: 1905*, pp. 337–41; H. de B. Parsons, "Disposal of Municipal Refuse and Rubbish Incineration," *Transactions of the ASCE* 57 (December 1906): 56–65; H. de B. Parsons, "City Refuse and Its Disposal," *Journal of the Society of Chemical Industry* 27 (30 April 1908): 376–79; "City Waste Studies in Ohio Cities," *Engineering News* 67 (28 March 1912): 608; "Disposal of Municipal Refuse," *Municipal Journal and Engineer* 35 (6 November 1913): 627ff.; "Uniform Statistics of Refuse Collection and Disposal," p. 678; Morse, "The Collection of Municipal Waste," pp. 569–70; "Refuse Disposal and Street Cleaning," *Municipal Journal and Engineer* 36 (12 March 1914): 361; "Refuse Collection and Disposal," *Municipal Journal and Engineer* 39 (11 November 1915): 725–27; Morris Irwin Evinger and Daniel C. Faber, "The Collection and Disposal of City Refuse," *Bulletin of Iowa State College of Agriculture and Mechanical Arts* 14 (1 January 1915): 6–8; A. Prescott Folwell, *Municipal Engineering Practice*, pp. 320–21; Capes and Carpenter, *Municipal Housecleaning*, pp. 167–68; Pittsburgh, Commission on Garbage and Rubbish Collection and Disposal," *Report*, pp. 14–15; Hering and Greeley, *Collection and Disposal of Municipal Refuse*, pp. 28, 37, 40; Parsons, *The Disposal of Municipal Refuse*, p. 56; Harry R. Crohurst, "Municipal Wastes: Their Character, Collection, Disposal," *U.S. Public Health Service Bulletin* 107 (October 1920): 11, 17, 20.

Yet few public-works departments assumed that the volume of waste would diminish or that their workloads would decrease over time.[18]

Population size was an important variable in the impact of the refuse problem on American cities. Table 9 shows the average annual tonnage and the range of annual tonnage of refuse for cities according to population size in 1907. Besides having larger populations than their smaller counterparts, major cities supported arrays of business, hotels, restaurants, and services which contributed greatly to the tonnage figures.

Still other factors influenced the quantities of wastes in the various cities, such as the affluence of the citizens and the relative density of residential dwellings.[19] Although statistics are not particularly reliable for these variables, a few contemporary surveys produced some intriguing "findings." A survey made in Chicago in 1912, for example, attempted to correlate nationality or ethnic background with the production of refuse. The survey demonstrated that "Americans" (presumably native-born white Americans of the pre–"New Immigrant" era) produced substantially more waste than their "foreign" (Italian, Polish, Bohemian, German, and Russian) counterparts. The average per capita annual production by "Americans" was 120.7 pounds of garbage and 630.7 pounds of ashes and rubbish, a total of 751.4 pounds of refuse. The "foreign" group annually produced 90.5 pounds of garbage and 582.3 pounds of ashes and rubbish per capita, a total of 672.8 pounds. These figures are not representative of the entire nation, but they give credence to the theory that there is an important correlation between affluence and refuse production (if it can be assumed that the "Americans" were generally more affluent than the "foreigns" in Chicago).[20] It is curious, therefore, that those grappling with the

---

[18] Parsons, *The Disposal of Municipal Refuse*, p. 56; *Stastics of Cities Having a Population of over 30,000: 1905*, p. 337; U.S. Department of Commerce and Labor, Bureau of the Census, *Statistics of Cities Having a Population of over 30,000: 1907*, p. 452. Total tonnage figures did not always increase since certain kinds of refuse varied each year and changed over the years. For instance, as electrical heating became more popular, coal and wood consumption dropped markedly, and consequently the volume of ash residue dropped.

[19] A survey conducted in ten New England cities in 1909 demonstrated that cities with large residential populations (such as Cambridge and Somerville, Massachusetts) produced more than twice as much garbage per capita as manufacturing cities (such as New Bedford, Lawrence, and Lynn, Massachusetts, and Manchester, New Hampshire) produced, and about one-third more ashes and rubbish. See Hering and Greeley, *Collection and Disposal of Municipal Refuse*, p. 37.

[20] Ibid., pp. 38–39. Figures were calculated by wards, which is an inexact measure for

TABLE 9
Tons of Refuse Collected by City Size, 1907

Population	Number of Cities	Average Tonnage	Range of Tonnage
Over 300,000	14	521,009	3,042,308–75,000
100,000 to 300,000	26	59,405	301,211–4,868
50,000 to 100,000	34	25,449	67,501–1,047
30,00 to 50,000	49	9,030	22,893–400

SOURCE: U.S. Department of Commerce and Labor, Bureau of the Census, *Statistics of Cities Having a Population of over 30,000: 1907* (Washington, D.C., 1910), pp. 452–57.

refuse problem tended to place excessive responsibility on the immigrant populations for generation of wastes.

The huge quantities of waste pointed to the need for not only efficient collection but effective disposal as well. City officials faced substantially different problems in dealing with disposal from those attendant on collection. For one thing, collection practices affected all members of the urban population, while disposal problems affected urbanites variously. City dwellers living close to open dumps, landfills, loading docks, reduction plants, and incinerators suffered the greatest inconveniences, annoyances, and dangers from disposal methods, while a large portion of the population encountered little direct contact with them. Thus city officials were little inclined to worry about whether disposal methods were offensive to the senses and more inclined to select methods that were expedient and inexpensive or that offered the promise of much greater efficiency. In other words, popular protests tended to be of much less consequence in the selection of a disposal method than they were in the choice of a collection method. It is no wonder that urbanites criticized the primitiveness of many disposal methods. Cities, however, were painfully slow in abandoning them. Breaking old habits was difficult, especially if a lake or stream was nearby or vacant lots were available for dumping. Also the cost of conversion to newer methods frustrated many cities, especially smaller ones.

Table 10 shows the array of methods (many of them primitive) employed by cities to dispose of garbage in the early twentieth century. Table 11 shows the methods used to dispose of rubbish or combustible wastes be-

---

evaluating volume of waste per ethnic group. Another variable, of course, is the efficiency of collections in each ward.

TABLE 10

Disposal of Garbage in Cities, Selected Years

Method	Year of Survey, Percentage and Number of Cities											
	1899	1901	1902	1902	1903	1913	1913	1915	1916	1918	1918*	1924
Dumping on land, used as fill, or buried	27% (10)	23% (6)	32.0% (7)	24% (39)	24% (44)	3.5% (1)	18.5% (25)	11% (21)	29% (10)	27.5% (29)		17% (16)
Farm use (fertilizer, animal feed)	16% (6)	19% (5)	13.5% (3)	21% (33)	32% (59)	14.5% (4)	28.0% (37)	8% (15)	14% (5)	20.0% (21)	15.5% (2)	38% (37)
Dumping in water	8% (3)	23% (6)	9.0% (2)	6% (10)	8% (14)	3.5% (1)	7.5% (10)	2% (4)		1.0% (1)		
Burning or incineration	16% (6)	8% (2)	32.0% (7)	22% (36)	20% (36)	25.0% (7)	26.5% (35)	30% (56)	43% (15)	13.5% (14)	15.5% (2)	29% (27)
Reduction	22% (8)	4% (1)	13.5% (3)	9% (15)	10% (19)	43.0% (12)	19.5% (26)	10% (19)	14% (5)	20.0% (21)	69.0% (9)	2% (2)
Combination of methods				12% (19)		3.5% (1)		7% (13)		17.0% (18)		1% (1)
Other methods												9%† (9)
No systematic method	11% (4)				6% (11)							
No data		23% (6)		6% (9)		7% (2)		32% (61)		1.0% (1)		4% (4)
Total cities	37	26	22	161	146‡	28	133	189	35	106	13	96

*Cities with 247,000 or more population.
†Sanitary landfill.
‡Responses totaled 183, but only 146 cities were surveyed.

SOURCE: "Garbage Collection and Disposal," *Engineering News* 42 (28 September 1899): 214; "Methods of Garbage Disposal," *Municipal Journal and Engineer* 11 (September 1901): 123–124; "Methods of Garbage Disposal," *Municipal Journal and Engineer* 13 (July 1902): 28; B. E. Briggs, "Cost of Collection and Disposal of Garbage," in *Proceedings of the Association for Municipal Improvements, Twelfth Annual Convention (1905)*, p. 149; Rudolph Hering and Samuel A. Greeley, *Collection and Disposal of Municipal Refuse* (New York: McGraw-Hill Book Co., 1921), p. 106; "Disposal of Municipal Refuse," *Municipal Journal and Engineer* 35 (6 November 1913): 627; "Refuse Collection and Disposal," *Municipal Journal and Engineer* 39 (11 November 1915): 728–30; "Methods of Garbage Collection," *Municipal Journal and Engineer* 41 (7 December 1916): 701–702; William Parr Capes and Jeanne Daniels Carpenter, *Municipal Housecleaning*, New York E. P. Dutton and Co., 1918), table vi; Pittsburgh, Commission on Garbage and Rubbish Collection and Disposal, *Report on Methods of Garbage and Rubbish Collection in American Cities* (1918); "Garbage Collection and Disposal," *City Manager Magazine* (July 1924): 12–13.

TABLE 11

Method of Disposal of Rubbish or Combustible Wastes in Cities, Selected Years

Method	Year of Survey, Percentage and Number of Cities		
	1899	1902	1913
Dumped on land	70%	46.5%	61%
	(26)	(75)	(17)
Dumped in water	3%	2.5%	3%
	(1)	(4)	(1)
Burning or Incineration	16%	29.5%	7%
	(6)	(47)	(2)
Sanitary fill			7%
			(2)
Combination of methods		1.5%	11%
		(2)	(3)
No systematic method	11%	0.5%	
	(4)	(1)	
No data		19.5%	11%
		(31)	(3)
Total cities	37	161	28

SOURCE: "Garbage Collection and Disposal," *Engineering News* 42 (28 September 1899), 214; C. E. A. Winslow and P. Hansen, "Some Statistics of Garbage Disposal for the Larger American Cities in 1902," in American Public Health Association, *Public Health: Papers and Reports* 29 (October 1903): 141–53; Rudolph Hering and Samuel A. Greeley, *Collection and Disposal of Municipal Refuse* (New York: McGraw-Hill Book Co., 1921), p. 106.

tween 1899 and 1913. Table 12 indicates the methods used to dispose of ashes in 1902. Dumping on land continued to be the primary method of disposal of rubbish and ashes, but no single method of garbage disposal dominated, despite the ballyhoo over incineration and reduction. As primitive methods faced greater scrutiny and more careful evaluation, city officials and sanitary engineers came to believe that they could be modified for or restricted to certain kinds of disposal needs. More cities began taking into account what they expected to achieve by using a specific method, rather than simply accepting a method because it was expedient or rejecting it out of hand. This was the real revolution in collection and disposal practices in the early twentieth century, not technological innovation. More and more municipal leaders were abandoning the "out of sight, out of mind" attitude of the nineteenth century for a thoughtful consideration of the means and ends of refuse management.

TABLE 12
Method of Disposal of Ashes in Cities, 1902

Method	Percentage of Cities	Number of Cities
Dumped on land (including fill)	79.0	127
Dumped in water	3.0	5
Burning or incineration	1.5	3
Combination of methods	0.5	1
No systematic method	0.5	1
No data	15.0	24
Total cities		161

SOURCE: C. E. A. Winslow and P. Hansen, "Some Statistics of Garbage Disposal for the Larger American Cities in 1902," in American Public Health Association, *Public Health: Papers and Reports* 29 (October 1903): 141–53.

Of all the primitive methods dumping of waste into water was the most universally condemned practice. As indicated in table 10, the method was waning by 1902. Several reasons—not necessarily environmental considerations—led to the end of water dumping. In the early 1900s, New York City temporarily curtailed dumping refuse at sea because too much of it floated back to the shoreline and also because officials in the Street-Cleaning Department believed that the waste could be put to better use as landfill.[21] A relatively common complaint about sea and lake dumping was that for all but the largest cities it was too costly to tow wastes to deep water, especially because a large portion of the material would not sink and washed up on adjacent beaches. Dumping into rivers or streams also had serious legal ramifications. Downstream cities began filing lawsuits against upstream cities that used the rivers for dumping. In time the federal government began trying to stop the disposal of refuse in interstate waterways to end these confrontations.[22] Evaluations of water dumping eventually

[21] Frederick L. Stearns, *The Work of the Department of Street Cleaning*, p. 210. See also *Engineering News* 48 (17 July 1902): 48; "The Sanitary Disposal of Municipal Refuse," *Transactions of the ASCE* 50 (1903): 104; Charles A. Meade, "City Cleansing in New York City," *Municipal Affairs* 4 (December 1900): 738.

[22] Crohurst, *Municipal Wastes*, pp. 42–43; Parsons, *The Disposal of Municipal Refuse*, p. 93; William P. Munn, "Collection and Disposal of Garbage," *City Government* 2 (January 1897): 6–7; Capes and Carpenter, *Municipal Housecleaning*, p. 175. See also U.S. Commit-

moved beyond the following rationalization that appeared in a New Orleans Board of Health report for 1898–99:

> To dump the garbage of a large city into a running stream from which is also derived the water supply of the city, might seem, at first glance, a rather crude and imperfect, as well as unsanitary, method of getting rid of the city's waste; but when it is remembered that the Mississippi River is at this point a half mile wide, from fifty to one hundred feet deep, with an average current of three miles per hour, as much as one million five hundred thousand cubic feet of water passing a given point during every second at the stage of high water, we may readily imagine how little influence a boat-load or two of garbage per day can have upon such an immense body of water in constant motion.[23]

Like dumping into water, dumping on land came under increasing criticism in the early twentieth century. Dumping garbage on land, including landfills and burial, represented up to 32 percent of the disposal methods used. Dumping of ashes or combustible materials, considered less objectionable than dumping organic matter, remained as high as 70 to 80 percent. The method was common because of its convenience. Several cities employed land dumping not because they considered it the theoretically best method but because it was a practical alternative until capital outlay for a better system, such as incineration or reduction, could be implemented. Many cities were, so to speak, "cities in waiting," resigned to dumping until they could afford to end the practice. Answers to a questionnaire mailed in 1913 to ninety cities with populations of 30,000 or more illustrate this point. Of the sixty-eight cities that replied, fifty-nine maintained dumps, and thirteen relied exclusively on dumping for the disposal of garbage. In answering the question "Is the public dump a proper means of garbage disposal?" however, sixty-four of the sixty-eight answered no.[24]

Criticism of dumping did not necessarily result in the abandonment of the practice, though the intensity of the protests might lead a casual observer to assume so. Boards of health and public-works departments of several cities were continually hounded with complaints about open dumping. In a 1917 report Cleveland's Committee on Housing and Sanitation

---

tee on Interstate and Foreign Commerce, *Hearings on Bill to Prevent the Dumping of Refuse Material in Lake Michigan or Near Chicago* (Washington, D.C.: Government Printing Office, 1910).

[23] Louisiana, Board of Health, *Annual Report* (1898–99), p. 177.

[24] C. E. Terry, "The Public Dump and the Public Health," *American Journal of Public Health* 3 (April 1913): 338–39.

stated that the dumps "caused the most complaint in the collection and disposal system for refuse." The city owned twenty-five dumps, and private concerns maintained many more. According to the report they constituted "breeding places for rats and cockroaches and the homes in the vicinity are infested with them. Paper and other light articles blow over the surrounding territory and are a great source of annoyance. Fires break out on the dumps frequently not only endangering the adjoining property, but the smoke and smudge are very offensive especially when the fires often smolder for months."[25] C. E. Terry, a physician of Jacksonville, Florida, told an audience at the APHA convention in 1912: "In its simplicity and carelessness, as a means of waste disposal, the dump probably dates back to the discarding of the first apple core in the Garden of Eden, and its subsequent train of evils is ample testimony of the Eternal Wrath elicited by that act."[26]

As land and water dumping drew increased criticism, other primitive methods, especially filling and burial, began attracting the renewed interest of engineers and sanitarians who believed that, properly managed, they held the best promise for the future. There was a growing sentiment that a method was only as good as its management. In *Collection and Disposal of Municipal Refuse*, Hering and Greeley commented:

The natural methods (land dumping, filling, burial) . . . need, in our opinion, more consideration than they have received in the past. Their simplicity and economy heretofore have tended toward neglecting a sufficient study of their efficiency and cost; yet they constitute an important branch of city refuse disposal work, and, as some of them have an extensive application, they need greater study.[27]

In 1905, in an *Engineering News* story entitled "The Land Disposal of Garbage: An Opportunity for Engineers and Contractors," the editors noted that experiments in plowing waste into the land in Saint Louis "might well lead engineers and sanitarians to give more attention to the possibilities in

---

[25] Cleveland, Chamber of Commerce, Committee on Housing and Sanitation, *Report on Collection and Disposal of Cleveland's Waste*, p. 7. See also Boston, Health Department, *Annual Report* (1905), pp. 40–41; *Annual Report* (1909), pp. 12–13; *Annual Report* (1916), pp. 89–90; Detroit, Board of Health, *Annual Report* (1907), p. 17; *Annual Report* (1908), p. 16; *Annual Report* (1909), pp. 23–24; *Annual Report* (1910) pp. 27–28.

[26] Terry, "The Public Dump and the Public Heath," p. 338.

[27] Hering and Greeley, *Collection and Disposal of Municipal Refuse*, p. 257. See also Capes and Carpenter, *Municipal Housecleaning*, pp. 174–75; Franz Schneider, Jr., "The Disposal of a City's Waste," *Scientific American* 107 (13 July 1912): 24–25; "Dumping Garbage Unsanitary," *Municipal Journal and Engineer* 24 (22 April 1908): 493.

the treatment of garbage by burial on agricultural lands. The system is already in quite extensive use, but is generally regarded as more or less a makeshift, as indeed it is when conducted in the ordinary manner."[28] An article in a 1917 issue of *Municipal Journal and Engineer* drew much the same conclusion: "It is possible to deposit garbage and refuse mixed, or even garbage alone if properly treated, on low land without creating a nuisance."[29]

Landfill programs never supplanted dumping as a primary disposal method in this period. They were generally a supplementary means of dealing with inorganic materials. The use of organic wastes alone to fill ravines or to level roads had always been regarded as highly objectionable. When garbage was mixed with large amounts of other materials, the practice was more acceptable, but it rarely provided an adequate means for cities to dispose of all refuse materials. As utilization and recycling of wastes came into vogue, however, filling low places with refuse or reclaiming marshland and coastal land became desirable for many cities. The "sanitary landfill" was the breakthrough which revived interest in filling, though it would not become a primary disposal method until the 1920s. The sanitary fill was a modification of the primitive program, but more carefully supervised and maintained. The basic principle was to utilize all forms of waste and at the same time eliminate the problem of putrefaction of organic materials. Typical sanitary fills were layered: twelve inches of garbage were covered with eighteen to twenty-four inches of ashes, street sweepings, or rubbish; then another layer of garbage; and so forth. Chemicals were sometimes sprayed on the fill to retard putrefaction. The method took some time to catch on because it was expensive and labor-intensive. Nonetheless, in the 1910s cities as diverse as Seattle, New Orleans, and Davenport, Iowa, implemented it.[30]

Using fill for reclamation purposes, with or without the new sanitary procedure, was becoming more popular. Davenport, Iowa, situated on the west bank of the Mississippi River, used fill to build up its levies. In Oak-

[28] "The Land Disposal of Garbage: An Opportunity for Engineers and Contractors," *Engineering News* 53 (6 April 1905): 367–69.

[29] "Dumping City Refuse," *Municipal Journal and Engineer* 42 (25 January 1917): 103.

[30] Crohurst, *Municipal Wastes*, pp. 43–45; Parsons, *The Disposal of Municipal Refuse*, pp. 78–80; D. C. Faber, "Collection and Disposal of Refuse," *American Municipalities* 30 (February 1916): 185–86; Robert H. Wyld, "Modern Methods of Municipal Refuse Disposal," *American City* 5 (October 1911): 207–208.

land, California, refuse was used as fill along the shoreline of San Francisco Bay.[31] The best-known reclamation project was begun at Rikers Island, in the East River in New York City. The project, begun under Colonel Waring, was not without controversy. In 1900 the United States War Department, which controlled the harbor lines, forbade the dumping of material behind the enclosing cribwork until a properly constructed seawall was completed. This decree sparked a jurisdictional dispute among city departments: the Street-Cleaning Department, which wanted to use the enclosure for ash dumping; the Department of Correction, which occupied the island and wanted to reclaim more land for its uses; and the Dock Department, which would be required to improve the seawall.[32]

The enthusiasm for waste utilization also produced a renewed interest in feeding garbage to swine.[33] Some sanitarians remained skeptical about the healthfulness of pork from garbage-fed hogs, but others were not willing to dismiss the method so quickly. Almost everyone agreed that it was ill-suited to large cities, especially because it would require a dramatic increase in collections (to ensure the freshness of the garbage) and because the herds of pigs maintained outside the city would have to be enormous.[34] The scale of these problems could be avoided in medium- and small-sized

[31] A. M. Compton, "The Disposal of Municipal Waste by the Burial Method," *American Journal of Public Health* 2 (December 1912): 925–29; "Refuse Disposal in California," *Municipal Journal and Engineer* 42 (25 January 1917): 100–101.

[32] Charles A. Meade, "City Cleansing in New York City," *Municipal Affairs* 4 (December 1900): 735–36; New York City, Department of Street Cleaning, *Annual Report* (1902–1905), p. 74; City Club of Philadelphia, *City Club Bulletin* 2 (24 March 1910): 116; Charles W. Staniford, *Report on the Disposal of City Wastes*, pp. 1–19; "Waste-Material Disposal of New York," *Engineering News* 77 (18 January 1917): 119. Burial of garbage, about which there had been many of the same complaints as those about dumping and filling, was being reconsidered by some cities. See Faber, "Collection and Disposal of Refuse," p. 186; Crohurst, *Municipal Wastes*, pp. 45–47; Parsons, *The Disposal of Municipal Refuse*, pp. 93–94.

[33] This method became especially popular during World War I, when garbage was fed to hogs to produce more food for the war effort. See F. G. Ashbrook and A. Wilson, "Feeding Garbage to Hogs," *Farmer's Bulletin*, No. 1133, pp. 3–26; Charles V. Chapin, "Disposal of Garbage by Hog Feeding," *American Journal of Public Health* 7 (March 1918): 234–35; and U.S. Food Administration, *Garbage Utilization, with Particular Reference to Utilization by Feeding*, pp. 3–11.

[34] Parsons, *The Disposal of Municipal Refuse*, p. 94; Capes and Carpenter, *Municipal Housecleaning*, p. 173; Charles V. Chapin, "The Collection and Disposal of Garbage in Providence, R.I.," *Public Health: Papers and Reports* 28 (1903): 48–50; D. C. Faber, "Collection and Disposal of Refuse," *American Municipalities* 30 (February 1916): 184–85.

cities, and some did experiment successfully with modern swine-feeding techniques. Samuel Greeley calculated that it would take only seventy-five pigs to dispose of one ton of garbage per day. By properly sorting the garbage and possibly cooking it to avoid spoilage, small cities surrounded by isolated farms could profit from such a method.[35]

Worcester, Massachusetts, operated one of the most highly regarded swine-feeding programs in the country. According to X. H. Goodnough, of the Boston Society of Civil Engineers, Worcester's program was "a remarkable development of that method of garbage disposal." The city maintained a piggery from which, he reported, "a considerable income is derived."[36] Worcester was but one of sixty-one cities and towns in Massachusetts which employed some form of swine feeding. Outside New England the practice was not as widespread; however, Grand Rapids, Saint Paul, Omaha, Denver, and even Los Angeles (until 1914), used swine feeding as major parts of their disposal programs.[37] Feeding garbage to swine had come a long way from the days when pigs, geese, cows, and other animals roamed the streets scrounging for castaway items to eat.

The modification of some primitive methods had not deterred efforts to find modern alternatives to nineteenth-century practices. After a decade or so of practical experience with incineration and reduction—the two "solutions" of the 1890s—engineers and city officials were reluctant to claim that they had found a single best disposal method. Unbridled enthusiasm for the so-called technological wonders from Europe was replaced by healthier skepticism and more deliberate evaluation of the methods. By 1902 experts had begun taking a closer look at incineration and reduction to determine whether they, put to a practical test, really could supplant the older practices.

Of the two methods incineration managed to retain the greatest number of adherents.[38] The general consensus was that burning waste in furnaces, crematories, or incinerators offered the most sanitary method of disposal yet devised and was possibly the most efficient and economical

---

[35] Capes and Carpenter, *Municipal Housecleaning*, p. 174.

[36] X. H. Goodnough, "The Collection and Disposal of Municipal Waste and Refuse," *Journal of the Association of Engineering Societies* 40 (May 1908): 246–47.

[37] Hering and Greeley, *Collection and Disposal of Municipal Refuse*, pp. 258–59. See also Alvah W. Brown, "Garbage Piggeries," *American Journal of Public Health* 2 (December 1912): 930–36.

[38] Few, however, gave sufficient attention to the smoke produced by the incinerators.

method available.[39] While many engineers and city officials believed that incineration was a theoretically perfect disposal method, they also expressed considerable dissatisfaction with the first generation of American furnaces and crematories installed in the late 1880s. These original crematories (which continued to be built through 1910), had been impulsively adapted from European models, had never lived up to expectations, and were almost without exception branded as failures. Of the 180 furnaces erected between 1885 and 1908, 102 had been abandoned or dismantled by 1909.[40]

The initial American experience with incineration was unsuccessful because American engineers did not apply the technology with proper attention to what it was capable of achieving. In the excitement over the new method few bothered to consider whether European-designed equipment would meet American needs. For Europeans—the English in particular— destruction of waste by fire offered many advantages. In England, which lacked cheap undeveloped land, urban dumps had become impractical and costly. Extensive ocean dumping was impractical because of the proximity of neighboring countries. A method had to be devised which reduced waste to the smallest volume possible. Furthermore, because of England's limited energy resources disposal had to be carried out with minimum transportation costs and fuel consumption. The British "destructors" met these criteria. They burned mixed refuse at high temperatures—in excess of 1,000° F.—without the use of additional fuels. The only by-product of the process was an inert clinker, which could be disposed of with relative ease. In addition, destructors could be connected to steam boilers for generating heat or electricity. Similar practices on the Continent produced equally impressive results, especially in Germany.[41]

[39] Robert H. Wyld, "Modern Methods of Municipal Refuse Disposal," *American City* 5 (October 1911): 208; "Garbage Disposal in St. Louis," *Municipal Journal and Engineer* 19 (November 1905): 220; E. N. Stacy, "Refuse Collection and Disposal," *Journal of the Association of Engineering Societies* 54 (January 1915): 15; J. J. Jessup, "Refuse Incineration," *Pacific Municipalities* 27 (May 1913): 258; Cleveland, Chamber of Commerce, Committee on Housing and Sanitation, *Report on Collection and Disposal of Cleveland's Waste*, p. 9; Boston, American Garbage Cremation Co., *Cremation of Garbage*, p. 13.

[40] "Refuse Disposal in California," *Municipal Journal and Engineer* 42 (25 January 1917): 101; Chamber of Commerce of the United States of America, Construction and Civic Development Department, *Refuse Disposal in American Cities*, pp. 15–16.

[41] W. F. Goodrich suggested that, of the more than 250 plants constructed in Great Britain in the thirty years before 1908, fewer than 10 were dismantled or abandoned. W. Francis

Circumstances of space and demography were much different in the United States. The American population was dispersed over a larger area and in many regions was substantially less dense. The availability of cheap land in the United States afforded greater opportunity for dumping, making it a practical alternative to other, more expensive or labor-intensive methods. Moreover, energy sources were more plentiful and cheaper in America, which meant that wastes could be hauled greater distances for dumping or fuels could be used for burning.[42]

The unique spatial and human dimensions of the American urban society, along with considerations of expediency, led to the adoption of European incinerators modified to meet American needs. Unfortunately, the modifications were too severe to make incineration a competitive or reliable disposal method in the late nineteenth century. Most important, the early American furnaces were intended primarily for burning organic wastes. Mixing refuse, the common practice in Europe, was not as widespread in the United States. Programs of primary separation, along with the availability of land and water dumping sites, provided convenient, if not always judicious, means of disposing inorganic materials. With such a wide array of disposal choices for rubbish, combustible waste, and ashes, incineration was viewed as having a specialized function—the disposal of garbage. Compounding the problem was that American furnaces used large amounts of fuel to produce the heat necessary to destroy wet garbage. Since coal and fuel oil and, later, natural gas were abundant, little attention was given to designing crematories which were fuel-efficient or self-burning. This practice nonetheless added to the cost of incineration and tended to make the method less attractive. Also, as fuel consumption and costs rose, there was a temptation to lower the temperature of the furnaces for the sake of conservation, with the result that waste was not completely burned and gas and smoke emissions from the furnaces increased alarmingly. These modifications which were intended to meet American needs and conditions, actually negated the advantages of the British destructors.[43]

Goodrich, *Modern Destructor Practice*, pp. 15–30; William F. Morse, "Utilization and Disposal of Municipal Waste," *Journal of the Franklin Institute* 157 (June 1904): 420–21; "British Refuse Destructors and American Garbage Furnaces," *Engineering News* 53 (13 April 1905): 388–89; Morse, *The Collection and Disposal of Municipal Waste*, pp. 216–79.

[42] See Hering and Greeley, *Collection and Disposal of Municipal Refuse*, pp. 311–12.

[43] Ibid. See also Chamber of Commerce of the United States of America, *Refuse Disposal in American Cities*, pp. 15–16; "British Refuse Destructors and American Garbage Furnaces," pp. 388–89; Wyld, "Modern Methods of Municipal Refuse Disposal," p. 208; "San-

American sanitary engineers were the first group to criticize openly the performance of the American-modified crematories. Although they had been among the first advocates of the British method, they had become increasingly suspicious of the faulty designs and inefficient operation of the furnaces built in the United States.[44] In 1911, Joseph B. Rider, a consulting engineer of New York City, charged that the early cremation plants had been constructed by rule-of-thumb methods: "What the old horse car is to the modern traction, the ox team is to the automobile, the hour glass is to the chronometer, so are crematories of the past to the modern incinerators or destructor."[45]

The frustration of sanitary engineers went beyond faulty designs and improper operation of crematories. They were critical of unscrupulous companies that built and promoted poor-quality equipment, and they particularly resented city officials who adopted the equipment without consulting them. They often felt that their authority had been usurped or their advice circumvented by untrained bureaucrats. Colonel William F. Morse, a sanitary engineer and author of many tracts on waste disposal, led the assault on the "extravagant claims" of the peddlers of the first-generation incinerators. He charged that the "sharp competition of opposing interests [builders of crematories and city authorities] developed mutual misrepresentation and recrimination. Contracts were obtained by personal and political favor, by influential pull, by manipulation and graft, with little regard to the interests of the city or town."[46] Interestingly, Morse had been the manager of the New York office of Engle Sanitary and Cremation Company, founded in 1886, the first American company to manufacture crematories in quantity. In 1898 and 1899, Morse and Benjamin Boulger built

itary Disposal of Municipal Refuse," *Transactions of the ASCE* 50 (1903): 106; Morse, *Collection and Disposal of Municipal Waste*, p. 137; M. N. Baker, "Condition of Garbage Disposal in United States," *Municipal Journal and Engineer* 11 (October 1901): 147; "Refuse Disposal in America," *Engineering Record* 58 (25 July 1908): 85; William F. Morse, "The Utilization and Disposal of Municipal Waste," *Journal of the Franklin Institute* 158 (July 1904): 28; *Proceedings of the ASMI* (1910), p. 58.

[44] Chamber of Commerce of the United States, *Refuse Disposal in American Cities*, p. 16; Joseph G. Branch, "Garbage Disposal," *Municipal Journal and Engineer* 20 (January 1906): 4–5; William F. Morse, "The Disposal of the City's Waste," *American City* 2 (May 1910): 224–27; "Garbage Disposal in St. Louis," *Municipal Journal and Engineer* 19 (November 1905): 220.

[45] Joseph B. Rider, "Public Refuse Destruction a Municipal Asset, Not a Liability," *Fire and Water Engineering* 54 (15 October 1913): 311.

[46] Morse, *The Collection and Disposal of Municipal Waste*, p. 98. See also Morse, "The Utilization and Disposal of Municipal Waste," pp. 28–30.

the Morse-Boulger Destructor and in 1902 formed the Morse-Boulger Destructor Company. The company held American rights to Meldrum Brothers' Destructors, of Manchester, England, but did not construct equipment under its patents. In 1904, Morse retired from the company and assumed control of Meldrum Destructors and later developed other equipment. Therefore, he had a substantial vested interest in the English-style destructors, which accounts for much of his vehemence against the early promoters of incinerators in the United States.[47]

Although few sanitary engineers were as openly critical of crematory promoters as Colonel Morse was, substantial numbers of them echoed his sentiments that American municipalities had too quickly adopted the new method without adequate investigation and the sound advice of the experts. The 1901 report of the APHA Committee on Disposal of Refuse stated, "No city in America has yet undertaken a systematic comparative test of the several types of destructors that are recommended."[48] Rudolph Hering charged, "In but a few instances did city officials take the initiative in devising proper methods of disposal; hardly one American city can be found where exhaustive preliminary investigations were made and where the solutions suggested and practiced have been as yet entirely satisfactory and final."[49] The ASMI Committee on Refuse Disposal and Street Cleaning noted that some municipalities made mistakes in adopting incineration or reduction plants without necessary investigations: "Again dissatisfaction, in our opinion, in some instances has been brought about by some contractors of plants making guarantees that only technically can be lived up to under special conditions."[50] *Engineering News* asked, "Why do so many of our cities persist in building discredited types of garbage and refuse furnaces?"[51]

In leveling these criticisms, sanitary engineers exonerated themselves of blame, reasserting that disposal, especially by the incineration method, was an engineering problem. E. N. Stacy commented in a typical manner:

[47] Morse, *The Collection and Disposal of Municipal Waste*, pp. 148–49, 161–63, 191–93.

[48] "Report of the Committee on Disposal of Refuse Materials," in APHA, *Public Health: Papers and Reports* 27 (1901): 184.

[49] Hering, "Disposal of Municipal Refuse: Review of General Practice," *Transactions of the ASCE* 54 (1904): 266.

[50] *Proceedings of the ASMI, Twenty-third Annual Convention* (1916), p. 245.

[51] *Engineering News* 64 (11 August 1910): 153. See also William F. Morse, "The Disposal of Municipal Waste," *Municipal Journal and Engineer* 22 (6 March 1907): 235.

"The question of refuse disposal is purely an engineering problem and in the majority of cases the committees appointed to investigate and report on the various designs of incinerators available, are not competent to make a selection that would prove satisfactory."[52] M. N. Baker said that it would be "hard to name a sanitary or mechanical engineer of national reputation who was ever prominently connected with the design of an American garbage disposal plant of either the cremation or reduction type."[53] Sanitary engineers tenaciously guarded the territory they had come to dominate in the late nineteenth century. As far as they were concerned, refuse collection and disposal were their province.

After 1902 the serious criticisms of the engineering community and the mediocre to poor performance of the first-generation crematories led to more careful scrutiny of the practice of burning refuse. In that year experts in the field conducted the first major investigation of American crematories. The resulting debate over the value of incineration lasted fifteen or twenty years.[54] In 1906 engineers made the first successful adaptation of an English-style destructor in Westmount, Quebec. This project was followed by similar ones in Vancouver, British Columbia; Seattle; Milwaukee; and West New Brighton, New York (Milwaukee had the largest incinerator in America in its time).[55] By 1910 many engineers were claiming that a new generation of incinerators had finally arrived.[56] By 1914 approximately three hundred incinerating plants were in operation in the United States and Canada, eighty-eight of them built between 1908 and 1914. About half the plants constructed after 1908 were built in the South, an indication of

[52] E. N. Stacy, "Refuse Collection and Disposal," *Journal of the Association of Engineering Societies* 54 (January 1915): 16.

[53] Baker, "Condition of Garbage Disposal in United States," p. 148. See also Jessup, "Refuse Incineration," p. 258; "British Refuse Destructors and American Garbage Furnaces," pp. 388–89; "Refuse Incineration and Engineering Problems," *Engineering News* 67 (15 February 1912): 311; William F. Morse, "Garbage Disposal Work in America," *Municipal Journal and Engineer* 17 (October 1904): 158; Howard G. Bayles, "The Incineration of Municipal Waste," *Municipal Engineering* 29 (October 1905): 255.

[54] Morse, *The Collection and Disposal of Municipal Waste*, pp. 98–99; J. T. Fetherston, "Incineration of Refuse," *American Journal of Public Health* 2 (December 1912): 943–45.

[55] "Modern Refuse Disposal Plants," *Municipal Journal and Engineer* 32 (30 May 1912): 832; Chamber of Commerce of the United States of America, *Refuse Disposal in American Cities*, p. 16. For the most detailed chronology of incinerators in America between 1885 and 1908, see Morse, *The Collection and Disposal of Municipal Waste*, pp. 114–19.

[56] *Engineering News* 63 (23 June 1910): 729; Wyld, "Modern Methods of Municipal Refuse Disposal," p. 208; Hering and Greeley, *Collection and Disposal of Municipal Refuse*, p. 314.

the movement of the technology from the industrial Northeast and the Middle West into areas of increasing urbanization (and also an indication of the new popularity of incinerators in smaller cities and towns).[57]

The controversy surrounding the incineration method was mild in comparison with the storm over the reduction process. The views of Dr. Quitman Kohnke, city councilman of New Orleans and chairman of that city's Committee on Health, reflected the general disillusionment with reduction. At the meeting of the League of American Municipalities in 1898 he complained, "We have been seduced by the glowing promises of rich rewards which the reduction process has failed to give us."[58] Plants built on the European design in the 1880s in Milwaukee, Saint Paul, Chicago, Denver, and elsewhere were proving to be failures. Newer plants built in the 1890s on modified patterns were faring little better. By November 1914 only twenty-two of the forty-five reduction plants in the country were in use. Of the twenty-two, nine had changed management and ownership, two had been turned over to municipal operation, and one had burned down and was not replaced. Overall, reduction plants were going out of service much more quickly than were incinerators.[59]

The problems of the reduction process were substantially different from the problems of incineration. Critics of the early crematories continued to favor the burning of waste as a method of disposal, despite the recurrent technical problems. Critics of reduction, however, tended to question the viability of the method itself. Unlike incineration, reduction was a distinctively American process. Although the original plants were applications of the Merz method imported from Vienna, reduction as a practical disposal method never attained success in Austria or other European countries. Except for a plant in Charlottenburg, a suburb of Berlin, the reduction method was not used in Europe during this period.[60] In large

---

[57]"Recent Refuse Disposal Practice," *Municipal Journal and Engineer* 37 (17 December 1914): 849–50. For additional statistics on refuse incinerating plants and their operations in the early twentieth century, see Crohurst, *Municipal Wastes*, pp. 62–63; "Refuse Collection and Disposal," *Municipal Journal and Engineer* 39 (11 November 1915): 731–34.

[58]"Disposal of Garbage," *City Government* 5 (August 1898): 67.

[59]"Recent Refuse Disposal Practice," *Municipal Journal and Engineer* 37 (10 December 1914): 848–49. See also Morse, "The Disposal of the City's Waste," *American City* 2 (June 1910): 272; A. Prescott Folwell, *Municipal Engineering Practice*, pp. 334–35; "Refuse Collection and Disposal," *Municipal Journal and Engineer* 39 (11 November 1915): 730–32; U.S. Department of Commerce, Bureau of the Census, *General Statistics of Cities: 1909*, p. 49.

[60]Franz Schneider, Jr., "The Disposal of a City's Waste," *Scientific American* 107 (13

measure reduction was a product of American affluence. As Hering and Greeley stated, "Without doubt, the greater wastefulness of the American people is one reason for this development, as it produced a garbage rich in recoverable elements."[61] Another observer theorized that people of other nations "throw away too little valuable food matter to make the process profitable."[62] As an American method of disposal reduction had to be evaluated without the benefit of comparative performance in other locations under different conditions.

A comparison of the reduction process with incineration was inevitable. Several critics suggested that, instead of trying to improve the reduction process, cities should abandon it for incineration. A major criticism— not without validity—was that reduction had limited applicability; it could handle only garbage; 70 to 90 percent of the waste had to be disposed of by other means.[63] Cost was also a major consideration. According to one source, the cost of installing a reduction plant varied between $4,000 and $8,000 per ton capacity, which was much higher than the cost of installing an incinerator of equivalent capacity. Some experts also claimed that the cost of disposal was substantially higher (available statistics are not reliable enough to verify that claim).[64] It was suggested that for cities and towns with populations under 75,000 to 100,000 reduction was prohibitively expensive; only in communities in which large volumes of organic waste were produced was reduction economically feasible.[65]

Until about 1905 cities shied away from municipal ownership of reduction plants because of the cost factor. Ironically, several privately oper-

July 1912): 25; Chicago City Waste Commission, *Report of the City Waste Commission of the City of Chicago*. p. 25; Morse, "The Disposal of the City's Waste," p. 271.

[61] Hering and Greeley, *Collection and Disposal of Municipal Refuse*, p. 444.

[62] Folwell, *Municipal Engineering Practice*, p. 333.

[63] Morse, "The Disposal of the City's Waste," p. 274; "British Refuse Destructors and American Garbage Furnaces," p. 389; H. de B. Parsons, "City Refuse and Its Disposal," *Scientific American Supplement* 66 (4 July 1908): 8; Walter F. Goodrich, *The Economic Disposal of Towns' Refuse*, p. 236; Baltimore, Department of Street Cleaning, *Annual Report* (1906), p. 5.

[64] Mansfield Merriman, *Elements of Sanitary Engineering*, p. 229; Crohurst, *Municipal Wastes*, p. 77; "Street Cleaning and Refuse Disposal," *Municipal Journal and Engineer* 30 (4 January 1911): 16; Parsons, "City Refuse and Its Disposal," pp. 8–9; Goodrich, *The Economic Disposal of Town's Refuse*, pp. 236–38.

[65] B. F. Miller, "Garbage Collection and Disposal," *Proceedings of the ASMI, Twenty-second Annual Convention* (1915), p. 8; "Street Cleaning and Refuse Disposal," *Municipal Journal and Engineer* 30 (4 January 1911): 16; "Recent Refuse Disposal Practice," *Municipal Journal and Engineer* 37 (10 December 1914): 850.

ated reduction plants were showing a profit, largely because they had acquired highly favorable contracts with cities that hired their services; the contracts usually stipulated that the city would pay for collecting and transporting the garbage. At the ASMI convention in 1907, Frederick P. Smith commented, "While it may be true that the contract may be profitable to the operating company, it is doubtful if it is the best method to serve the city's interests."[66] In other words, municipalities were footing the bill for reduction, with little control over the operation of the plants and none of the profits.

When city officials realized what was happening, the calls to make reduction a municipal utility increased markedly. Several obstacles stood in the path, however. Some cities were hamstrung by their charters, which prohibited them from manufacturing goods, and reduction produced marketable by-products from waste. City officials also operated at a severe disadvantage because private companies, for obvious reasons, intentionally kept municipal governments ignorant of their expenses and profits, and there were no figures on which to base determinations about the feasibility of municipally owned reduction systems.[67] Some cities, nonetheless, tried to gain control of privately operated facilities or sought funds to build their own. Several Ohio cities led in the effort. In fact, municipal ownership and operation of garbage-reduction plants has been termed an Ohio idea. In 1905, Cleveland became the first American city to establish a municipal reduction plant. Soon after the publication of statistics showing the profitability of the Cleveland facility, other Ohio cities—Columbus, Akron, and Dayton (as well as cities in other states, such as Chicago, Schenectady, and Detroit)—built their own plants.

In 1915, Columbus officials claimed that during the four and a half years in which the city owned and operated its reduction plant the revenue from the operation paid the entire operating expenses and fixed costs of the plant, including interest and depreciation. In 1914 the plant treated 21,600

[66] Frederick P. Smith, "Final Disposition of Garbage and Rubbish," *Proceedings of the ASMI, Fourteenth Annual Convention* (1907), p. 169. See also F. Allen Phillips, "Selling Garbage for Reduction at Los Angeles," *Engineering News* 70 (28 August 1913): 429–30; Merriman, *Elements of Sanitary Engineering*, pp. 230–32.

[67] "The Unsatisfactory Condition of Garbage Disposal in the United States," *Proceedings of the League of American Municipalities* (1901), p. 20; "Four Garbage-Disposal Contracts," *Engineering News* 70 (9 December 1913): 718–19; M. N. Baker, "Condition of Garbage Disposal in United States," *Municipal Journal and Engineer* 11 (October 1901): 147; Folwell, *Municipal Engineering Practice*, pp. 330–31; Irwin S. Osborn, "Disposal of Garbage by the Reduction Method," *American Journal of Public Health* 2 (December 1912): 939.

tons of garbage at an average cost of $1.86 a ton, and the sale of grease, tankage, and other by-products yielded a revenue of $3.085 a ton. The net earnings for the city in that year were $26,500. Cleveland experienced similar good fortune. In 1905 the city purchased the reduction works from the Newburg Reduction Company. In the first year it incurred a net loss (or net charge) of $5,243. After 1905, however, there was a net annual gain. In 1910 it amounted to $72,532, or about $1.62 a ton. National figures for 1914 were similarly encouraging. Twenty-five reduction plants in the country produced about 60 million pounds of grease and 150,000 tons of tankage having an average market value of $3.5 million. Of course, most of these plants were still in private hands.[68]

The success of municipal ownership in Ohio seemed to give the reduction method renewed practicability. In many locations, however, the problems could not be overcome by a change in control. Over and above the limited application of the reduction method, the high cost of construction and operation, the dependence on a large and constant supply of organic waste, and the unreliability of the by-product market was the overriding problem of the stench. Reduction facilities polluted the air with the pungent odor of huge quantities of putrefying wastes, which were "cooked" as part of the process of recovering grease and other by-products. In addition dark-colored liquids from the compressing process often ran off into nearby streams.[69] Mayor J. J. Williams of Memphis was extremely critical

[68] "The Success of Two Municipal Garbage-Reduction Plants," *Engineering News* 73 (27 May 1915): 1042; "Operating Results of the Garbage-Reduction Works of Cleveland and Columbus, Ohio," *Engineering News* 66 (30 November 1911): 633–65; "Two Years' Operations of the Municipal Garbage Reduction Works, Cleveland, O.," *Engineering News* 57 (2 May 1907): 487–90; "Garbage Reduction in Cleveland, Ohio," *Municipal Journal and Engineer* 19 (December 1905): 274–75; "Cleveland's Garbage Reduction Plant," *Municipal Journal and Engineer* 22 (13 February 1907): 147–48; "Municipal Garbage Reduction," *Municipal Journal and Engineer* 22 (13 February 1907): 149–51; "Street Cleaning Methods in Cleveland," *Municipal Engineering* 31 (December 1906): 437–38. See also Morse, "The Disposal of the City's Waste," pp. 272–73; "Recent Refuse Disposal Practice," *Municipal Journal and Engineer* 37 (10 December 1914): 848; Osborn, "Disposal of Garbage by the Reduction Method," pp. 940-41.

[69] Merriman, *Elements of Sanitary Engineering*, p. 230; Folwell, *Municipal Engineering Practice*, p. 336; "The Garbage Disposal Problem in Boston and Elsewhere," *Engineering News* 48 (7 August 1902): 96–97; Stacy, "Refuse Collection and Disposal," p. 13; Rider, "Public Refuse Destruction a Municipal Asset, Not a Liability," p. 312. An additional problem with reduction was the volatility of the naphtha used in the process. Explosions were not uncommon. In May 1908 a large tank of naphtha exploded at the Chicago Reduction Company plant, killing one man and seriously injuring five, with eight reported missing. Morse, *The Collection and Disposal of Municipal Waste*, pp. 307–308.

of the reduction process at a meeting of the League of American Municipalities in 1899. The hopes, he said, that reduction plants would answer the
need

> have not been realized, and, from a financial standpoint, these plants have proven
> failures, chiefly because their output commands a very low price in the market.
> From a sanitary point of view they have proven worse than failures. The air for
> miles around them is so contaminated that the courts and lawmakers have been
> appealed to, and have, as a rule, given relief to the sufferers by abating the foul,
> disease-breeding business. I may mention here that, for no other cause, the laws
> should prohibit these establishments, because it is degrading and inhuman for
> human beings to spend their days in such an occupation as assorting the filth of our
> cities.[70]

Williams' poignant and sensitive criticisms were not taken to heart by
those who had faith in the profitability of reduction. Environmental considerations were ignored or rationalized in cities that had decided upon reduction with the hope of recovering revenue. To avoid the perpetual complaints about the smell, plants were built on sites distant from the central
city, which tended to increase costs by requiring longer garbage hauls to
them.[71]

Problems of location were acute for cities like New York, in which
reduction was economically viable but low-density property was scarce. In
1916 and 1917 a local debate over the placement of a reduction plant grew
into a statewide controversy. During negotiations to secure a five-year contract for garbage disposal (to begin January 1, 1917) a decision was made to
transport garbage from the boroughs of Manhattan, the Bronx, and Brooklyn to a reduction plant on Staten Island (this plant was to replace plants in
Brooklyn which had been closed because of the odor problem). Residents
of the island protested and asked Governor Charles S. Whitman to inter-
vene in their behalf. After a preliminary hearing he referred the matter to
the state commissioner of health, who in turn referred it to his deputy, who
eventually held a formal hearing. The hearing lasted twelve days, producing 1,700 pages of testimony. Dr. George C. Whipple, professr of sanitary
engineering at Harvard University and a member of Hazen, Whipple, and
Fuller, a New York City engineering firm, wrote a summary report based
on the testimony. Whipple declared that neither the transportation of waste

---

[70] "Garbage Collection and Disposal," *City Government* 7 (September 1899): 50.

[71] "Garbage Destruction," *Pacific Municipalities* 9 (October 1903): 81; Schneider, "The
Disposal of a City's Waste," p. 25.

by scows nor the treatment of garbage by the proposed reduction system would be a health menace. He added, however, that the plant would cause some local nuisance and recommended that officials choose another site. Governor Whitman concurred with Whipple's findings but surprisingly declared that he had no jurisdiction over the matter. His show of concern had turned to indifference or insensitivity to local protests, and contractors began the project without further delay.[72]

The Staten Island controversy highlighted the clash between economic and environmental interests over the reduction method. The attraction of potential revenue led supporters to argue that the drawbacks to reduction were only temporary, readily overcome by technical improvements. Under the new system, they claimed, odors could be eliminated. Many city officials remained suspicious, considering the investment too great and the potential benefits too uncertain. In time the controversy over the reduction method—and other disposal methods as well—made municipal authorities more wary of the claims of promoters of new equipment and, indeed, of promises of ready solutions to what had become a major issue of the cities.[73]

While the reduction method failed to attract widespread support in American cities, it did help generate interest in the broader area of utilization of wastes and recycling. By World War I the perception of waste as a

[72] "Garbage Reduction Plant for New York City," *Municipal Journal and Engineer* 41 (9 November 1916): 568–69; "New York Garbage-Reduction Works Controversy May Be Over," *Engineering News* 77 (18 January 1917): 125; "New York's Garbage-Reduction Fuss," *Engineering News* 77 (1 February 1917): 201–202; Richard Fenton to Martin Melosi, October 27, 1980. The Barren Island reduction plant in New York, the world's largest reduction plant, was also the subject of controversy and complaint because of the noxious odors it emitted. See New York City, Board of Health, *A Report as to the Existing Conditions on Barren Island*, pp. 1–31; "Collection of Garbage," *Municipal Journal and Engineer* 39 (8 July 1915): 43; "Reduction of New York's Garbage," *Municipal Journal and Engineer* 39 (8 July 1915): 37; Charles F. Bolduan, *Over a Century of Health Administration in New York City*, p. 27; Morse, *The Collection and Disposal of Municipal Waste*, p. 350.

[73] Parsons, "City Refuse and Its Disposal," p. 9; Hering and Greeley, *Collection and Disposal of Municipal Refuse*, pp. 501–502; Morse, "The Disposal of the City's Waste," p. 273; Howard G. Bayles, "Incineration of Municipal Waste," *Municipal Engineering* 29 (October 1905): 255; Walter F. Goodrich, *The Economic Disposal of Town's Refuse*, pp. 238–39; "Recent Refuse Disposal Practice," *Municipal Journal and Engineer* 37 (10 December 1914): 848–50; Crohurst, *Municipal Wastes*, p. 76; Osborn, "Disposal of Garbage by the Reduction Method," pp. 939–42; Sterling H. Bunnell, "Municipal Refuse Sorting and Utilization Plant, Pittsburgh, Penn.," *Engineering News* 71 (30 April 1914): 980–84; "Reduction of New York's Garbage," pp. 37–38; "Collection of Garbage," *Municipal Journal and Engineer* 39 (8 July 1915): 43.

menace had been supplanted in some circles by the notion of "waste as wealth." George E. Dyck, an industrial chemist for the Chicago Bureau of Waste, wrote the following poem in 1916:

> There is wealth in waste,
> Also waste in wealth;
> Save the waste of wealth,
> Turning waste into wealth.[74]

Although hardly Shakespearean, Dyck's quatrain reflected the optimism of many engineers, chemists, city officials, journalists, and sanitarians who saw a way to turn a liability into an asset. As noted earlier, new and varied methods of recycling were introduced in the twentieth century. In an article in *Cosmopolitan Magazine* entitled "The Chemical House That Jack Built," Theodore Waters extolled the manner in which "every possible substance we use and throw away comes back as new and different material—a wonderful cycle of transformation created by the scientist's skill."[75] Charles Zueblin, the author of *American Municipal Progress* (1916), wrote about the utilization of all kinds of refuse, from street sweepings as fill to the sorting of rubbish for resale.[76] Engineers like Colonel Morse claimed that "almost every article used in a household, after it has been worn out and thrown away, can by the proper agency be turned to some new purpose."[77]

For the most part "waste as wealth" was induced primarily by economic rather than by environmental motives. Profits were to be made in recycling and waste utilization, and people were always ready and willing to promote a new method of disposal or a new cleaning device. This view was manifest in a promotional pamphlet circulated by the United States Garbage Reduction Company:

The fortunes of the future will be made from the crumbs that fall from the world's table. The worthless chips of leather of ten years ago make the valuable leatherboard of to-day. The cast-off woollens of thirty years ago now clothe in handsome-looking cloths the poorest in the land. Cotton seed, a waste in the early seventies, is to-day the source of a substitute for lard, better than the original itself.

---

[74] Geroge E. Dyck, *The Treatment of Garbage*, p. 4.

[75] Theodore Waters, "The Chemical House That Jack Built," *Cosmopolitan Magazine* 43 (July 1907): 290–93.

[76] Charles Zueblin, *American Municipal Progress*, pp. 78–79.

[77] William F. Morse, *The Disposal of Refuse and Garbage*, p. 3. See also "A Chance to Save Money from the Refuse of New York City," *Engineering News* 67 (8 February 1912): 265.

The flax stalk of the western linseed grower, until recently burned up, has become the fiber from which American linen is made.

But greater than all these is the conversion of the greatest menace to public health, the garbage of the townsman, into a useful and valuable commercial product. This is what the United States Garbage Reduction company will do.[78]

Experiments in turning waste into wealth multiplied rapidly in the early twentieth century. Older techniques were adapted to the new conditions, as in finding innovative ways to use waste materials as fertilizer. In the late 1890s the United States Department of Agriculture had begun investigating the value of street sweepings as fertilizer. Machines were invented to pulverize inorganic materials to be used as fill or fertilizer. Clinker from incineration plants, which had traditionally been used as fill, was tested as a possible improvement on gravel for concrete.[79]

Sorting and reselling items found in rubbish were becoming profitable for some cities, especially because of the growing demand for old rags and used paper by manufacturers of paper products. By the turn of the century the United States was the world's leading producer of paper and paper goods, with an annual output of approximately 640,000 tons in 1908. Americans were also the leading consumers of paper products. They used about 38.6 pounds per capita a year, as compared with 34.3 pounds used by the English, 29.9 pounds by the Germans, 20.5 pounds by the French, 19 pounds by the Austrians, and 15.4 pounds by the Italians. Because of the increasing demand and the fear of deforestation, manufacturing companies eagerly purchased any material which could be turned into paper pulp quickly and cheaply. In 1913 the United States imported 123,000 tons of rags and 380,000 tons of wastepaper. When foreign sources diminished during World War I, paper manufacturers depended even more heavily on domestic sources to be found in abundance in the cities. In 1916 the United States produced more than 15,000 tons of paper a day, using 5,000 tons of old paper in the process. Demand for paper goods continued to outstrip

[78] Albert C. Day, *The Garbage Question: A Profitable Solution*, p. 1. See also Edgar L. Culver, *Value at City Waste*.

[79] Ervin E. Ewell, *The Fertilizing Value of Street Sweepings*, U.S. Department of Agriculture Bulletin no. 55 (1898), pp. 7–19; "Fertilizer from City Refuse," *Municipal Journal and Engineer* 30 (28 June 1911): 918; Arturo Bruttini, *Uses of Waste Materials*, pp. 1–5; Edward A. Oldham, "Value of Steet Sweepings," *Municipal Engineering* 16 (February 1899): 80–84; "Concrete from Refuse Clinker," *Municipal Journal and Engineer* 31 (9 August 1911): 175; "Value of Coal Ashes," *City Government* 4 (January 1898): 31.

supply, however, and prices rose steadily. Manufacturers employed innovative technology which allowed them to remove printer's ink from old newspapers through a defibering process. Other techniques were devised to turn old paper into cardboard and pasteboard.[80]

The most promising experimentation took place with conversion of waste into energy, the precursor of modern biomass technology. One approach was to turn refuse into liquid or solid fuels. At a reduction plant in Columbus, Ohio, for example, experiments were conducted in converting garbage into alcohol, to compete with alcohol derived from corn, wheat, and potatoes. In Austin, Texas, E. L. Culver patented a method of turning refuse into fuel bricks called "oakoal" (so named because of the similarity of its burning properties with those of oakwood). According to Dr. William B. Philips, of the University of Texas, the fuel bricks contained about the same amount of heat units per pound as the best bituminous lump coal. In the meantime scientists in England developed "coalesine," a fuel briquette made from pulverized refuse. Coalesine gained widespread attention in the United States.[81]

English and German projects to convert waste into steam and electrical power eventually prompted similar experiments in the United States. The writings of W. F. Goodrich and Joseph G. Branch introduced to American engineers the English method of using high-temperature destructors to produce power. Colonel Morse called Goodrich's first book on the subject "a revelation to American engineers and town officials." Goodrich and other English engineers designed destructors to perform a number of power-producing functions. In 1897 a destructor was connected to the steam engines of a sewage pumping station in Hereford. The excess steam generated by the destructor was used to pump the sewage to its final destination. Also in the mid-1890s a destructor plant was combined with an electricity works. The steam produced by the destructor ran turbines which generated power. By 1912 there were approximately seventy-six combined destructors and electricity works in operation or under construction in the

---

[80] Thomas J. Keenan, "How Waste Paper Is Treated to Make New Paper," *Scientific American* 115 (23 December 1916): 574–75; "Where Waste Newspapers Go," *Scientific American* 111 (5 December 1914): 471; "Sale of Waste Material," *Municipal Journal and Engineer* 41 (31 August 1916): 261–62; Morse, *The Collection and Disposal of Municipal Waste*, pp. 421–25.

[81] "Alcohol from Garbage," *Municipal Journal and Engineer* 42 (24 May 1917): 707–709; Robert H. Moulton, "Turning Garbage into Fuel," *Independent* 89 (5 February 1917): 222; Morse, *The Collection and Disposal of Municipal Waste*, pp. 444–46.

United Kingdom and about seventeen such installations in other countries throughout the world. These works helped generate light, supplied power for traction, and pumped water. In other forms power generated from waste was connected to gasworks or other municipal operations requiring power. For example, in Nottingham enough steam was produced by the destructor system to provide one-third of the electricity needed to operate the tramway.[82]

The generation of steam and electrical power through incineration was one of several experiments in ways to obtain wealth from waste.[83] In 1905, New York City began a project to combine a rubbish incinerator and an electric lighting plant. The steam was to run dynamos and provide power to light several city structures, including an East River bridge. Little came of the project, however. Before World War I there was talk of several incineration plants to be coupled in a similar manner. Only a few were completed. Electric generators were installed in the huge Milwaukee incinerator in December, 1913, but, as Samuel Greeley noted, "With this exception no new record of actual steam utilization on a full output basis has been made in this country." A few small-scale projects were developed, such as one in Minneapolis to light and heat a hospital and to light some city streets. In Seattle power from waste was used for some manufacturing functions; a Rochester, New York, plant furnished power to an adjacent reduction plant; Miami, Florida, generated steam for a municipal hospital to help operate the kitchen and laundry; and Savannah, Georgia, sent power to a steam heater in a nearby waterworks plant.[84]

[82] William F. Morse, "Refuse Disposal and Power Production," *Municipal Journal and Engineer* 17 (September 1904): 107–109; W. Francis Goodrich, *Refuse Disposal and Power Production*, pp. v–vii, 1–26; Joseph G. Branch, *Heat and Light from Municipal and Other Waste*, pp. 1ff.; William F. Morse, "Utilization and Disposal of Municipal Waste," *Journal of the Franklin Institute* 157 (June 1904): 420–21; "City Refuse Destructors as Power Plants," *California (Pacific) Municipalities* 2 (April 1900): 85–86; Louis L. Tribus. "Disposal of Garbage, a Large City's Problem," *Proceedings of the ASMI* (1917), p. 250; William F. Morse, "Steam Power from City Waste," *Municipal Journal and Engineer* 10 (March 1901): 90–91; Morse, *The Collection and Disposal of Municipal Waste*, pp. 216–79; Fetherston, "Municipal Refuse Disposal," pp. 384–86; "Running Municipal Trolley Cars with Garbage and Refuse," *Scientific American* 96 (1 June 1907): 446.

[83] It should be noted that the development of industrial-waste heat boilers to generate steam antedated municipal incinerators in the United States.

[84] "New York Light from Rubbish," *Bulletin of the League of American Municipalities* 4 (December 1905): 190; *Engineering News* 53 (5 January 1905): 17; *Municipal Journal and Engineer* 19 (July 1905): 40–41; Samuel A. Greeley, "Refuse Disposal and Street Cleaning," *Engineering Record* 69 (3 January 1914): 15; Zueblin, *American Municipal Progress*, p. 80;

Cost was a major deterrent to large-scale projects in heat and power generation from waste before World War I. A report of the Chamber of Commerce of the United States in 1931 concluded that "only a small number of American incinerators develop steam, the more common practice being to erect plants of cheaper initial cost which are neither designed nor equipped for steam production."[85] Gaining sufficient value from a steam-producing incinerator required utilizing the steam generated day and night, effectively regulating the collection of wastes to ensure proper content for the burning process, calculating the requirements for auxiliary fuel to create the steam, and, of course, determining the market for the energy produced. Although proponents of the method argued the advantages of energy-producing incinerators, it was difficult to overcome the objection that the initial costs of construction were higher than those for traditional crematories. Colonel Morse calculated that the initial cost of a steam-producing plant, which used 30 to 75 tons of waste a day, was 15 percent higher than the cost of a simple incinerator. A strong proponent of the new technology, Morse tried to demonstrate to his peers that the investment was worthwhile, but many remained convinced that higher construction costs and potentially higher operating costs (a hotly debated point) made steam-generating incinerators hardly worth the effort.[86]

Most other forms of waste utilization met similar resistance. Although some local experiments proved successful, the idea of obtaining wealth from waste never found wide acceptance in American cities. Sanitarian Charles V. Chapin argued that, aside from feeding garbage to swine, he knew of no utilization method "where the value of the products sold yielded a net profit over and above the cost of collection and disposal."[87] Utilization as a means of reducing municipal expenditures for collection and disposal had other detractors as well. Some engineers claimed that the

---

Tribus, "Report of the Committee on Street Cleaning and Garbage Disposal," pp. 61–62; Wyld, "Modern Methods of Municipal Refuse Disposal," pp. 208–209; Goodrich, *Modern Destructor Practices*, p. 194.

[85] Chamber of Commerce of the United States, *Refuse Disposal in American Cities*, p.17.

[86] Morse, *The Collection and Disposal of Municipal Refuse*, pp. 431–32; P. M. Hall, "Report of the Committee on City Wastes: The Economics of Waste Collection and Disposal," *American Journal of Public Health* 5 (November 1915): 1164–67.

[87] Charles V. Chapin, "Profit from Garbage," *American Journal of Public Health* 1 (April 1911): 288.

composition of American refuse, with its allegedly high moisture content, would make the energy-generating processes unsuitable to large-scale incineration and would prove to be very costly.[88]

Utilization failed to make its anticipated impact because it was out of step with certain realities of industrial America. The availability of cheap energy sources—wood, coal, petroleum, and electric power—made the conversion of waste into heat and light seem unnecessary. Private power companies frustrated efforts at extensive experimentation with European innovations. Furthermore, the United States had so many disposal methods available to it that utilization was inevitably compared with them on a cost-benefit basis. The advent of the sanitary landfill, in particular, undercut several utilization programs by offering a disposal method that seemed to combine both economical and efficient means of disposal.

Interest in the utilization of wastes, though limited in actual practice in the United States, did point to a significant change in the questions which engineers and city officials were asking about refuse management. While sanitation practices continued to vary widely from city to city, the nineteenth-century notion that waste collection and disposal were necessary for the health and well-being of the citizens had long since become dogma. Although contemporaries did not fully comprehend the broad ecological implications of efficient and effective refuse management, they paid more than lip service to the importance of sanitation services in curbing the most obvious nuisances and environmental dangers. As collection and disposal techniques underwent more careful scrutiny and as reformers convinced urbanites that an "out of sight, out of mind" mentality no longer fit the circumstances, some cities began making the hard choices necessary to provide organized, effective, and consistent service for their citizens. The biggest problem confronting city officials was trying to balance the three pillars of modern refuse management—efficiency, sanitation, and

---

[88] It was widely believed that American waste had a much higher water content than European waste and a higher percentage of organic materials. Contemporary statistics—at least those for the major cities—do not bear out this belief. For example, in a table reproduced in Hering's "Disposal of Municipal Refuse: Review of General Practice" (*Transactions of the ASCE* 54 [1904]: 271), the average percentage of moisture in American garbage was 70 percent; in English garbage it was 65 percent, and in Berlin garbage, 60 percent. See also William Mayo Venable, *Garbage Crematories in America*, pp. 271–74; Parsons, *The Disposal of Municipal Refuse*, p. 20; Morse, *Collection and Disposal of Municipal Waste*, p. 37; "Some Financial, Political, and Sanitary Phases of Garbage Disposal," *Engineering News* 45 (14 February 1901): 120–21.

cost. The best-run cities effectively balanced their needs against available resources; the worst-managed cities favored expedience. Although the "perfect" system had yet to be devised, a universally conscientious public had not yet been born, and officials with vision were rare, refuse management was never the same after Colonel Waring and those who took heed of his programs.

7

Third Pollution and Modern
Solid-Waste Management

THE economic revolution of the nineteenth century forced city dwellers to confront a wide array of environmental challenges posed by rapid large-scale industrialization and urbanization. The staggering quantities and innumerable varieties of waste presented unusually difficult problems with few immediate solutions. The environmental consciousness of the era had led to the establishment of modern refuse management, which produced the first reliable statistics on the solid-waste problem and offered more efficient methods of collection and disposal. Progress between 1880 and 1920, however, was limited to waste elimination. Little if any thought was given to controlling the generation of waste. As American society after World War I grew more affluent and as industrial cities made way for the modern metropolises, the refuse problem grew in magnitude and complexity. The scale of urban growth after 1920, plus the changing economy of the nation and the impact of scientific and technological innovations, contributed to this monumental issue. On the positive side, the lessons learned in the late nineteenth and early twentieth centuries provided the basis for more sophisticated means of addressing the refuse problem.

It is ironic that the new era of urbanization ushered in confounding waste problems while at the same time offering city officials, engineers, and civic organizations the means to control them. By the mid-twentieth century metropolitan growth had become increasingly regional. Cities were no longer densely populated enclaves surrounded by sparsely populated hinterlands. Urban development spread over much of the country, especially into the South and West, where several cities emerged as centers with regional dominance. For the first time in the history of the nation urban populations were distributed more uniformly over a vast geographic area. Regions of continuous urban development, such as the one stretching from Boston to Richmond, Virginia, were of unprecedented dimensions. The change in the scale of urban growth meant that the United States was no longer a nation with cities but an urban nation. By 1920 more than half of all Americans (51.4 percent) lived in urban areas, and by the 1970s that figure had soared to about 75 percent. The scale of growth also meant that the refuse problem, largely confined to urban islands in the nineteenth century, was spreading over an enormous area and was becoming a national problem.[1]

The patterns of metropolitan growth seriously affected the further development of sanitation services. Expansion in the form of annexation, especially in the South and West, and suburbanization, made possible by the automobile and the post–World War II housing boom, meant that sanitation services had to span great distances. Geographic expansion accelerated to such a degree that suburbs frequently became centers of regional economic and political power as well as of population. This phenomenon raised serious questions about responsibility for sanitation services. Major cities, of course, continued to grow upward as well as outward. After 1930 skyscrapers increasingly dominated the inner-city skylines. Although central cities would be hard hit by "white flight" and other forms of migration to the suburbs, they still had to contend with mounting environmental problems, including solid waste. The twentieth-century metropolis, vital and dynamic along its fringe and decaying at its core, offered serious challenges to those accountable for collection and disposal.[2]

The transformation of the national economy after World War I also had a significant effect on the changing nature of wastes. The dramatic rise in the automobile, chemical, and electrical industries during the 1920s superimposed a consumer-oriented, service-oriented economy over the nation's industrial-agricultural base.[3] The most obvious impact of this change, with respect to the refuse problem, was the appearance of numerous and diverse products and packaging materials—such as paper goods, plastics, toxic chemicals, and synthetics—which would ultimately find their way into American trash heaps. Not only did these goods add signifi-

[1] See David R. Goldfield and Blaine A. Brownell, *Urban America: From Downtown to No Town*, pp. 18–21, 296–331.

[2] Ibid. See also Charles N. Glaab and A. Theodore Brown, *A History of Urban America*, 2d ed., pp. 245–71, 291–312.

[3] See Goldfield and Brownell, *Urban America*, pp. 332–54.

cantly to the quantities of waste, but they posed new collection and disposal problems as well.

Finally, the changing relationship between the federal government and the cities after World War I had a great influence on the refuse problem. In immeasurable ways the federal government became deeply involved in the affairs of the modern city, sometimes as adviser, sometimes as partner, and sometimes as interloper. In housing, transportation, and social welfare it became the primary source of funding and policymaking. Before long several city services had also attracted the attention of Washington, D. C., including refuse management. What had been an exclusively local function rapidly gained larger dimensions through federal legislation and other actions.[4]

The confluence of urban regionalism, relentless outward and upward metropolitan growth, the transformation of the national economy, and the changing relationship between local and federal government complicated and made more serious the refuse problem in American cities. Knowledge of the context, therefore, is crucial to an understanding of the magnitude and nature of the problem. This chapter will attempt to explain the effects of a new urban and national context on trends in garbage and rubbish generation, collection and disposal practices, and refuse management. This evaluation also hints at the potential future problems posed by wastes.

Despite the changes in the urban setting after World War I, contending with the sheer quantities of waste remained the single most confounding aspect of refuse management. In 1968 cities collected and disposed of 140 million tons of solid waste. If this material were dumped in a landfill of average density, it would cover an area thirty-five miles square and ten feet deep.[5] Waste estimates for the 1970s were 127 to 250 million tons annually. For a city of 200,000 to 300,000 people this represented 400 to 500 tons a day.[6] More incredible than the amounts of waste generated after World

[4] See Glaab and Brown, *A History of Urban America*, pp. 272–90; Mark I. Gelfand, *A Nation of Cities: The Federal Government and Urban America, 1933–1965*.

[5] American Public Works Association, *Municipal Refuse Disposal*, 3d ed., p. 10 (hereafter cited as APWA).

[6] Garry D. McKenzie and Russell O. Utgard, eds., *Man and His Physical Environment: Readings in Environmental Geology*, p. 111; Peter Kemper and John M. Quigley, *The Economics of Refuse Collection*, p. 5; E. S. Savas, *The Organization and Efficiency of Solid Waste Collection*, p. 7; National League of Cities and United States Conference of Mayors, Solid Waste Management Task Force, *Cities and the Nation's Disposal Crisis*, p. 17.

War I was the rate of growth. One estimate is that solid waste increased about five times as rapidly as population.[7] In 1920 per capita production of waste was about 2.75 pounds per day; in 1970, about 5 pounds per day; and in 1980, about 8 pounds per day. This means that in the fifty years after 1920 the production of solid waste increased 45 percent and in the decade of the 1970s increased approximately 37.5 percent. Some cities, such as New York and Los Angeles, experienced much larger increases than the national average. Between 1955 and 1965 the amount of refuse in New York rose 78 percent; between 1958 and 1968 the refuse in Los Angeles increased 51 percent.[8]

It is all the more staggering to realize that municipal refuse represents only about 5 percent of the total solid waste produced annually in the United States. Agricultural and mining wastes account for 91 percent, and industrial wastes comprise about 4 percent.[9] Yet municipal waste represents a major problem because it is much less homogeneous than mining and agricultural wastes and must be removed quickly from concentrated centers of population before it creates environmental risks. Statistics for 1968 indicate that 74 percent of household wastes came from urban areas in that year and that cities must contend with approximately 20 percent more household waste than that of their rural counterparts. Since 74 percent of Americans lived in cities in 1970, it can readily be seen that the municipal waste problem can hardly be ignored.[10] An additional problem is

[7] National League of Cities and United States Conference of Mayors, Solid Waste Management Task Force, *Cities and the Nation's Disposal Crisis*, p. 1.

[8] National Academy of Sciences–National Research Council, Committee on Pollution, *Waste Management and Control*, pp. 13–14; APWA, *History of Pubic Works in the United States, 1776–1976*, ed. Ellis L. Armstrong, Michael C. Robinson, and Suellen M. Hoy, p. 431; U.S. News and World Report, *Our Poisoned Planet: Can We Save It?* p. 127; Kemper and Quigley, *The Economics of Refuse Collection*, pp. 4–5. Compared with other countries, the United States produces an exceptionally large amount of waste. One study indicates that urban and industrial waste in the United States in the 1970s was 4.5 times greater than that in Japan, 6 times greater than that in the Netherlands, and 7.2 times greater than that in West Germany. See George Tchobanoglous, Hilary Theisen, and Rolf Eliassen, *Solid Wastes: Engineering Principles and Management Issues*, p. 8.

[9] U.S Environmental Protection Agency, *Legal Compilation: Statutes and Legislative History, Executive Orders, Regulations, Guidelines and Reports* supplement 2, vol. 1, *Solid Waste*, p. 2 (hereafter cited as EPA).

[10] National League of Cities and United States Conference of Mayors, Solid Waste Management Task Force, *Cities and the Nation's Disposal Crisis*, p. 1; D. Joseph Hagerty, Joseph L. Pavoni and John E. Heer, *Solid Waste Management*, p. 7.

that the uncompacted volume of waste has been increasing faster than the weight, owing to the composition of modern discarded materials. As a result, those charged with solid-waste management must reevaluate current collection and disposal techniques to meet the change in volume-to-weight ratios.[11]

Collection and disposal methods had to be adapted not only to the increased volume and quantities of waste but also to its rapidly changing composition. In many ways the change in composition reflects the growing affluence and consumer orientation of the postindustrial United States. In these technologically sophisticated times certain types of wastes, such as horse manure, have ceased to be important, while newer ones, such as plastics, have become critically important. With the growing demand for electrical power the production of wood and coal ashes dropped off sharply. As late as 1939, 43 percent of New York City's refuse was ashes, but figures for middle-western cities in the 1960s show that ashes represented only 10 percent of their total waste. In statistical surveys for the 1970s a special category for ashes was no longer deemed necessary.[12]

The most dramatic change in the composition of waste was the massive increase in the proportion of paper, reaching as much as 50 percent of all municipal refuse in 1975.[13] Rampant consumerism, which fostered a boom in the packaging industry, was largely responsible for this phenomenon. Other items identified with growing consumerism showed a marked increase, such as glass (used for bottles and other containers), metals (such as aluminum), and plastics. These materials represented much smaller percentages of total waste materials than paper, as indicated in table 13.

The affluence which produced the "throwaway" culture of recent years is stigmatized by its role in generating increasing volumes of waste. A study of refuse production in New Haven, Connecticut, demonstrates the significant relationship between affluence and waste. A two-person household in New Haven earning $6,000 a year in the late 1960s or early 1970s produced 800 pounds of waste annually. A four-person household earning $12,000 a year produced 4,000 pounds annually. This means that

[11] Alfred J. Van Tassel, ed., *Our Environment: The Outlook for 1980*, p. 460; Kemper and Quigley, *The Economics of Refuse Collection*, pp. 5–6.

[12] Laurent Hodges, *Environmental Pollution: A Survey Emphasizing Physical and Chemical Principles*, p. 214.

[13] APWA, *History of Public Works in the United States*, p. 443.

TABLE 13
Composition of Municipal Waste, 1977*

Component	Percent of Total
Paper	31.3
Glass	9.7
Metal	9.5
Plastic	3.4
Rubber and Leather	2.6
Textiles	1.4
Wood	3.7
Food (garbage)	17.6
Yard waste	19.3
Miscellaneous inorganic	1.5
Total	100

*Waste generated, not collected.

SOURCE: George Tchobanoglous, Hilary Theisen, and Rolf Eliassen, *Solid Wastes: Engineering Principles and Management Issues* (New York: McGraw-Hill Book Co., 1977), p. 10.

doubling a family's size and income increased the production of waste by a factor of five.[14] If these figures were accurate for the entire nation, the chance of bringing the refuse problem under control would seem very unlikely.

The affluent society which produces this overwhelming volume of waste is also burdened with the astronomical costs of dealing with it. As with volume and quantities of waste, the cost of collection and disposal has soared in recent years. In 1980 the annual cost of collection and disposal in American cities exceeded $4 billion. Among the various expenditures for public services, this amount was surpassed only by the costs for schools and for roads. The rate of increase for collection and disposal costs has likewise been staggering. In the early 1960s local governments spent approximately $1 billion; in 1940 the figure was only $300 million. With rampant inflation in the 1970s and into the 1980s expenditures for collection and disposal show little sign of stabilizing in the near future.[15]

[14] Kemper and Quigley, *The Economics of Refuse Collection*, p. 88.

[15] National Academy of Sciences–National Research Council, *Waste Management and Control*, p. 14; U.S. Department of Health, Education, and Welfare, Public Health Service, Environmental Health Service, Bureau of Solid Waste Management, *Solid Waste Manage-*

Accompanying the changes in the refuse problem has been a significant attitudinal change about the nature of that problem. Most significantly, experts in the field have come to view it as one element of an environmental dilemma centered in the cities. Many recent observers, without the benefit of historical perspective, assume that this new perception is a product of the ecology movement, which made its appearance in 1970 with Earth Day and the establishment of the Environmental Protection Agency (EPA). The origins of environmental consciousness in the cities go back at least to the 1880s, as we have seen. Nonetheless, refuse as an environmental problem has undergone substantial metamorphosis in recent years. What was once referred to as "rejectamenta," "offal," or other imprecise terms has become "solid waste." Once regarded as merely a nuisance, refuse is now "third pollution." In his book of that title, William E. Small stated:

> Environment and ecology are popular subjects today. Public concern over air and water pollution has been strong for some years. But only very recently have more than a scattered handful of city government officials, sanitary engineers, and backers of beautification projects paid much attention to the critical problem of solid waste disposal. Not long ago, the city or township dump was considered an unsightly but seemingly manageable appendage, and the scars on the countryside from other kinds of refuse disposal were regarded as ugly but scarcely endangering. Today, there is general recognition that solid wastes are a cancer growing on the land, awful in themselves and awful in the way they further foul the already polluted air and waters near them—a third pollution inextricably interlocked with the two that have been longer recognized as unacceptable environmental hazards.[16]

Characterizing refuse as "third pollution" or "land pollution" reflects a rediscovery of the problem in recent years—a renewed sensitivity rather than a revelation. The editors of *Sourcebook on the Environment* proclaim that the solid waste problem "took the nation by surprise in the 1960s."[17] That may be true, but at the same time the recent generations of environmentalists look at the refuse problem with different eyes from those of their predecessors in the nineteenth century. William D. Ruckelshaus, former administrator of the EPA, asserted that solid-waste management is "a fun-

---

ment: Abstracts and Excerpts from the Literature, 1:29; and Arthur H. Purcell, *The Waste Watchers: A Citizen's Handbook for Conserving Energy and Resources*, p. 17.

[16] William E. Small, *Third Pollution: The National Problem of Solid Waste Disposal*, p. 7.

[17] Kenneth A. Hammond, George Micinko, and Wilma B. Fairchild, eds., *Sourcebook on the Environment: A Guide to the Literature*, p. 327.

damental ecological issue. It illustrates, perhaps more clearly than any other environmental problem, that we must change many of our traditional attitudes and habits. It shows us very directly and concretely that we must work to adjust our institutions, both public and private, to the problems and opportunities posed by our traditional disregard for the pollution effects of disposal, and particularly for our misuse of natural resources."[18]

As an ecological problem refuse is criticized not only for its intrinsic hazards but also for its place in the total ecological matrix. In other words, solid waste is a serious pollution problem because it is one element of a more pervasive environmental problem and compounds the damage done by water and air pollution. This concept was understood in only rudimentary form in the late nineteenth and early twentieth centuries. The linking of health problems with waste, a major contribution of the nineteenth century, has retained its significance in recent years, especially as scientists acquired a better understanding of the dangers of toxic substances in refuse, the linkage between certain communicable (and other) diseases and waste, and the high incidence of rat and insect infestation of open dumps.[19] Previous generations of city officials, engineers, and civic leaders were less sensitive to the broader implications of refuse pollution—its impact not only on the land but on the atmosphere and on watercourses. EPA studies in the early 1970s revealed that "no more than a handful" of municipal incinerators met existing air-quality standards. The EPA took several actions, including requiring newly constructed incinerators to meet emission standards and by sponsoring, in cooperation with local authorities, stiffer air-pollution laws to curtail open burning of municipal waste. New furnace designs and better preparation of waste before burning gave the cities the

[18] William D. Ruckelshaus, "Solid Waste Management: An Overview," *Public Management* (October 1972). See also Hagerty, Pavoni, and Heer, *Solid Waste Management*, pp. 1–2; Douglas B. Cargo, *Solid Wastes: Factors Influencing Generation Rates*, research paper 174, pp. 1, 75.

[19] Esber I. Shaheen, *Environmental Pollution: Awareness and Control*, pp. 156–57; Van Tassell, ed., *Our Environment*, pp. 455, 467; APWA, *History of Public Works in the United States*, p. 443. According to APWA: "Probably the first substantial scientific evidence in the United States that implicated a method of refuse disposal as a cause of a disease in human beings was obtained in the 1930's through studies of the incidence of trichinosis. Using raw garbage as feed was identified as an important factor in the infection of hogs with the parasitic nematode trichinella spiralis. It was also determined that the infection was transmitted to humans when undercooked meat from the infected animals was eaten." (APWA, *Municipal Refuse Disposal*, pp. 4–5.)

technical capability of complying with the new laws. Under the Harbors and Refuse Act attention was given to the problem of dumps adjacent to rivers and other waterways. Closing some of these dumps was a way to reduce water pollution immediately, and EPA began by closing seven large dumps. Some states responded to these problems by establishing programs to license land disposal sites and initiated air- and water-pollution standards and zoning laws to reduce the risk of pollution emanating from disposal plants.[20] These actions offered a beginning for controlling refuse pollution from several different vantage points and indicate more sophisticated approaches to the problem than those of the past.

In recent years solid-waste management has undergone some important refinements in response to the changing nature of cities and their wastes. The question of municipal responsibility for collection and disposal has long since been resolved, but the mechanisms for carrying out those tasks have been modified. The trend toward municipal sanitation services continued steadily into the 1920s and 1930s. By the late 1930s virtually every city with a population exceeding 100,000 had converted to municipal collection and disposal.[21] In the 1960s circumstances began to change at the local and later the federal levels. With increased regulations, requirements for various permits, and stepped-up monitoring of pollution, responsibility for the various aspects of collection and disposal fragmented and was ultimately divided among many agencies, councils, and other groups. Furthermore, as city boundaries became unworkable as limits for determining responsibility, multicounty corporations, countywide programs, and interlocal agreements began replacing more traditional collection and disposal arrangements. For example, the Southern West Virginia Regional Health Council, representing a nine-county area, initiated a regional plan for waste disposal which immediately provided service to 200,000 people, or 50 percent of the area's total population. In 1966, Broome County, New York, established a countywide system which required the county to assume responsibility for disposal of all solid wastes. The state of Tennessee passed the Interlocal Cooperation Act, which permitted local government units to enter into interlocal agreements and contracts to provide services and facilities more efficiently. In 1951 the city of

[20]Ruckelshaus, "Solid Waste Management: An Overview"; APWA, *Municipal Refuse Disposal*, pp. 199–200.
[21]Donald C. Stone, *The Management of Municipal Public Works*, p. 241.

Maryville and Blount County entered into an agreement to operate a sanitary landfill jointly. From this beginning sprang several other agreements over a wider geographic area.[22]

Cost also became a factor in forcing cities to rethink means of collecting and disposing of their wastes. In the early 1970s the forty-eight largest cities in the country were spending nearly 50 percent of their environmental budgets on solid-waste management. Several cities began investigating whether municipal services, as opposed to cooperative ventures, were an economical way to deal with refuse.[23]

Although statistics indicate that municipal services have continued to maintain primary responsibility for collecting and disposing household wastes while contracted services have handled primarily commerical and industrial wastes, the balance has varied markedly. Factors other than jurisdiction and cost came into play. During the 1960s large hauling firms absorbed smaller companies throughout the nation, and in many cities these "agglomerates" began controlling a substantial portion of the residential as well as the industrial collection business. It was estimated that by 1974 the agglomerates held contracts in more than three hundred municipalities. Since the firms offered comprehensive services, many cities turned over to them all their collection and disposal operations. Cities found it attractive to pass on to the companies the requirements for meeting environmental regulations as well as responsibility for financing the operations and contending with labor disputes. The large volumes of waste which the agglomerates could handle often made resource recovery more feasible. In many ways the arguments for the services of the agglomerates were updated versions of what procontract people had been saying since the nineteenth century.[24]

Despite the impact of the agglomerates, the trend away from municipal operation of collection and disposal has not been widespread. In 1973, 39 percent of 661 North American cities surveyed had municipal collection exclusively; only 16 percent had contraced collection, and only 12 percent had private collection. Sixty-five percent of the cities had some form of

[22] U.S. Environmental Protection Agency, *Guidelines for Local Governments on Solid Waste Management*, pp. 7ff. (hereafter cited as EPA); Hagerty, Pavoni, and Heer, *Solid Waste Management*, p. 270.

[23] National League of Cities and United States Conference of Mayors, Solid Waste Management Task Force, *Cities and the Nation's Disposal Crisis*, pp. 3, 32.

[24] APWA, *History of Public Works in the United States*, pp. 446–47; APWA, *Municipal Refuse Disposal*, pp. 82–83.

municipal collection, when figues for various combinations of municipal, contracted, and private services were added to the total for exclusive municipal collection. Thus most cities have maintained some degree of municipal control, though exclusively municipal collection is steadily declining.[25]

The growing complexity of the refuse problem and the nagging question of responsibility for providing adequate sanitation services forced many cities to look to state and federal government for help. The federal government's increasing interest in the refuse problem became noticeable in the 1960s. Before that time it had been restricted to a small group of researchers in the Public Health Service, who conducted modest investigations on the relationship of sanitation to public helath, and to the military, which developed programs for disposing of wastes at federal installations.[26]

Solid-waste disposal emerged as a significant national problem when it was linked with other forms of pollution. A report issued by the Department of Health, Education, and Welfare (HEW) stated that high rates of production and consumption of goods plus the rising urban population had created "a refuse disposal problem that far outstrips the waste handling resources and facilities of virtually every community in the nation." It added that the results of the problem were "obvious and appalling—billowing clouds of smoke drifting from hundreds of thousands of antiquated and over-burdened incinerators, open fires at city dumps, wholesale on-site burning of demolition refuse . . . , acres of abandoned automobiles that blight the outskirts of our greatest cities, and veritable mountains of smoldering wastes abandoned at mining sites."[27]

Considered as part of the national environmental problem, the issue of solid waste received long-overdue recognition in 1965. In a special message on conservation and restoration of national beauty, President Lyndon B. Johnson called for "better solutions to the disposal of solid waste" and recommended federal legislation to assist state governments in developing comprehensive disposal programs and to provide research-and-development funds. Soon after that call to action Congress passed the Solid Waste

[25] APWA, *Municipal Refuse Disposal*, pp. 82–83.

[26] Cargo, *Solid Wastes*, p. 73; APWA, *History of Public Works in the United States*, p. 453.

[27] Stanley D. Degler, *Federal Pollution Control Programs: Water, Air, and Solid Wastes*, rev. ed., p. 36. See also National League of Cities and United States Conference of Mayors, Solid Waste Management Task Force, *Cities and the Nation's Disposal Crisis*, pp. 4–6, 7–12, 37–40.

Disposal Act of 1965—interestingly, as title 2 of the 1965 amendments to the Clean Air Act. The Disposal Act recognized the ever-mounting volume and changing character of refuse. It also noted the inability of current methods to deal with the problem and the failure of resource-recovery programs to convert waste into usable by-products economically. It further stated:

. . . while the collection and disposal of solid wastes should continue to be primarily the function of State, regional, and local agencies, the problems of waste disposal . . . have become a matter national in scope and in concern and necessitate Federal action through financial and technical assistance and leadership in the development, demonstration, and application of new and improved methods and processes to reduce the amount of waste and unsalvageable materials and to provide for proper and economical solid-waste disposal practices.

The primary thrust of the act would be to "initiate and accelerate" a national research-and-development program and to provide technical and financial assistance to state and local governments and interstate agencies in the "planning, development, and conduct" of disposal programs.[28]

The Solid Waste Disposal Act, while representing the first significant recognition of refuse as a national issue, was incomplete in its assessment of the problem. Its primary focus was on disposal of waste, not collection or street cleaning. Unfortunately, the link between street cleaning and collection and disposal had weakened since the advent of the automobile. Furthermore, the act failed to mandate a regulatory authority to deal with broader issues related to solid waste.[29] As these shortcomings became apparent, further actions were taken to give federal refuse policy greater comprehensiveness without seriously eroding local authority. Not satisfied with legislation alone, President Johnson, with the advice of his Scientific Advisory Committee, directed that a special study be made of the national problem of solid waste. Members of the White House staff, with representatives of the Public Health Service, the Departments of Agriculture, Defense, and the Interior, and other groups, produced the 1968 National Survey of Community Solid Waste Practices. It was the first truly national study of its kind in the twentieth century. Although the samples chosen were incomplete and the execution was imperfect, the survey nonetheless

[28]C. L. Mantell, *Solid Wastes: Origin, Collection, Processing, and Disposal*, pp. 3–7; APWA, *Municipal Refuse Disposal*, pp. 1–2; Hagerty, Pavoni, and Heer, *Solid Waste Management*, pp. 268–69.

[29]Savas, *The Organization and Efficiency of Solid Waste Collection*, pp. 169–70; APWA, *History of Public Works in the United States*, p. 453.

helped fill the "data gap" in the solid-waste field and led to other important statistical compilations.[30]

To refine the 1965 act, Congress passed the Resource Recovery Act in 1970. This piece of legislation did more than simply amend the 1965 act: it shifted the emphasis of federal involvement from disposal to recycling, resource recovery, and the conversion of waste into energy. Another significant feature of the act was the stipulation that a national system be implemented for storing and disposing of hazardous wastes.[31] Subsequent laws, such as the Resource Conservation and Recovery Act of 1976, built upon and essentially replaced earlier acts.[32]

Almost as important as the new legislation was the administrative structure established to oversee the implementation of the federal refuse program. At first too little attention was given to this aspect of federal involvement, and responsibility was passed from agency to agency like an orphan. Initially the enforcement of the 1965 act fell to the Public Health Service, an agency of HEW, and to the Bureau of Mines, in the Department of the Interior. The Public Health Service was given responsibility for municipal wastes, while the Bureau of Mines supervised mining and fossil-fuel waste from power plants and industrial steam plants. With the creation of the Environmental Protection Agency in 1970 responsibility for most refuse activities was transferred to it. In the 1970s the Office of Solid Waste acquired the authority to conduct special studies of problems related to solid waste, to award grants, and to publish guidelines.[33]

The establishment of the Office of Solid Waste provided a degree of stability and permanence for federal solid-waste programs, but not without controversy. Since a primary function of the EPA is to aid in the control and elimination of pollution, several officials preferred to concentrate on the problem of hazardous wastes and deemphasize solid-waste-management issues as envisioned in the 1965 and 1970 acts. In fact, in the mid-1970s the EPA proposed a drastic cutback in the federal solid-waste

[30] Tchobanoglous, Theisen, and Eliassen, *Solid Wastes*, p. 40; Mantell, *Solid Wastes*, pp. 11–12.

[31] Hagerty, Pavoni, and Heer, *Solid Waste Management*, p. 269; APWA, *History of Public Works in the United States*, p. 453; Tchobanoglous, Theisen, and Eliassen, *Solid Wastes*, p. 41; Hammond, Macinko, and Fairchild, *Sourcebook on the Environment*, pp. 332, 357.

[32] See League of Women Voters, *Federal Environmental Laws and You*, pp. 10–11.

[33] APWA, *History of Public Works in the United States*, p. 453; Tchobanoglous, Theisen, and Eliassen, *Solid Wastes*, pp. 40–43; Hagerty, Pavoni, and Heer, *Solid Waste Management*, p. 269; Cargo, *Solid Wastes*, p. 74.

program and recommended that federal activities be limited to regulating hazardous wastes. This stand drew substantial opposition, especially from Congress and state and local groups such as the Council of State Governments, the National Association of Counties, the National League of Cities, and the United States Conference of Mayors. Other groups with vested interests also stood in opposition to the EPA recommendation. As a result the EPA backed away from this extreme position and announced its willingness to continue to develop and promote resource-recovery systems and technology.[34] The commitment to a more comprehensive program did not automatically lead to increased allocations. In fact, there was some disparity between the amounts initially authorized under the 1965 and 1970 acts and the amounts appropriated and spent.[35]

If federal interest and involvement in the refuse problem has been inconsistent, it has nonetheless inspired a more activist role by state governments. At the time of the passage of the Solid Waste Disposal Act of 1965 there were no state-level solid-waste agencies in the country, and only five states had employees assigned to any phase of solid-waste management. Four and a half years after the first grant of technical assistance was awarded, forty-four states had active programs.[36] As one expert noted:

The decade since passage of the Solid Waste Disposal Act of 1965 has seen a virtual explosion of state legislation relating to solid waste management. An area that had been generally unregulated or, at most, regulated to prevent problems of public health or serious nuisances, became, in the matter of ten years, the subject of comprehensive legislation and administrative control.[37]

States enacted legislation to comply with federal law, which made the receipt of funds and participation in cooperative programs contingent on the submission of a solid-waste-management plan and designation of a single agency as responsible for all aspects of refuse services. By mid-1975 all the states but Wyoming, which was still drafting its rules and regulations, had enacted solid-waste-management statutes.[38] Refuse was no longer an exclusively local issue. The involvement of the state and federal governments offered hope for directing expenditures of funds, research, and administrative activities in a more comprehensive way, but it also confused

[34] APWA, *History of Public Works in the United States*, pp. 453–54.
[35] Degler, *Federal Pollution Control Programs*, p. 37.
[36] Van Tassel, ed., *Our Environment*, p. 468.
[37] Savas, *The Organization and Efficiency of Solid Waste Collection*, p. 176.
[38] Ibid., pp. 176–80.

and complicated questions of jurisdiction and responsibility for collection and disposal.

Operation of sanitation services largely remained a local obligation. Despite some innovative ideas about administrative techniques and new technology, street cleaning and refuse collection and disposal practices exhibited a remarkable continuity with those of the past. This was particularly true of street cleaning. Its purpose came to seem merely cosmetic as the era of the horse passed. With the manure problem removed and the streets paved, street cleaning came to be considered a matter of dealing with litter, street dirt, and obstructions such as abandoned automobiles. In later years certain environmental considerations promised to give street cleaning a renewed importance. Research indicated that fine dust remaining after street cleaning by mechanical sweepers could become a serious pollutant when it entered sewer systems after a rain. According to the American Public Works Association (APWA): "The time may soon arrive when street cleaning methods and operations will have to be directed to pick up this fine material along with the more visible sources of debris and litter. However, no pollution-control authority has currently expressed a demand for this more meticulous type of cleaning." An amendment to the Federal Water Pollution Control Act of 1972 placed strong emphasis on storm-water pollution and might prove to be the departure point for improving street-cleaning practices. Those charged with street cleaning were also becoming aware of the positive effects of good street cleaning on air pollution. Particulate matter from the streets adds to the general problem of air pollution. This fact was well known in the early twentieth century, when it was more simplistically referred to as the "dust problem."[39]

An APWA survey of street cleaning in 1975, however, indicated that city officials gave aesthetic considerations and efficient and effective service higher priority than environmental factors.[40] Consequently, street-cleaning departments placed greater emphasis on acquiring new equipment, which meant an increasing reliance on motorized vehicles and a reduction in manual labor. Labor-intensive methods, such as beat-patrol cleaning, gang sweeping, or hose flushing were being phased out in many cities. Machine sweeping (sometimes in conjunction with flushing) or vac-

[39] APWA, *Street Cleaning Practice*, ed. Rodney R. Fleming, 3d ed., pp. 33, 75, 79; William E. Korbitz, ed., *Urban Public Works Administration*, pp. 332–33. See also Chester C. Maxey, *Urban Democracy*, p. 365.

[40] APWA, *Street Cleaning Practice*, pp. 77–78.

uum cleaning became standard methods, especially in smaller cities which could not afford to maintain a large labor force. As we have seen earlier, these trends began in the early 1900s. Compared with changes in industrial technology, however, changes in street-cleaning methods and equipment have come slowly. Because of the limited demand for equipment manufacturers devoted minimal funds and staff to research and development in this area, and very few major cities had large enough programs to justify sustained research and development. Furthermore, street cleaning has been universally perceived as a local function. Thus no substantial federal funding has become available.[41]

Building on the administrative and organizational reforms of the past, modern-day street-cleaning officials have designed more efficient methods of accounting, cost keeping, and work scheduling. An attempt to use computers to plan routes failed in New York City in 1973–74 because there were too many variables to program. Yet efforts at route development have proved effective, as has the use of planning maps, which record topographical information, street conditions, and traffic information. Street departments have made the greatest strides in measurement of work effectiveness; in the past they could only guess at the effectiveness of their services. The Urban Institute, in the District of Columbia, developed a measurement technique using a series of photographs to determine levels of dirtiness and then numerically scoring these levels. The institute claimed that the method had universal application. "Project Scoreboard" in New York City developed a similar field-inspection rating system. Another method is to determine work output, especially as it relates to machine sweeping. Some efficiency experts even tried to devise a universal unit, the "cleaning mile," in an effort to establish a common measure of cleanliness. Most cities, however, employ the "curb mile," since machines operate in the gutters along the curb.[42]

Over the years the terminology has changed, and the dependence on sweeping machines has increased, but many of the same problems plague street cleaners today. Frequency of service has always been as important as thoroughness of cleaning. Statistics indicate little change in the effective-

[41] APWA, *History of Public Works in the United States*, pp. 439–40; Korbitz, *Urban Public Works Administration*, pp. 324, 327–32; APWA, *Street Cleaning Practice, pp. 8, 34;* Harold Zink, *Government of Cities in the United States*, rev. ed., pp. 423–24.

[42] Korbitz, *Urban Public Works Administration*, pp. 333–37; APWA, *Street Cleaning Practice*, p. 78.

ness of cities to supply consistent service. The APWA survey of 1975 stated that the most popular cleaning schedules were daily for central business districts, weekly for industrial streets and biweekly for residential streets. With the greater number of paved streets and the size of the modern metropolises, meeting these schedules has become increasingly difficult. Street-cleaning services also have to contend with the perpetual problem of labor relations, with substantial reductions in street crews, and with weather conditions—especially snowstorms in northern cities.[43]

While street cleaning has lost much of its importance in the eyes of city officials and the public, collection of household and commercial waste remains the major point of contact between city dwellers and sanitation services. People tend to take the collection of wastes for granted unless sanitation crews overlook their houses or businesses or until a labor strike shuts down service, leaving growing piles of waste lying about. City officials and municipal engineers are compelled to accept the importance of collection if for no other reason than that it commands 80 percent of the city's budget for solid waste management. The 1968 survey indicated that the typical community of 400,000 spent $900,000 a year for disposal and $2.5 million for collection.[44]

In addition to the staggering cost and scale of operations required for collection, controversies over responsibility and frequency of service, labor disputes, transportation needs, and so forth demand constant attention. During the 1930s and 1940s some progress was made in collection methods and practices, especially in equipment technology. In the early 1930s most horse-drawn equipment was retired in the major cities, and by the end of that decade enclosed collection vehicles were coming into use. This improvement helped reduce dust and litter blowing off the trucks. The addition of low-lift hoppers made the loading of refuse more convenient, with less physical strain on the collectors. Since the 1950s most changes in collection practices have been dictated by an increasing dependence on motorized vehicles with larger load capacities.[45]

The debate over who is responsible for the collection of refuse has been a preoccupation of American municipal leaders since the seventeenth

[43] APWA, *Street Cleaning Practice*, pp. 8, 161–62; Korbitz, *Urban Public Works Administration*, pp. 340–47.

[44] Hagerty, Pavoni, and Heer, *Solid Waste Management*, p. 13.

[45] APWA, *History of Public Works in the United States*, p. 442; Fenton to Melosi, October 27, 1980.

century. The choice between public, contracted, and private collection is not as clearcut as it once was. Typically in modern American cities several municipal-government bodies share the responsibility for collection or contract part of the responsibility to bidders. Yet some policymakers and commentators carry on as though there were a clear choice between municipal and nonmunicipal service. Many cities have public-works departments which collect residential wastes but may often have contract administrators who oversee concessions to private firms for collection of commercial and industrial refuse. There may also be officers in police departments who contend with abandoned vehicles; county health agencies that regulate containers, trucks, and storage; special sanitation districts that enact ordinances and administer contracts; county and state highway divisions that clean roadways and collect highway litter, and state environmental agencies that act as clearinghouses for grants, set state standards, and coordinate federal and state activities. Thus the wrong kinds of questions are often raised about responsibility for collection. Efforts to coordinate the various activities and establish clearer lines of jurisdiction seem more appropriate than trying to determine whether municipal collection is superior to contracted collection.[46]

If there is any clear trend in collection practices since the 1920s, it is toward the dominance of municipal collection supplemented by some form of contract or franchise arrangement (a franchise is a contractual arrangement with an individual, not a city). Between 1929 and 1975 the number of cities with some municipal collection ranged from 37.3 to 72 percent; the number of cities with some contracted collection ranged from 36 to 66.7 percent. In all cities municipal control of collection services dominated.[47] Table 14 gives statistics from four APWA surveys dealing with residential collections. Although the percentage of "municipal"-service arrangements declined steadily after the peak in 1955, cities with some municipal collection remained at 65 percent. The surveys also stated that municipal collection was greater in larger cities than in smaller ones, which is consistent with the findings for the early twentieth century. The statistics indicate that collection of refuse has remained a municipal function over the years; they also suggest that contracted collection, which fell into disfavor in the early

[46] Tchobanoglous, Theisen, and Eliassen, *Solid Wastes*, p. 443; APWA, *Solid Waste Collection Practice*, pp. 241–57; Zink, *Government of Cities in the United States*, pp. 437–38; Korbitz, *Urban Public Works Administration*, pp. 425–27.

[47] Savas, *The Organization and Efficiency of Solid Waste Collection*, p. 43.

TABLE 14

Comparison of Survey Results on Collection of Residential Waste, Selected Years

| Service Arrangement | Percentage of Cities Surveyed | | | |
	1939	1955	1964	1973
Municipal	38	55	45	39
Contract	4	15	18	16
Private (or franchise)	7	11	13	12
Municipal and contract	5	8	3	6
Municipal and private	31	6	15	16
Contract and private	11	2	5	7
Municipal, contract, and private	5	3	2	4
Totals	101	100	101	100

SOURCE: E. S. Savas, *The Organization and Efficiency of Solid Waste Collection* (Lexington, Mass.: D. C. Heath and Co., 1977), p. 43.

twentieth century, has rebounded to some extent. The typical configuration has become a combination of municipal and contracted collection with a smattering of private collection.

The major technical problems associated with collection revolve around familiar themes, primarily the manner and kind of pickup service provided to the public. Source separation, once viewed as the practice of the future, has been largely curtailed, at least in its most comprehensive form. Some cities have different segregation requirements for residential and commercial customers; some require yard wastes to be separated from garbage and other household wastes. The 1968 survey demonstrated that 56 percent of the cities surveyed collected mixed wastes, 33 percent collected separated wastes in some form, and the remaining 11 percent used both methods. The major reason for the limited use of the source-separation method was cost. Multiple collections are expensive, especially in light of the high cost of collection versus the relatively low cost of disposal. In recent years the resurgence of interest in conservation of resources has brought more attention to source separation, though voluntary segregation programs are much more common than municipal programs.[48]

The technical sophistication of home disposal systems has had some impact on collection practices. The in-sink grinder, or garbage disposal

[48] APWA, *Solid Waste Collection Practice*, pp. 36–39; Hagerty, Pavoni, and Heer, *Solid Waste Management*, p. 10; Korbitz, *Urban Public Works Administration*, p. 439.

unit is the best-known and most widely used of these devices. It had its origins in the 1930s but did not become popular until the 1950s. Although in-sink grinders have yet to become a standard home appliance—in the sense that a refrigerator or a stove is standard—they have made their greatest inroads in new middle-class suburban areas. In some of the largest cities, it is estimated, 25 to 30 percent of all garbage is ground. The 1968 survey disclosed that there were 63.5 home grinders per 1,000 residences nationwide. The grinder does not solve the collection problem, however; garbage generally represents only about one-tenth of the total volume of refuse collected. Furthermore, grinders can clog sewer lines and, more important, can be a health hazard and a source of pollution in cities lacking adequate sewage-disposal facilities to handle the volume of waste. Some cities have prohibited home grinders because of inadequate sewage facilities.[49]

Another device that has gained some influence as a home appliance is the trash compactor, which compresses household wastes to 10 to 20 percent of its original volume. The compactor has not attained widespread acceptance, however, being regarded as a luxury item enjoyed only by the more affluent. Compactors for industrial, commercial, or institutional use have gained wider application. And compaction has become a standard practice of sanitary services seeking to collect maximum loads in the fewest trips. In the mid-1970s compactor trucks represented over half the collection vehicles in operation.[50]

Technical improvements alone have not resolved many of the basic problems inherent in the collection of wastes. The forces of nature—climate, weather conditions, and so forth—continue to disrupt schedules, as do seasonal variations in the volumes of waste produced. The infusion of politics into city services is chronic. According to the APWA, solid-waste collection has some characteristics that

make it attractive for political exploitation. Patronage may be a factor because collection requires a large work force. There are innumerable contacts and relations with residents who are also voters, so opportunities for minor favors are numerous. The purchase of equipment and service also provides opportunities for political manipulation. Where such conditions occur, costs are liable to increase, even with good management control over other factors.[51]

[49] APWA, *Municipal Refuse Disposal*, pp. 64, 244, 265.
[50] APWA, *History of Public Works in the United States*, pp. 444–45; Shaheen, *Environmental Pollution*, p. 257; APWA, *Solid Waste Collection Practice*, pp. 6–7.
[51] APWA, *Solid Waste Collection Practice*, pp. 4, 29–30, 240.

Labor problems continue to be a source of concern even in the age of mechanization. Despite the use of gasoline-, diesel-, and electric-powered devices, collection has continued to be labor-intensive. Despite (or perhaps because of) the mechanization of collection services, the work of human beings is primarily unskilled or semiskilled—and highly unattractive. Stories of garbagemen's competitive salaries and short working hours are misleading at best. The job of the sanitation worker can be physically demanding, dangerous, low in esteem, and financially unrewarding. It is little wonder that job-turnover rates are very high[52]

High costs have been and remain the bane of collection services. In recent times the average community has spent $5.60 per capita a year for weekly collection and $6.82 for twice-weekly service. By conservative estimates the cost of collection for the whole nation in 1974 was $4 billion. Nearly 60 percent of this amount was earmarked for residential collection, and 70 percent of that went for salaries. The National Commission on Productivity and Work Quality estimated that most collection systems could increase their productivity by about 20 percent. Additional investigations indicate that variations in productivity are as high as 500 percent.[53] These staggering figures suggest the need for efficiency in collection as well as evaluation of methods of financing which will help cities cope with the rising rate of waste production. It is in the collection phase that bottlenecks continue to occur.

If problems of cost and scale of operations were not enough to confound most collection services, the constantly changing character of waste surely is. One of the major frustrations in establishing a workable system of solid-waste management is attempting to adapt to new sources or new combinations of waste that may require totally new collection and disposal procedures. During the late nineteenth century increased volumes of organic waste—not to mention ash—tested the capacity of the fledgling sanitation programs. In more recent times synthetic fibers and plastics have offered new challenges to public-works departments. The incredible volumes of paper changed the nature of residential and commerical waste

[52] Ibid., p. 8; Tchobanoglous, Theisen, and Eliassen, *Solid Wastes*, p. 447; John A. Burns and Michael J. Seaman, "Some Aspects of Solid Waste Disposal," in Van Tassell, ed., *Our Environment*, p. 467. Recent studies have dealt with how well garbagemen cope with their jobs. For example, see Edward J. Walsh, *Dirty Work, Race, and Self-Esteem*; and Stewart E. Perry, *San Francisco Scavengers: Dirty Work and the Pride of Ownership*.

[53] Hagerty, Pavoni, and Heer, *Solid Waste Management*, p. 13; APWA, *Solid Waste Collection Practice*, p. 1.

throughout the country. The unprecedented growth of the packaging industry, a direct response to rampant consumerism after World War I and again after World War II, was largely responsible for the creation of innumerable goods with short useful lives. Packaging took on special importance after World War II. One of the reasons was the rise of self-service merchandising through supermarkets and other consumer outlets. This new direction in marketing required packages that would help sell the product or reduce theft or damage of products. For the sake of convenience nonreturnable bottles and cans replaced returnables. The "throwaway society" was born amid a rising consumerism and the efforts of industry to cash in on it.[54]

Statistics reveal all too clearly the dangers of overconsumption in a throwaway culture. In recent years packaging waste has accounted for about 20 percent of all household refuse in the United States, with consumption steadily on the rise. Between 1958 and 1976 packaging consumption increased 63 percent. This percentage, translated into per capita figures, means that every person in the country contributed about 404 pounds of packaging in 1958 and approximately 661 pounds in 1976. In 1966 packaging cost the American public $25 billion, 3.4 percent of the gross national product. This does not include the cost of collection and disposal of that packaging once it was discarded.[55]

The heterogeneity of the packaging materials added to the problem of volume, as table 15 suggests. For the refuse collector this heterogeneity poses many problems. As one observer noted: ". . . the American consumer has a marked distaste for separating rubbish, and is, at the same time, an eager buyer of 'disposable' packaging." Lacking homogeneous composition, size, and shape, packaging waste cannot be dealt with easily:

Steel cans contain tin, lead, and organic adhesive, and are overwrapped with paper. Some glass bottles come with twist-off caps that leave a ring of aluminum adhering to the bottle neck. Steel bottle caps are commonly gasketed with plastic or cork. Paper is laminated to metal; coated with clay, plastics, or wax; fastened with organic glues or steel staples; printed with a variety of inks. Plastics are combined with paper or laminated with other plastics and sealed with steel or aluminum closures.[56]

[54] Hodges, *Environmental Pollution*, p. 220; Mantell, *Solid Wastes*, p. 31; U.S. News and World Report, *Our Poisoned Planet*, p. 132; APWA, *History of Public Works in the United States*, p. 443.

[55] Burns and Seaman, "Some Aspects of Solid Waste Disposal," in Van Tassel, ed., *Our Environment*, pp. 457–58; Hodges, *Environmental Pollution*, p. 219.

[56] Mantell, *Solid Waste*, p. 37.

TABLE 15
Packaging Waste and Other Throw-Away Items
(Average Annual Production, 1970–1974)

Type of Packaging	Number of Items or Weight
Cans	48–80 billion
Bottles	26–38 billion
Paper	30–100 million tons
Plastic	3–4 million tons
Metal and plastic caps	65 billion
Old tires	100 million
Junked cars and trucks	3–7 million
Television sets	7–8 million

SOURCE: Esber I. Shaheen, *Environmental Pollution: Awareness and Control* (Mahomet, Ill.: Engineering Technology, Inc., 1974), p. 255; National League of Cities and the U.S. Conference of Mayors, Solid Waste Management Task Force, *Cities and the Nation's Disposal Crisis* (Washington, D.C.; 1973), p. 17; Melvin A. Benarde, *Our Precarious Habitat* (New York: W. W. Norton and Co., 1970), p. 153; American Public Works Association, *History of Public Works in the United States, 1776–1976,* ed. Ellis L. Armstrong, Michael C. Robinson, Suellen M. Hoy (Chicago; APWA, 1976), p. 431; Bernard Baum, et al., *Solid Waste Disposal* (Ann Arbor, Mich.: Ann Arbor Science Publishers, 1974), 1:vi.

Some of the packaging not only compounds collecting but defies disposal, especially nonbiodegradable materials such as plastics. In 1966 officials of the Office of Solid Waste (then affiliated with HEW) branded polyethylene containers as possibly the "biggest problem" in solid-waste management at the time. Aside from being nonbiodegradable, polyethylene burns at temperatures high enough to melt conventional grates in incinerators. In one instance a truckload of polyethylene waste was sent by mistake to a conventional incinerator, causing $3 million in damages and a shutdown of the incinerator for a year.[57] Plastics were not used extensively in packaging until the 1960s. Although they still do not represent a major portion of solid waste in the United States, their growing use indicates a more serious problem for the future.[58]

If the problems posed by packaging wastes were restricted to residen-

[57] U.S. Department of Health, Education, and Welfare, Public Health Service, Environmental Health Service, Bureau of Solid Waste Management, *Solid Waste Management,* p. 35.

[58] Barnard Blum et al., *Solid Waste Disposal,* 1:4, 8; Burns and Seaman, "Some Aspects of Solid Waste Disposal," in Van Tassel, ed., *Our Environment,* p. 458.

tial and commercial collections, perhaps they would not have become so critical; however, the widespread general consumption of goods with a short useful life has seriously aggravated the litter problem in urban as well as rural communities. As George R. Stewart wrote in *Not so Rich as You Think*, "Litter does not present the most pressing of disposal problems, but it may well be the most difficult to solve." He goes on to argue that the problem is confounding because "it springs from the limitations of the individual human being." Recalling the "out of sight, out of mind" mentality of the nineteenth century, he concludes, "Monkeys cannot be housebroken."[59]

Considering the ubiquitousness of litter, Stewart may be correct. A recent survey conducted by the Highway Research Board of the National Research Council enumerated the items gathered up along a one-mile stretch of two-lane highway, including 770 paper cups, 730 cigarette packs, 590 beer cans, 130 soft-drink bottles, 120 beer bottles, 110 whiskey bottles, and 90 beer cartons.[60] Automobile drivers and passengers are among the worst litterers. In fact, approximately 95 percent of rural litter may be directly attributable to automobile users. Of course, litter is found everywhere that humans are—in streets, parks, parking lots, schoolyards, playgrounds. It is not merely a nuisance, however; each year hundreds of people are injured in accidents caused by vehicles hitting large pieces of litter or trying to miss them. Litter can be a fire hazard and a breeding place for disease. And it is costly: contending with litter may consume one-half of a community's budget for street cleaning.[61]

Next to recycling and resource recovery, the litter epidemic has inspired the most significant civic response of any aspect of the refuse problem in recent years. At first obvious and time-tested efforts were mounted. Cities posted fines for littering along streets and highways; radio and television public-service announcements promoted antilittering campaigns; civic groups underwrote the cost of trash cans and placed them at strategic points throughout the cities and along roadsides; and old-fashioned cleanup

[59] George R. Stewart, *Not so Rich as You Think*, p. 113.

[60] Baum, *Solid Waste Disposal*, p. 5.

[61] Stewart, *Not so Rich as You Think*, pp. 120–22. For more on discarded glass and metal containers see Amos Turk, Jonathan Turk, and Janet T. Wittes, *Ecology, Pollution, Environment*, p. 138; Hodges, *Environmental Pollution*, p. 220; Mantell, *Solid Wastes*, pp. 36, 915–19. For more on wastepaper see APWA, *Municipal Refuse Disposal*, p. 51; Burns and Seaman, "Some Aspects of Solid Waste Disposal," in Van Tassel, ed., *Our Environment*, p. 458; Mantell, *Solid Wastes*, pp. 32, 35.

campaigns reappeared in many areas. New York City initiated Project Scorecard, a program designed to measure the cleanliness of the city's streets and sidewalks and to evaluate the litter problem. One of the most innovative ideas was the so called bottle bill, which mandated returnable beverage containers to encourage citizens to collect the refund of the deposit for the containers rather than dropping bottles and cans along the roadside. Oregon led the way when "An Act Relating to Beverage Containers; and Providing Penalties" took effect in October 1972. The law declared that every beer and soft-drink container had a refund value of five cents, unless the container could be reused by more than one bottler, in which case it would have a two-cent refund value. The law also banned pull-tab cans. Although beverage and container companies and other opponents fought this approach to the litter problem, the Oregon idea spread to other states. By 1975, although few states had actual bottle laws, more than one thousand pieces of restrictive container legislation had been introduced at state and local levels throughout the country.[62]

The best-known national campaign against littering has been directed by Keep America Beautiful, Inc. (KAB). Founded in 1953 as an antilitter association, KAB has grown into a national organization which promotes several programs related to the environment. However, it has strong links with the beverage container industry, and has proved to be more interested in emphasizing individual and community responsibility for littering than in directing a critical eye at packaging products. KAB made "litterbug" a household word and in so doing brought the litter problem to public attention. In the 1970s the litterbug campaign was dropped because of its limited and almost juvenile appeal and was replaced by a more sophisticated and comprehensive program. The program's main thrust is to inspire action on the local level through its Clean Community System (CCS). By spring 1980 there were 181 CCS communities in the United States, representing a population of over 21 million in thirty-five states. KAB employs a behavioral-based systems approach to the litter problem, designed to educate citizens about the sources of litter and to encourage them to promote effective antilitter ordinances and efficient solid-waste-management practices. KAB

[62]APWA, *Street Cleaning Practice*, pp. 110–12, 122–29, 161; Korbitz, *Urban Public Works Administration*, pp. 337–38; Stewart, *Not so Rich as You Think*, pp. 125–29; Hammond, Macinko, and Fairchild, eds., *Sourcebook on the Environment*, pp. 332–33; David E. Wright and Robert E. Snow, "The Michigan Container Initiative as a Referendum on the American Technological Style" (Paper, August, 1978), p. 1. For public attitudes about littering and pollution see Susan L. Caris, *Community Attitudes toward Pollution*.

also conducts national and international campaigns. It produced television commercials featuring a "Crying Indian" (Iron Eyes Cody), who surveys the damage done to America by littering, shedding a tear for the sad state of affairs: "People Start Pollution, People Can Stop It." The message is a play on the "Indian as a conservationist" theme, and although it is almost as elementary as the litterbug campaign, it has made its case to millions of television viewers. KAB also was host to the 1980 Conference of Clean World International, a twenty-five-nation consortium of solid-waste-management organizations.[63]

Through direct grants and other means KAB has inspired other national organizations to become involved in the antilitter campaign. Under a KAB grant the APWA developed a litter-measuring technique, the APWA Photometric Index, to evaluate the extent of litter in a given location. The index measures the accumulation and spread of litter and provides a relatively simple means whereby cities can identify their major problem areas and then devise ways of dealing with them.[64] APWA also sponsors several other programs of research and information dissemination in the solid-waste field, especially through its Institute for Solid Wastes.[65]

Although the advent of the throwaway culture and the changing nature of wastes had a powerful effect on collection practices, especially after World War II, they affected disposal methods much more slowly and irregularly. Some older, outdated methods were abandoned, while others continued to flourish. Some traditional methods were modified to meet the new circumstances, and a few new methods were introduced. Interestingly, as late as the 1960s and 1970s, those people involved in solid-waste management, like their predecessors, were still seeking a single solution to the disposal problem. Also like their predecessors, they eventually came to the realization that no single method could predominate throughout the country. Criticisms of one method or another were echoes from the past. "Modern methods of trash disposal have not improved greatly over those used in

[63] APWA, *History of Public Works in the United States*, p. 440; APWA, *Street Cleaning Practice*, pp. 122–25; Stewart, *Not so Rich as You Think*, pp. 114–15; Keep America Beautiful, *Clean Community System Bulletin* (March–April 1980): 1–3; "A Clean Sweep in Georgia," *Time*, May 19, 1980, p. 51; Purcell, *Waste Watchers*, p. 121.

[64] APWA, *Street Cleaning Practice*, pp. 112–13; APWA, *History of Public Works in the United States*, p. 441.

[65] APWA was organized in 1937 from a merger of the American Society of Municipal Engineers and the International Association of Public Works Officials. For more details about its history and goals see APWA, *Municipal Refuse Disposal*, p. x; APWA, *History of Public Works in the United States*, pp. xi–xv, 673–75.

ancient Troy," a *U.S. News and World Report* publication stated. The 1968 National Survey of Community Solid Waste Practices concluded that collection and disposal management in the United States is "not only unsatisfactory, it is even alarmingly deficient." Two political scientists, George E. Antunes, of the University of Houston, and Gary Halter, of Texas A&M University, were sympathetic to the plight of municipalities trying to find adequate disposal methods. They argued that, while Americans were producing increasing amounts of waste, "constraints [were] being placed upon disposal methods." In other words, environmental regulations had reduced the options of disposal.[66] Regardless of the point of view, city officials and others interested in the waste problem are continually frustrated in their efforts to devise a technical or administrative solution to it.

An important legacy of refuse reform in the late nineteenth and early twentieth centuries was the practice of evaluating disposal methods to determine their effectiveness and possible side effects. In recent times this practice has led to the abandonment or modification of some primitive practices. An example is feeding garbage to swine, which fell out of favor in the late 1890s but had a resurgence during World War I, when the country needed to increase its food supply. The momentum of wartime needs helped sustain the practice through the 1930s. Surveys conducted between 1917 and 1930 indicate relatively consistent use of the method. In 1917, 216 of 610 surveyed cities (35 percent) employed swine feeding; in 1925, 423 of 967 cities (44 percent) followed the practice; and in 1930 the number was 218 of 557 cities (39 percent).[67]

In the 1930s scientific studies demonstrated that the use of raw garbage as feed was an important factor in the infection of pigs with the parasitic nematode *Trichinella spiralis*, which could be transmitted to human beings in undercooked meat from the animals. Despite this evidence the practice continued unabated until the 1950s. Between 1953 and 1955 owing to the rapid spread of vesicular exanthema, a swine disease which led to the slaughter of more than 400,000 pigs, the Public Health Service and state health departments instituted regulations forbidding the feeding of

[66] U.S. News and World Report, *Our Poisoned Planet*, p. 134; APWA, *Municipal Refuse Disposal*, p. viii; George E. Antunes and Gary Halter, "The Politics of Resource Recovery, Energy Conservation, and Solid Waste Management," *Administration and Society* 8 (May 1976): 56–57.

[67] Chamber of Commerce of the United States, Construction and Civic Development Department, *Refuse Disposal in American Cities: A Report*.

raw garbage to hogs. Although cooking the waste solved the problem, hog feeding dropped off steadily in the late 1950s and 1960s because the method became economically prohibitive. In the early 1970s only about 4 percent of collected food waste was being utilized as swine feed.[68]

Ocean or sea dumping of municipal solid wastes has also diminished in recent years. Although the method was going out of fashion by the 1920s, it was not until 1933 when New Jersey coastal cities went to court to force New York City to terminate its ocean dumping, that the practice ceased as a major means of disposal. The United States Supreme Court sustained the lower court's action, and effective 1 July 1934 all dumping of municipal waste at sea was to end. Industrial and some commercial wastes were immune from the ruling, however. At the end of the 1960s it was estimated that each year 50 million tons of waste were dumped into the ocean, (60 percent of which was dredging spills produced by harbor-deepening operations). In fact, industrial-waste dumping in the East more than doubled between 1959 and 1968. New York continued to dump sewage sludge over an area of several square miles which has been described by critics as a "dead sea of muck and black goo." In the mid-1970s there were nearly 120 ocean sites for waste disposal, supervised by the United States Coast Guard.[69]

Although some groups and individuals still believe that ocean dumping offers an acceptable alternative to land dumping, recent trends indicate a tightening of the regulations governing the dumping of industrial and commercial wastes at sea, though none as severe as those governing ocean dumping of municipal wastes. In 1967 the Atomic Energy Commission discontinued the disposal at sea of radioactive wastes from nuclear reactors and medical-research projects, but some European nations continued the practice. In 1972, Congress passed the Marine Protection, Research, and Sanctuaries Act "to prevent or strictly limit the dumping into ocean waters of any material which would adversely affect human health . . . or the marine environment." This so-called Ocean Dumping Act was a small step toward ending ocean dumping, but hardly a complete answer. The need

---

[68] Hodges, *Environmental Pollution*, pp. 214–15; Benarde, *Our Precarious Habitat,* pp. 168–69; APWA, *History of Public Works in the United States*, p. 448; APWA, *Municipal Refuse Disposal*, pp. 4–5, 65, 269–73. See also Zink, *Government of Cities in the United States*, p. 438.

[69] Richard Fenton, "Current Trends in Municipal Solid Waste Disposal in New York City," *Resource Recovery and Conservation* 1 (1975): 170; Hodges, *Environmental Pollution*, p. 217; APWA, *Municipal Refuse Disposal*, p. 91; Shaheen, *Environmental Pollution*, p. 260.

remains for a more comprehensive national policy on ocean dumping, though the efforts to curtail the dumping of municipal wastes helped render unacceptable one more primitive method of disposal.[70]

The two disposal "solutions" of the late nineteenth and early twentieth centuries, reduction and incineration, also fell on hard times after 1930. Interest in the reduction process, so highly touted in the 1890s, waned after 1910 and never recovered. After World War I few plants continued to operate. In 1959, Philadelphia became one of the last cities to abandon its reduction plant.[71] Incineration fared better and continued to be a viable disposal method, but not to the same extent as in the decade after 1910. In the late 1930s the number of incinerators declined sharply as they had greater competition from sanitary-landfill operations. In 1938 it was estimated that 600 to 700 cities and towns used incinerators for burning garbage and rubbish; by 1966 the total had declined to 265, and by the end of 1974 one expert estimated that only 160 plants were in operation.[72]

In addition to the high costs of construction and operation, Americans had developed a greater sensitivity to the relationship between incineration and air pollution. This issue, largely ignored at the turn of the century, became very significant in an more environment-conscious time. In the mid-1970s about 70 percent of the municipal incinerators in operation were judged to have inadequate air- and water-pollution controls; that had also been true in the late 1960s, when standards were much more lenient. A study of major atmospheric contaminants in several large cities indicated that incinerator particulates accounted for 18.2 percent of the total from all sources. Some cities began to legislate against incinerators; Los Angeles officials set standards so high that they virtually outlawed the plants. New York City passed a law making it mandatory to upgrade or close down incinerators in apartment buildings to reduce the high emissions.[73]

Clearly the technology was available to correct the flaws. Devices

[70] Mantell, *Solid Wastes*, pp. 341–47; Tchobanoglous, Theisen, and Eliassen, *Solid Wastes*, pp. 369–70; Ruckelshaus, "Solid Waste Management: An Overview," p. 1; League of Women Voters, *Federal Environmental Laws and You*, pp. 5–6; McKenzie and Utgard, *Man and His Physical Environment*, pp. 124–27.

[71] APWA, *Municipal Refuse Disposal*, pp. 337–38; Lent D. Upson, *Practice of Municipal Administration*, pp. 463–64.

[72] Fenton, "Current Trends in Municipal Solid Waste Disposal in New York City," p. 172; *History of Public Works in the United States*, p. 449.

[73] Ruckelshaus, "Solid Waste Management: An Overview," p. 1; Hodges, *Environmental Pollution*, p. 217; Mantell, *Solid Wastes*, pp. 13, 27-28; U.S News and World Report, *Our Poisoned Planet*, p. 134.

such as the wet scrubber and the electrostatic precipitator could effectively remove 90 to 95 percent of the pollutants. The cost of increasing the efficiency of incinerators and eliminating pollution was high, however. Because of the availability of what appeared to be an effective alternative, the sanitary landfill, the impetus to spend money on upgrading incinerators was not strong. Nevertheless, unlike other methods of disposal which have gone out of fashion, incineration has retained its advocates and may very well have a future in the United States. One of its major attractions is volume reduction; combustibles can be reduced to 10 to 20 percent of their original volume. This is an important consideration as landfills become scarcer. Another attraction is that incinerators can be harnessed to energy and materials-recovery systems. The water-wall incinerator, which has water tubes in the walls, can generate heated water or steam. As fuel costs soar, the capacity of the incinerator as an energy generator may make the investment more attractive.[74]

Probably no method of disposal caused more consternation over a longer period of time than has land, or open, dumping. The practice dates back to the origin of humankind and remains a problem to the present day. As late as the mid-1970s, 94 percent of the 17,000 land disposal sites surveyed did not meet the minimum requirements for a sanitary fill. In 1970 it was estimated that there were 15,000 authorized land disposal sites but that as many as ten times that number of unauthorized dumps were in use.[75] In 1939, Donald C. Stone, in *The Management of Municipal Public Works*, clearly summarized the criticisms against open dumping:

Refuse dumps in American cities have as a rule violated even elementary standards of municipal housekeeping. . . . Unsightly, often smouldering, and calling for a gas mask, such dumps inevitably push downward the living standard of all who reside in the area, and depress adjoining property values. They discredit the city in the eyes of those who chance to pass, for they inevitably reflect the level of culture of the community.[76]

---

[74] National Academy of Sciences–National Research Council, Committee on Pollution, *Waste Management and Control*, p. 85; Burns and Seaman, "Some Aspects of Solid Waste Disposal," in Van Tassel, ed., *Our Environment*, pp. 465–66; Tchobanoglous, Theisen, and Eliassen, *Solid Wastes*, p. 211; APWA, *Municipal Refuse Disposal*, pp. 148–50.

[75] Shaheen, *Environmental Pollution*, pp. 260–61; Mantell, *Solid Wastes*, p. 72. See also U.S. Department of Health, Education, and Welfare, Public Health Service, Environmental Health Service, Bureau of Solid Waste Management, *Solid Waste Management*, p. 29; Burns and Seaman, "Some Aspects of Solid Waste Disposal," in Van Tassel, ed., *Our Environment*, p. 462.

[76] Donald C. Stone, *The Management of Municipal Public Works*, pp. 259–60.

If Stone had written his harsh indictment of dumps forty years later, his assessment would probably have changed little. Dumps remained a breeding ground for disease, especially those transmitted by flies and rats. Former EPA Administrator Ruckelshaus estimated that about fourteen thousand communities relied on open dumps in 1972, and many allowed open burning of wastes. Smoke from open dumps has been a serious source of pollution: a smoldering dump near National Airport, in Washington, D.C., produced smoke that drifted across the airfield so thick at times that the field had to be shut down. The use of open dumps requires vast areas of land, which have become scarce in and around rapidly growing communities.[77] The defects of this primitive method clearly outweigh the advantages, but still the practice persists. A number of years ago the Public Health Service initiated "Mission 5,000" to close five thousand dumps by July 1972, and the EPA has been fighting the battle as well, but at this writing success is not in sight.[78]

After World War II the sanitary landfill became a preferable alternative to open dumping. In time it became the predominant disposal method in the country, supplanting incineration and reduction. In principle sanitary filling is not much different from open dumping, but in practice the method is considerably different, as described in chapter 6. Sanitary fills were in use in some areas before 1920, but the modern practice originated in Great Britain in the 1920s under the term "controlled tipping." The Americanized versions were first attempted in the 1930s in New York City and Fresno, California, and during World War II the Army Corps of Engineers experimented with landfills. After the war several cities adopted the technique. In the 1950s the Sanitary Engineering Division of the American Society of Civil Engineers prepared a manual on sanitary landfilling which became a standard guide. During the 1950s and 1960s the prevailing wisdom among those involved in solid-waste management was that sanitary landfilling was the most economical form of disposal and at the same time offered a sanitary method which produced reclaimed land.[79]

[77] Ruckelshaus, "Solid Waste Management: An Overview," p. 1; U.S. News and World Report, *Our Poisoned Planet*, p. 135; Turk, Turk, and Wittes, *Ecology, Pollution, Environment*, p. 141; Hodges, *Environmental Pollution*, p. 215.

[78] See Fenton, "Current Trends in Municipal Solid Waste Disposal in New York City," p. 170.

[79] McKenzie and Utgard, *Man and His Physical Environment*, p. 111; Tchobanoglous, Theisen, and Eliassen, *Solid Wastes*, p. 20; Mantell, *Solid Wastes*, p. 71; APWA, *History of Public Works in the United States*, p. 450.

By the 1970s, however, officials began to doubt the long-range potential of the method and the extent of its apparent success. A major reason for concern was the problem of acquiring adequate sites. Why this problem had not been foreseen, given the experience with open dumping, is difficult to understand. Cities had to seek sites farther and farther from the centers of population, making transportation more difficult and costly. Multijurisdictional agreements did not solve the siting problem. Some cities tried to fill bays and backwater areas, but, as San Francisco learned, these efforts had detrimental effects on the local ecology, such as reducing the marshlands suitable for wildlife habitation. As one authority noted: "A constant headache to local government managers and politicians alike is the problem of selecting a site for a new sanitary landfill. . . . The general public is often aroused at the very thought of a sanitary landfill . . . being sited in their neighborhood." In 1975, Richard Fenton, formerly of the New York City Environmental Protection Administration, estimated that the city's available landfill sites would be exhausted by 1985. "In past years," he stated, "it was much simpler to obtain sites in swampy areas. Today, these shorefront areas are considered wetlands and important in the chain of sea life. Before wetlands can be used, State permission is required, as well as a public hearing."[80]

Other unforseen or overlooked problems arose. The objective of using the fill for land-reclamation purposes was promising. As it turned out, however, land reclaimed in this manner, while suitable for parks, recreational areas, and even parking lots, was not always suitable for residential and commercial sites (this was especially true of newer, less stable, landfills). A dramatic example occurred in the East Bronx. Row houses were erected on filled land in 1959. Within six months cracks developed in the walls. By 1965 the floors were badly tilted, and larger cracks had appeared along the brick walls. A year later the housing commissioner condemned

---

[80]Fenton, "Current Trends in Municipal Solid Waste Disposal in New York City," p. 171. See also Korbitz, *Urban Public Works Administration*, p. 447; Burns and Seaman, "Some Aspects of Solid Waste Disposal," in Van Tassel, ed., *Our Environment*, pp. 462–63; Benarde, *Our Precarious Habitat*, p. 162; National League of Cities and United States Conference of Mayors, Solid Waste Management Task Force, *Cities and the Nation's Disposal Crisis*, p. 2; Mantell, *Solid Wastes*, p. 71; APWA, *Municipal Refuse Disposal*, p. 92; J. J. Dunn and Penelope Hong, "Landfill Siting—An Old Skill in a New Setting," *APWA Reporter* 46 (June 1979): 12–13; Hagerty, Pavoni, and Heer, *Solid Waste Management*, pp. 16–20.

the dwellings and ordered them demolished. The owners lost their homes and investments in the property. Nor have sanitary fills prevented pollution problems. They often contaminate groundwater and sometimes produce noxious fumes and gases if they are not properly monitored. Unless the fills are properly vented, methane can migrate through fissures and cause fires and explosions.[81]

At the beginning of the 1980s no major new methods have replaced the sanitary fill and the incinerator. Many of the primitive methods, especially open dumping, still dominate in some communities. Periodically new variations appear. Composting, a method of converting organic waste into humus, has gained some popularity in recent years. The method was practiced by farmers in Europe for a long time, but the idea of using composting as a means of disposal and treatment of municipal waste did not come into use until 1920. In 1932 a full-scale plant was operating in the Netherlands. Since 1960 about 2,600 composting plants have begun operating outside the United States, about 2,500 of them in India alone. For a long time, because of the skepticism of public-works officials and the availability of arable land, composting did not receive much attention in America. In fact, little scientific investigation of the composting of municipal refuse occurred in the United States before 1950. In that year, through the efforts of the University of California, Michigan State University, and the Public Health Service, research was finally begun, and one of the few successful plants in this country began operation in Altoona, Pennsylvania, in 1950. The high costs of processing and distributing the compost have prevented this method from becoming a practical alternative to traditional disposal methods.[82] Other techniques, such as baling waste to reduce its size, have suffered the same fate.[83]

Construction, operation, transportation, and labor costs, plus political considerations—legal, extralegal, and illegal—have stood in the path of innovation in disposal methods. Modifying existing systems which

[81] Hodges, *Environmental Pollution*, p. 216; J. Ernest Flack and Margaret C. Shipley, eds., *Man and the Quality of His Environment*, p. 113; Bernarde, *Our Precarious Habitat*, pp. 161–62; Antunes and Halter, "The Politics of Resource Recovery, Energy Conservation, and Solid Waste Management," pp. 58–59.

[82] Mantell, *Solid Wastes*, pp. 223–24; Shaheen, *Environmental Pollution*, p. 271; APWA, *History of Public Works in the United States*, pp. 450–51; APWA, *Municipal Refuse Disposal*, pp. 293–98.

[83] Mantell, *Solid Wastes*, p. 115.

seems the most practical alternative, is unlikely to resolve the inherently difficult health, environmental, economic, and political problems attendant on disposal practices.

Periodically resource recovery has been put forth as a possible alternative to disposal or destruction of wastes. In the late nineteenth and early twentieth centuries refuse reformers perceived of material and energy recovery as a way to make collection and disposal more efficient and to reduce costs. Progress in resource recovery was slow at best.[84] During both world wars and especially World War II, resource recovery was regarded as a patriotic duty, a means to acquire or save valuable resources to aid in the prosecution of the war. Wartime industrial expansion increased the demand for tin, rubber, aluminum, paper, and other materials. Conservation of food and fuel were encouraged on the domestic front to increase supplies for the war effort.[85] Later, in the 1970s, interest in resource recovery emerged again, this time in the wake of the ecology movement and the energy crisis. Could the nation really turn "garbage into gold"? The question suggested a possible turning point in modern refuse management.[86]

The new interest in resource recovery was widely publicized. *Time* magazine lured by the hope of "wealth from waste," was guilty of overt optimism in a January 1978 article, "Moving to Garbage Power." The article mistakenly concluded that resource recovery "seems to have caught on almost overnight" and that turning trash into fuel was becoming increasingly popular.[87] Few experts in the field shared *Time*'s Pollyanna view; they were more cautious—even pessimistic—about the viability of resource recovery. In 1973 a report by the National League of Cities and the United States Conference of Mayors flatly stated that resource recovery and recycling "are not viable because they are not economically profitable," even though there seemed to be a strong desire for their application. An EPA report in 1974 sounded the same note: ". . . many cities increasingly are viewing resource recovery as both an environmentally and economically

[84] See chap. 6.

[85] See Suellen M. Hoy and Michael C. Robinson, *Recovering the Past: A Handbook of Community Recycling Programs, 1890–1945*, pp. 4, 8–10, 15–19, 22.

[86] APWA, *History of Public Works in the United States*, p. 454; Korbitz, *Urban Public Works Administration*, p. 443; Institute of Gas Technology, *Symposium Papers: Clean Fuels from Biomass and Wastes*, pp. 279–80; National League of Cities and United States Conference of Mayors, Solid Waste Management Task Force, *Cities and the Nation's Disposal Crisis*, pp. 29–30.

[87] "Moving to Garbage Power," *Time* (9 January 1978): 46.

desirable alternative to disposal. Unfortunately, this option is most often not available because demand for materials from wastes is nonexistent or severely limited." Solid-waste experts D. Joseph Hagerty, Joseph L. Pavoni, and John E. Heer, Jr., while emphasizing the potential of recycling, warned that "recycling and reuse are not magic actions to get rid of the [waste] problem." It is not surprising that, given these evaluations, Franchot Buhler, director of the Florida Resource Recovery Council, concluded in 1979: "Although greeted with such fanfare in the early Seventies—over 100 congressional hearings have been published on the subject—resource recovery has had a rocky road since."[88]

Often too cautious and too pessimistic, experts in the field have nevertheless become aware of the real problems facing cities interested in material or energy recovery. Market instability for "secondary materials" has been a constant problem. An EPA study indicated that, while the federal government is potentially a good source for recycled materials, it alone could not command a sufficient portion of the market to create a stable demand for them. State and local governments, as well as the private sector, would have to play larger roles in moving away from the purchase of virgin resources and helping recycle or convert various wastes into usable materials. In recent years the instability in the market has led to declining demand for many recyclable materials. The paper-recycling rate, for instance, dropped from 35 percent in 1944 to half that in 1973. Rubber reclaiming also decreased: in 1958 reclaim consumption was 19 percent of total consumption; in 1969 it was 8.8 percent. Similar declines were noted for nonferrous metals, such as aluminum, copper, and lead, as well as for iron and steel scrap. The EPA has argued that the low recycling rate is due to several factors: (1) the price of virgin materials to manufacturers is competitive with secondary materials and is considered generally higher in quality; (2) many natural resources appear to be abundant; (3) technology to utilize virgin materials has been perfected, while technology to exploit waste has not; (4) virgin materials tend to be more homogeneous in composition, even in unprocessed form; (5) synthetics in combination with natural materials cause contamination of the latter, limiting their recovery;

---

[88] National League of Cities and United States Conference of Mayors, Solid Waste Management Task Force, *Cities and the Nation's Disposal Crisis*, pp. 2–3, 19–22; EPA, *Legal Compilation*, p. 45; Hagerty, Pavoni, and Heer, *Solid Waste Management*, p. 56; Franchot Buhler, "Is There Gold among the Garbage?" *Sky: Delta Airlines Inflight Magazine* (April 1979): 11–12. See also Korbitz, *Urban Public Works Administration*, pp. 445–46.

and (6) artificial economic barriers, such as tax-depletion allowances, favor virgin materials over secondary materials.[89] These are important factors working against the recycling of waste materials, and similar barriers exist for turning waste into energy and other forms of conversion.

Conditions may change in the coming years. As the price of oil and other fossil fuels skyrockets, as transportation and labor costs soar, as inflation eats away at the dollar, as certain natural resources become scarcer, and as waste mounts, resource recovery may become more attractive. Much of the basic technology has already been devised and provides a departure point for future development. In the area of materials recovery several processes exist to aid in the recycling process. De-inking equipment and other devices make it easier to recycle old newsprint into new. Pilot plants have been established to separate and recover the major metal and mineral values in residues from municipal incinerators. New administrative techniques, such as a system for reclaiming aluminum cans, also provide examples for adaptations to other materials.[90]

The most promising, though not yet practicable, dimension of resource recovery is the conversion of waste into some form of energy. Research and recent applications have moved primarily along three lines: incinerator-generated heat and electricity (especially through water-wall incinerators), solid fuels from waste, and pyrolysis. Of the three processes only pyrolysis is relatively new; the others originated in the late nineteenth century. As mentioned earlier, experiments with incinerator-generated energy date back to the English destructors of the 1880s and have continued intermittently in the United States since that time. In the late 1960s, for the first time since the turn of the century, Americans began to consider seriously this means of acquiring energy. Improved design to increase efficiency and lessen air pollution has made incinerators more acceptable to the citizenry and local authorities. One expert estimated that a typical community might be able to obtain 10 percent of its electric power from burning its own refuse. Few cities have leaped at the opportunity, but some success has been achieved on a small scale. Although such plants are common in European cities, probably fewer than twenty were in operation in

[89] Antunes and Halter, "The Politics of Resource Recovery, Energy Conservation, and Solid Waste Management," p. 74; Hodges, *Environmental Pollution*, p. 225; EPA, *Legal Compilation*, pp. 45–48; APWA, *History of Public Works in the United States*, p. 431.

[90] EPA, *Legal Compilation*, pp. 81ff.; Mantell, *Solid Wastes*, pp. 756, 800–803, 833, 883–91; Buhler, "Is There Gold among the Garbage?" p. 16; Korbitz, *Urban Public Works Administration*, p. 443.

the United States in the 1970s. New York City, Chicago, Milwaukee, Saint Louis, Atlanta, Miami and other cities have experimented with the method. In Saugus, Massachusetts, a plant using a design developed in Switzerland burns 1,200 tons of refuse a day from thirteen towns and produces the steam equivalent of 12 to 17 million gallons of oil a year for a nearby General Electric plant. In Nashville, Tennessee, the Hyatt Regency Hotel uses energy from the city's garbage and trash to heat and air-condition its 440 rooms. Private firms are becoming interested in these methods. Wheelabrator-Frye, Grumman Corporation, and UOD, Inc., are sales agents representing successful European designers of steam-generating incinerators in the United States.[91]

Another alternative is turning wastes into a solid form as a substitute for fossil fuels. The potential advantage of this method is the production of a fuel which is easily stored and easily transported, as well as being low in polluting sulfur (the latter claim is a point of debate, however). With minor equipment modification this type of fuel can be used in coal-burning boilers (of course, many areas of the country do not have utility boilers equipped to burn solid fuels). Reminiscent of the "oakoal" production of an earlier time is a fine brown powder made for use in power plants, by a proprietary process, primarily from cellulose found in refuse, which is treated with chemicals and then pulverized. It is claimed that the end result can be stored without decomposing, burns more efficiently than raw garbage, and can be combined with other fuels, such as oil, coal, and natural gas. A plant in New England has been designed to convert 1,200 tons of garbage daily into this type of synthetic fuel; the material would then be combined with oil to generate steam for a power plant.[92] At this writing, this fuel is still in the experimental stage.

Pyrolysis technology offers another method of converting solid waste into a storable, transportable fuel. Pyrolysis produces gaseous, liquid, and

---

[91]Hodges, *Environmental Pollution*, p. 224; "Moving to Garbage Power," p. 46; "Is There Gold among the Garbage?" pp. 11–16; Korbitz, *Urban Public Works Administration*, p. 444; APWA, *Municipal Refuse Disposal*, pp. 149, 340–41; McKenzie and Utgard, *Man and His Physical Environment*, p. 127; Fenton, "Current Trends in Municipal Solid Waste Disposal in New York City," pp. 172–75. Energy recovery from urban organic wastes is one phase of what has come to be referred to as "biomass" energy retrieval (biomas energy "comes from the photosynthetic resources of the earth"). See Institute of Gas Technology, *Symposium Papers*, pp. 441–43; Kenneth Salvesen and Lauren Chun, eds., *Biomass Energy for Hawaii*, vol. 3, *Mixed Municipal Refuse*, pp. 5-1–5-2.

[92]Korbitz, *Urban Public Works Administration*, p. 89; "Is There Gold among the Garbage?" p. 13; "Moving to Garbage Power," p. 46.

solid fuels from organic waste by heating them in a low-oxygen or oxygen-free atmosphere where chemical decomposition but no combustion occurs. The Pittsburgh Energy Research Center, a subsidiary of the Bureau of Mines, studied pyrolysis for many years. In 1929 the bureau's pyrolysis unit was established to study carbonization of coal. Various substances have been subjected to the method, including municipal wastes, which produced materials with significant thermal value. Monsanto has also carried out pyrolysis experiments. Although demonstration plants have been constructed and cities such as San Diego and Baltimore have experimented with the method, it is among the least advanced energy-retrieval systems and has not established a clear record of reliability.[93]

The interest in resource recovery in recent years suggests a further shift away from viewing disposal as a means of getting waste out of sight, out of mind. It also, however, indicates that local authorities on their own are incapable of financing research and development in this area or of paying for operation and maintenance of new recovery systems. Consequently, the role of the federal government is critical. The EPA has provided federal resource-recovery funds and has underwritten the costs of demonstration plants. The Department of Energy has congressional approval for demonstrations emphasizing energy retrieval. The Resource Conservation and Recovery Act of 1976 indicated that congressional support was forthcoming. Still the commitment was insufficient in the 1970s to stimulate extensive local interest in resource recovery.[94] Citizen action will continue to be crucial, but although citizen-sponsored recycling centers have appeared intermittently throughout the country, they have been too limited in scale to have any major impact.

An even more fundamental question than the need for federal support is whether local authorities perceive real value in large-scale recovery programs. Recently, skepticism about the garbage-to-energy conversion process has raised doubts about the prospects of wide acceptance of resource recovery. Criticism of these facilities has focused on periodic explosions occurring during the processing stage, stifling odors, and expensive operating costs. In the spring of 1980, Thomas Stelson, assistant secretary for

---

[93]Mantell, *Solid Wastes*, pp. 255–56; Korbitz, *Urban Public Works Administration*, p. 445; *History of Public Works in the United States*, pp. 454–55.

[94]Antunes and Halter, "The Politics of Resource Recovery, Energy Conservation, and Solid Waste Management," p. 25; "Is There Gold among the Garbage?" pp. 16–18.

conservation and solar energy in the Department of Energy, stated that gar-bage-to-energy conversion uses only 3 percent of the available waste sup-ply (and this after ten years' work to complete the initial projects). At the current rate, some experts argue, only one-third of the nation's waste will be undergoing recycling by the year 2000.[95]

Technological barriers are not the major reason for the less-than-spec-tacular results of energy-generation programs. Economic barriers seem to be the most significant ones. James Abert, of the National Center for Re-source Recovery, stated in early 1980 that the "profits for the most part have been almost nonexistent to date." Sanitary fills, despite their prob-lems and the lack of sufficient sites, are still less expensive, at least in the short run. Other considerations are of an institutional nature. Refuse plants are under municipal control and operation, while electrical generation is not (an exception is an electric-power-generating plant in Ames, Iowa, where both the refuse plant and electrical generation are under municipal control and operation). As long as jurisdictional and operational control is split between private and public authorities, little momentum toward major resource-recovery programs will likely be achieved.[96]

Resource recovery may not be the complete or even a large portion of the answer to the refuse problem. Many substantive questions remain to be answered: Who owns the garbage and trash? Can a municipality charge citizens a collection-and-disposal charge and then utilize or sell the waste to someone else to generate energy which may be resold? Does resource recovery require a constant supply of waste to be economical? Is it possible that municipalities might have to encourage waste production to have enough material to burn in incinerators or convert into fuel bricks?

As fanciful as some of these questions seem, they suggest the extent to which the refuse problem tends to focus on disposal rather than on waste reduction. As the report by the National League of Cities and the United States Conference of Mayors asserted:

If solid waste management were graphed as a linear process, 99 percent of the line would depict the attention given the middle phases (collection and transportation, column reduction or compacting) and the end phases (disposal). The other one per-

[95] Jonathan Dedmon, "Conversion of Garbage to Energy May Be a Dud," *Houston Chronicle*, March 15, 1980, p. 12.

[96] Ibid.; Fenton, "Current Trends in Municipal Solid Waste Disposal in New York City," pp. 172–76; Fenton to Melosi, October 27, 1980.

cent would reflect recycling efforts. The front end of the solid waste management process, source reduction, has been unattended for too long.[97]

Controlling or monitoring the sources of waste is the one area of refuse management which has few antecedents in the nineteenth and early twentieth centuries. In the past few years, however, more acute environmental consciousness and greater attention to the *national* waste problem have given impetus to a dialogue on waste generation and how best to develop a meaningful program of waste reduction.[98]

Although President Johnson's Science Advisory Committee stressed conservation to minimize the generation of waste in 1965, the first major step in that direction did not take place until 1975 with the EPA-sponsored Conference on Waste Reduction. In the foreword to the proceedings Sheldon Meyers, deputy assistant administrator for solid-waste management of EPA, stated:

For our society, geared to intensive consumption of resources, establishment of waste reduction as a basic goal would require major shifts in attitudes, industrial practices, and consumer behavior. The wide-ranging implications were apparent in the interests represented by the approximately 200 persons attending the Conference on Waste Reduction—industries, citizen and public interest groups, labor unions, government at all levels, research and development organizations, consumers, universities, and environmentalists. As might be expected, the conference was characterized by keen interest, controversy, and variety in the facts presented and their interpretation.

Another, high-ranking EPA official evaluated waste reduction as a "radical concept." "We might as well recognize that at the outset," he stated. "It means basic change in our ways of approaching day-to-day activities. In this sense it is analogous to various other environmental and safety issues." Predictably, the conference participants represented thinking from across the spectrum of American society. One EPA official asserted that faith in the free-market economic approach and in technology must not be depended upon to resolve the problem of waste generation. "I think the energy crisis that we're now in, and are going to be in for some time no matter what we do in the very near term, illustrates that well," he concluded.

---

[97] National League of Cities and United States Conference of Mayors, Solid Waste Management Task Force, *Cities and the Nation's Disposal Crisis*, p. 29.

[98] Waste reduction in the late twentieth century is not to be confused with the reduction, or "Merz," process of the late nineteenth century.

Other speakers pilloried federal and state governments for their lack of participation in efforts at waste reduction. Some criticized state governments for restricting the battle too narrowly to ordinances on bottles and cans.

William Sadd, president of the Glass Container Manufacturers Institute, took up the free-market banner characterizing the hope of controlling resources and population and thus providing the good life through government action, as a "utopian dream." He further asserted that, though waste reduction might be a worthy goal, it obstructed material growth and progress. Expressing his belief that the United States was not in a crisis state on pollution issues, and asserting his faith in the technical fix and the marketplace to solve the problem, he continued:

I agree that there is a need to do a better job of husbanding our finite resources. I believe that we are already moving in that direction. . . . Increased technology is necessary and can help us in reaching this goal. The pricing mechanism in a free market can and is already starting to cause shifts in products and processes to reduce resource depletion. The role of the government in the marketplace concerning this problem should be minimal except in extreme situations. If that position is a call for laissez faire, so be it, for I do have more faith in our free market system than I do in our present bureaucratic structure.

He added, "Let source reduction begin right here at home in Washington with the Federal establishment." A representative from MacDonald's took a more apologetic stance, defending the company's use of packaging as a response to consumer demand and citing figures suggesting that less packaging was employed for a meal at MacDonald's than was used for a meal at home. Labor representatives, as predictably as every other vested interest present, questioned the impact on jobs of a stringent waste-reduction program.[99]

The attitudes and ideas expressed at the conference indicated the complex and radical nature of this relatively new idea. Some questioned the costs involved in programs of waste reduction; others advised caution and proceeding carefully before advocating massive changes in business or consumer behavior. Some spoke of practical ways to package goods to give consumers what they needed and at the same time provide economically and environmentally sound packaging. Some spoke with great optimism about a future when conservation and waste reduction could preserve the

[99] U.S. Environmental Protection Agency, *Proceedings: 1975 Conference on Waste Reduction, Washington, D.C., April 2–3, 1975*, pp. 1ff.

nation's environment and resources and even help resolve the energy crisis. Others were more skeptical. One commentator wondered how, for instance, the debate between the EPA and the Food and Drug Administration (FDA) over proper packaging could be reconciled; that is, the EPA demanded a reduction in packaging, while the FDA wanted packaging that would ensure safety and good health.[100]

If nothing else, the conference brought together many interest groups who interacted to produce the first national dialogue on waste reduction. It also helped set solid-waste management on a significantly different course from that of the past. In the wake of the Conference on Waste Reduction, the Resource Conservation Committee was established under the Resource Conservation and Recovery Act of 1976. This cabinet-level committee was directed to study federal "incentives and disincentives to materials conservation." The committee, with EPA Administrator Douglas Costle as chairman, included the secretaries of Commerce, Energy, Interior, Labor, and Treasury; the chairman of the Council on Environmental Quality; the chairman of the Council of Economic Advisers; and a representative from the Office of Management and Budget. In 1979 the committee issued a major report entitled "Choices for Conservation." The report included the following statement by Barbara Blum, EPA deputy administrator:

While we do not appear to be facing an imminent shortage of material resources similar to that which we face with energy resources, we have no cause for complacency about the rate at which we consume our national endowment. Our materials use practices affect environmental quality, energy consumption, waste generation, the balance of trade, and other important national concerns. Individuals, private companies, local governments and the Federal Government all make choices every day which affect our use and conservation of resources.

The report evaluated legislation on beverage containers, taxing of the extraction of virgin materials, national solid-waste disposal charges and local user fees, resource-recovery subsidies, a national litter tax, and other issues. Although it did not produce a comprehensive program or end the debate on these matters, it did offer an important focus for discussing resource conservation, especially as it relates to waste.[101]

Whether the new emphasis on waste reduction will provide answers to the perplexing problem of refuse has not become clear at the beginning of the 1980s. What does seem clear is that the present and past problems with

[100] Ibid.
[101] Press release, Resource Conservation Committee, July 13, 1979.

refuse have been linked by some significant continuities and discontinuities. Modern programs of solid-waste management still combat refuse with many of the technical and administrative tools developed in the late nineteenth and twentieth centuries in a time filled with urban problems on a scale and of a complexity that men like George Waring could not have imagined. As in all previous eras of human existence, the refuse problem has not begun to subside. It has only changed in form and magnitude.

Conclusion

THE refuse problem in urban America between 1880 and 1980 had many dimensions. It was, foremost, an environmental problem of no less importance than air, water, and noise pollution. It also stimulated vigorous debate over the extent and limits of individual versus community responsibility. It became a significant focal point for municipal reform efforts. Refuse, the seemingly mundane and oft-neglected residue of human activity, came into the public consciousness in a major way during the late nineteenth century and raised several uncomfortable questions about health, aesthetics, affluence, technology, and the quality of urban life.

Refuse and the Environment

The rampant increase in solid wastes was a central feature of the environmental crisis of American cities in the late nineteenth and early twentieth centuries. As Eric Lampard might agree, this was a period of "disorder," as Americans sought to accommodate themselves to the many changes wrought by industrialization and urbanization. For the first time in the nation's history cities confronted garbage and rubbish in quantities far beyond the capacities of traditional collection and disposal practices. More important, the perception of the problem also became outdated. Refuse had been considered not an environmental danger but rather a nuisance that brought temporary discomfort or inconvenience. When the waste was removed from the range of human senses, it ceased to be an eyesore, a bad odor, an obstacle to traffic, or a bothersome annoyance. Few individuals cared what became of the refuse after it had been disposed of.

An "out of sight, out of mind" approach to the problem was inappropriate and impractical in an industrial age. Big-city life especially made individual disregard obsolete. As the mounds of waste piled up on every street corner and in every alley of the nation's cities, urbanites were compelled to address the problem. Beginning in the 1880s, city dwellers began to take the "garbage nuisance" seriously. Individual acts of neglect were perceived as community-wide dangers, especially after it became common knowledge that there was a direct relationship between disease and waste. With the realization that inadequate or inappropriate collection and disposal threatened the physical city as well as the public health came the awareness that refuse was a serious environmental problem. A change in attitude about the problem was a necessary first step in seeking a solution.

The purported threat to health undercut the notion of refuse as simply a nuisance. This was also true of other kinds of pollution—tainted water supplies, billowing coal smoke, unnecessary noise—which accompanied rapid urbanization and industrialization.[1] In the effort to deal with refuse, environmental sanitation came to be regarded as the most effective safeguard against the ravages of communicable diseases. Despite its flawed theoretical base, environmental sanitation mobilized urbanites to deal forthrightly with garbage and rubbish. The perception of refuse as a danger to health led the way to an examination of other unwanted properties of that blight which might further undermine urban living conditions or the surrounding physical environment. Existing methods of disposal, such as sea dumping, filling with untreated wastes, swine feeding, and open burning came under scrutiny. Experts like George Waring experimented with collection methods such as source separation to try to improve disposal practices.

During this period some effort was made to link the refuse problem with various other physical and social phenomena of the emerging urban-industrial age. Overcrowded residences—especially in tenement districts—and human and transportation congestion in business districts were viewed as conditions obviously contributing to the refuse problem. Sometimes, however, these observations were carried too far, especially when foreign-borns were blamed for the major part of the problem or when "cleanliness" was equated with "civilization." On the periphery of the new urban environmental consciousness was some vague connection between refuse and resource conservation. The experiments with the reduction process, recycling programs, and sanitary landfills were obvious ex-

---

[1] See Martin V. Melosi, ed., *Pollution and Reform in American Cities, 1870–1930.*

amples of that relationship. Austin Bierbower, in a 1907 issue of *Overland Monthly*, made one of the clearest statements on this subject:

> Nowhere in the world is there such a waste of material as in this country. In our eagerness to get the most results from our resources, and to get them quickly, we destroy perhaps as much as we use. Americans have not learned to save; and their wastefulness imperils their future. Our resources are fast giving out, and the next problem will be to make them last.
>
> In passing the alleys of an American city, a foreigner marvels at the quantity of produce in the garbage boxes. The thrifty Germans would have saved this; and there is no excuse for letting it spoil in these days of cold storage and quick transportation.[2]

This glimmer of conservationist thinking was not central to the environmentalism of refuse collection and disposal in the late nineteenth and early twentieth centuries, however. Primary attention was given to the eradication of waste rather than to the origins of that waste. Reflections on the broader implications of the refuse problem, resource conservation in particular, were ignored primarily because an immediate, practical solution to waste disposal seemed imperative to prevent the ravages of disease. Despite the limitations on their environmental perspective, contemporaries did recognize the physical threat of "land pollution" and sought to control it.

In the years since the 1880s the refuse problem and the perception of refuse as an environmental threat have undergone a substantial evolution. The changing nature of waste—synthetics, new chemical compounds, less organic material, more paper products—meant different environmental challenges and more complex methods of collection and disposal. The scale of metropolitan growth and the regional and national significance of cities placed even greater significance on controlling the problems associated with solid wastes. The advent of widespread consumerism, especially after 1920, did little to curb the staggering volumes of refuse; indeed, it increased them. Despite a keener awareness of the environmental repercussions of "third pollution," modern Americans continued to face the challenges of bountiful wastes in a throwaway culture.

In recent years, however, some valuable lessons are being drawn from the long-term experience with the refuse problem. The study of urban ecol-

---

[2] Austin Bierbower, "American Wastefulness," *Overland Monthly* 49 (April 1907): 358–59.

ogy suggests that pollution can best be understood as part of the urban process. As demographic, geographic, climatic, economic, political, and social conditions change over time, pollution problems such as solid waste continue in flux. Density and distribution of population, geographic variables, fluctuations in weather, ratios of residential to commercial establishments, and so forth, are now being considered before new collection and disposal systems are implemented. This is not to say that municipal officials design sanitation services based exclusively on environmental factors, only that they no longer neglect such factors in making their assessments. The recent popularity of the term "third pollution" also attests to the significance accorded to the refuse problem in the general environment of the city.

The more recent ecological or holistic view of the urban environment has led to a greater appreciation of the "front end" of the refuse problem, namely, waste generation. Nineteenth-century Americans, like the little Dutch boy with his finger in the dike, could do little more than deal with the environmental problems as they became critical. It was typical to view environmental problems as distinctive one from the other. Refuse, noise, smoke, dirty water appeared to have separate causes, requiring separate and specific solutions. Later refuse reformers, having the advantage of hindsight, were better equipped to suggest the means to reduce the production of waste, rather than simply to devise more imaginative ways of collecting and disposing of it. Even in the modern era, however, the sheer volume of wastes has made it difficult to do more than cope with the daily deluge. Substantive programs in waste reduction wait for the future.

The evolution of environmentalist thought with respect to the refuse problem is, nevertheless, a positive sign of the growing understanding of urban American life. As historian Donald Worster suggested, nineteenth-century Americans began the search for more relevant environmental models, characterized not by farmland, open spaces, and natural wonders but by cities, factories, and national politics. Once they began to understand that the new cities represented not only a quantitative but also a qualitative change from the past, they could better begin to evaluate those factors which determined the quality of life that best met their needs.[3] The refuse problem became one of those issues which city dwellers began to compre-

---

[3] Donald Worster, *American Environmentalism: The Formative Period, 1860–1915.*

hend. Although solutions to the problem were rarely achieved, the attitudinal change with respect to the physical environment offered hope.

Solid Waste Management as a City Service

Successfully coping with the refuse problem required more than a change in attitude about the threat of pollution. Implementing programs to eradicate waste had to be devised. Yet it was extremely important that refuse was perceived as an environmental problem which threatened the entire community. This awareness enabled urbanites to consider collection and disposal as a municipal responsibility. The scale of urbanization in the late nineteenth century made private action impractical. A community perspective may not have been necessary for some services, but for refuse, as well as for sewerage, the acquisition of pure water, and so forth, any other approach was unreliable. Consequently the development of municipal environmental services was not a radical notion but a pragmatic one. As Allen Wakstein noted, problems which were most threatening (such as fire) or solutions which offered the most immediate return (such as transportation) were receiving the most immediate attention.[4] What nineteenth-century city dwellers came to understand was that decent physical surroundings were a necessity, not a luxury.

Recognized first as a health hazard and later as a technical problem, refuse—it was believed—could not be left to the laymen to dispense with but must be the responsibility of those trained in sanitation, public health, and engineering. Individuals with such training had already been attracted to municipal-government service to deal with health problems, sewerage, and water supplies. These activities had effectively linked technical experts with municipal authorities in efforts to protect some of the basic features of the urban physical environment (more elusive forms of pollution, such as smoke and noise, came under municipal authority later and in a much less successful way).[5]

Transforming refuse collection and disposal into a municipal function also grew more generally out of the cities' efforts to establish "home rule."

[4] Allen M. Wakstein, ed., *The Urbanization of America: A Historical Anthology*, pp. 115–16.

[5] Many cities had smoke inspectors and even noise inspectors, but they were dealing with forms of pollution which defied more tangible means of control, such as refuse or sewerage.

Municipal authorities actively discouraged state legislatures from interfering in sanitation services and especially tried to gain or maintain control over city health departments. Criticism of contracted services also represented an attempt by city officials to head off any challenge to their growing authority. The controversy over contracted versus municipally operated programs was secondarily a debate over the operation of a community-wide system of collection and disposal. Sometimes the question of control (or responsibility) was confused with the question of operation, but there was little doubt that cities would ignore the refuse problem any longer.

Colonel Waring introduced modern refuse management to the United States, drawing on European precedents, past American practices and experiments, and his own experiences as a sewerage and drainage engineer. Waring's emphasis was on developing a total sanitation system which took into consideration social, political, and economic considerations, as well as technical and organizational improvements. None of the individual parts of his program was particularly new or innovative—with the possible exception of the White Wings and the Juvenile Street Cleaning League, which were promotional masterpieces. His real accomplishment was uniting a commitment to municipal responsibility with the application of technical and organizational expertise, the rallying of civic action, and the cultivation of good public relations. Waring's effective coalition of municipal leaders, technical experts, and community activists demonstrated that a community-wide sanitation program could work. That was his legacy to the twentieth-century city.

Waring's example led to the institutionalization of more professional street-cleaning and refuse services throughout the nation's cities in the twentieth century. Street-cleaning practices benefited from improved pavements and more sophisticated sweeping and flushing devices. In street cleaning and refuse collection and disposal, however, improved administrative and organizational techniques were as important as, if not more important than, technical advances. Better scheduling of tasks to be completed, better routing of workers and vehicles, and more competent cost-keeping and budgeting methods were effective tools in making refuse management and street cleaning more reliable. The gathering of statistics about past and present practices, especially by sanitary engineers, added to a more comprehensive knowledge of the waste problem, which also contributed to more successful programs. The emphasis on "technique" or "the one best way" of doing things was meant not to pay homage to the fashionable efficiency ethic of the day but to solve a pressing environmental problem. These organizational and administrative improvements often proved more effective than the "technical fix," as experiences with incinerators and reduction plants attest.

The practices established in the early twentieth century have been remarkably adhered to in recent times. Collection and disposal practices have been modified by motorized vehicles and other technical innovations, but the administrative and organizational functions of modern public-works departments are largely refinements of past practice. Of course, questions of responsibility and control have been and continue to be adjusted to meet the demands of the metropolis and regional urban development. Jurisdictional boundaries for providing service may be set along county or district lines rather than restricted to city limits. The magnitude of the task often requires a greater degree of cooperation among cities or counties. These changes in jurisdiction have led to a rethinking about which services municipal governments should provide and which might be best accomplished through contracted work. Municipal control over sanitation services, however, has not been seriously eroded. Even with recent federal interest in the refuse problem, local control of solid-waste management has not been challenged. The role of the federal government remains indirect, through programs of research in collection and disposal practices, the establishment of environmental guidelines, and the discussion of solid-waste programs in national forums. The historical role of the federal government in the area of refuse management has been largely benign. What the future holds is unclear.

The efforts of Waring and the contemporary promotion of "home rule" and "municipal socialism" guaranteed that a mechanism for dealing with the collection and disposal of refuse was firmly implanted in the urban American bureaucracy. Yet the success of a program of solid-waste management depends on more than a permanent system. Street cleaning, collection, and disposal are expensive services. The level of funding determines the choice of disposal methods, the quality and extent of collection practices, and the frequency of cleaning. The degree to which a city maintains a financial commitment to its sanitation services determines its effectiveness. It should also be remembered that the establishment of refuse-management programs only ensured attention to the "back end" of the refuse problem—that is, the elimination of the waste after it is created. Refuse management programs are not designed to deal with problems of waste generation. Consequently, the knotty problem of how to curb the creation of waste still requires a mechanism of its own.

Refuse and Reform

Sanitation reformers of the late nineteenth and early twentieth centuries succeeded in convincing city officials and the public that the refuse problem could no longer be ignored (a major accomplishment of civic reform) and that it could be controlled through the mechanism of municipal government (a major accomplishment of Waring and other sanitary engineers). Operating primarily in the public realm outside municipal government, civic reformers encouraged compliance with sanitation ordinances, promoted citizen involvement in cleanup projects, and lobbied for better collection and disposal methods. Working primarily away from the public gaze within municipal government, sanitary engineers set about to shape a workable refuse-management program. Civic reformers articulated the problem in laymen's terms; sanitary engineers focused on finding solutions. Having an external and an internal sphere, both a popular and a professional dimension, refuse reform had an excellent chance for success. Refuse reform was particularly effective when the two dimensions were united, as in Colonel Waring. It was least effective when the two failed to achieve some linkage.

For the future sanitation reform provided two major legacies. First, it contributed to the institutionalization of refuse management. Second, it offered a departure point for a more sophisticated environmentalism among American city dwellers. Much has been made of the contributions of the conservation movement of the early twentieth century to the ecology movement of the 1960s and beyond. Too little has been made of the contributions to modern environmentalist thought of sanitation reform in particular and urban environmental reform in general. Certainly there were limits to urban environmental reform at the turn of the century. There were no omnibus environmental organizations, only specialized groups interested in particular forms of pollution or specific environmental issues—antismoke groups, noise-abatement leagues, sanitation groups, and so on. Few people recognized the important interrelationships among all forms of pollution or any other physical threats to the city. Even city planners, who seemed best qualified to merge the myriad reform interests into a general program for change, contributed little of substance.[6] Nevertheless, contemporary environmental reformers rejected the notion that pollution of any kind was an unavoidable by-product of industrialization, that a trade-off had to be made between a clean environment and material progress. There was never a rejection of the economic benefits of industrialization and urbanization, but an assertion that material progress had meaning only if concern for the quality of the physical surroundings was not abandoned in the process. Refuse reformers in particular did not question an economic system and a society which generated the most abundant waste materials in the world. They rarely made the connection between affluence and quantity of refuse. Instead, they contended that the physical environment should not be sacrificed to high productivity and consumerism. This was, of course, a compromise, but a compromise acceptable to a great number of people. A more incisive ecological perspective, one that would be less conciliatory to the rampant exploitation of natural resources, would have to find its context in a later period of American history.

The modest environmentalist goals of sanitation and urban environmental reform also encompassed a faith in professional expertise, technique, and scientific method in solving pollution problems. A society which grew powerful because of its mastery of machines, acquisition of vast resources, and massive production of goods was not likely to abandon a faith in and a dependence on technology and scientific method to help curb the excesses of those activities. Yet the civic phases of refuse reform, for instance, were not totally dependent on the technical fix or scientific expertise; they were accompanied by aesthetic considerations and a humanism that demonstrated great faith in the ability of citizens to rally to the civic call. American urbanites had not totally abandoned the natural world for a manufactured one; they simply tried to adapt to onrushing economic change without accepting the inevitability of defilement of the physical world. The echoes of this brand of environmentalism can be heard in more modern times.

[6] See Jon A. Peterson, "The Impact of Sanitary Reform upon American Urban Planning, 1840–1890," *Journal of Social History* 13 (Fall 1979): 83–103. Peterson argues that the establishment of elaborate sewer lines played a central role in determining the physical layout of cities and tended to dictate plans for city development. Planners, therefore, had to follow the lead established by the application of this form of technology.

The refuse problem in American cities posed a challenge to urbanites that could not be resolved in a generation or a century. Credit should be given to civic reformers, engineers, and city officials who confronted the mounds of waste and sought practical solutions. The experience of the late nineteenth and early twentieth centuries provided guidelines for effective methods of collecting and disposing of waste. It also offered broader guidelines for comprehension of the intricacies of the urban environment. It is to be hoped that in the near future Americans will be able to deal more effectively with the generation of waste and acquire a better understanding of the forces which shape the metropolitan environment.

Bibliography

Unpublished Works

Cabeen, Mrs. F. von A. "The Proper Disposal of Household Refuse and the Care and Cleanliness of Cellars." Paper read at a meeting of the Department of Social Science, Civic Clubs, Philadelphia, Pa., 1895.

Conant, E. R. "Refuse Disposal in Southern Cities with Particular Reference to Savannah, Ga., and Its New Incinerator." Paper read at the American Public Health Association Convention, Jacksonville, Fla., 1914.

Emerson, Guy C. "Individual Responsibility for Clean Streets." Address delivered at the First New England Conference on Street Cleaning, Providence, R.I., 1910.

FitzSimons, Neil. "Pollution Fighter: George Waring." Manuscript, n.d.

Morse, William F. "Methods of Collection, and the Disposal of Waste and Garbage by Cremation." Paper read at the Sanitary Convention of State and Local Boards of Health of Pennsylvania, Erie, Pa., 1892.

New York, N.Y. New York Public Library. Richard W. G. Welling Papers.

Soper, George A. "Modern Methods of Street Cleaning." Address delivered at the First New England Conference on Street Cleaning, Providence, R.I., 1910.

Waring, George E., Jr. "House-Drainage and Sewerage." Paper read before the Philadelphia Social Science Association, Philadelphia, Pa., 1878.

———. "The Memphis System of Memphis and Elsewhere." Paper read at the American Public Health Association Convention, Mexico City, 1893.

———. "The Sewering and Draining of Cities." Paper read at the American Public Health Association Convention, Nashville, Tenn., 1879.

Welch, Fred B. "History of Sanitation." Paper read at the First General Meeting of the "Wisconsin Section" of the National Association of Sanitari❧s, Inc., Milwaukee, Wis., December, 1944.

Reports and Proceedings

American Public Health Association [APHA]. *Public Health: Papers and Reports.* 1886–1903.

————. Committee on the Disposal of Garbage and Refuse. *Report.* 1897.

Ashbrook, F. G., and Wilson, A. *Feeding Garbage to Hogs.* Farmer's Bulletin No. 1133. Washington, D.C.: U.S. Department of Agriculture, 1921.

Baltimore. Department of Street Cleaning. *Annual Report.* 1882–1916.

Boston. Board of Health (Health Department). *Annual Report.* 1879–1917.

————. Joint Special Committee on the Disposing of City Offal. *Report of the Joint Special Committee on the Disposing of City Offal.* 1893.

————. Public Works Department. *Annual Report.* 1911–17.

————. Special Commissions on Collection and Disposal of Refuse. *Reports of the First and Second Special Commissions to Investigate the Subject of the Collection and Disposal of Refuse in the City of Boston.* 1908, 1910.

————. Street Department. *Annual Report.* 1891–1909.

Chapin, Charles V. "Sanitation in Providence." In *Proceedings of the Providence, Rhode Island, Conference for Good Government and the Thirteenth Annual Meeting of the National Municipal League.* Edited by Clinton Rogers Woodruff. 1907.

Chicago. City Waste Commission. *Report of the City Waste Commission of the City of Chicago.* 1914.

————. Civil Service Commission. *Reports on the Bureau of Streets, Department of Public Works, City of Chicago.* 1913.

————. Department of Health. *Report.* 1881–1918.

————. Department of Public Works. *Annual Report.* 1882–1914.

————. Plan Commission. *Chicago Can Get Fifty Million Dollars for Nothing!* 1916.

————. Special Committee on Garbage Disposal. *Report of Special Committee Relating to the Disposal of Garbage.* 1901.

Citizen's Association of Chicago. *Annual Report.* 1880–87.

City Club of Philadelphia. *Annual Report.* 1911.

City of Newton, Mass. *Report of the Board of Health upon the Sanitary Disposition of Garbage and Other Municipal Waste, and the Reorganization of the Department.* 1895.

Civic League of Saint Louis. *Yearbook.* 1907–14.

Cleveland [Ohio]. Board [Department] of Public Service. *Annual Report.* 1905–14.

————. Chamber of Commerce. Committee on Housing and Sanitation. *Report on Collection and Disposal of Cleveland's Waste.* 1917.

Crohurst, Harry R. *Municipal Wastes: Their Character, Collection, Disposal.* U.S. Public Health Service Bulletin 107. October 1920.

Darlington, Thomas. "Civics and Sanitation." *Proceedings of the New York Conference for Good Government and the Eleventh Annual Meeting of the Na-*

tional Municipal League. Edited by Clinton Rogers Woodruff. 1905.

Detroit. Board of Health. *Annual Report*. 1882–1910.

Ewell, Ervin E. *The Fertilizing Value of Street Sweepings*. U.S. Department of Agriculture Bulletin no. 55. Washington, D.C., 1898.

Fisher, Edward A. *Report of J. G. Cutler, Mayor, on the Collection and Disposal of Garbage and Other City Refuse in the City of Rochester, New York*. Rochester, N.Y.: Department of Engineering, 1906.

Great Britain. Local Government Board. *Report on the Destruction of Town Refuse*. [By T. Codrington.] 1888.

International Association of Public Works Officials. *Report of Proceedings—Conference of Street Cleaning Officials*. 1919.

Louisiana. Board of Health. *Report*. New Orleans. 1894–1905.

———. ———. *Report of President of the State Board of Health*. 1896–97.

Merchants Association of San Francisco. *Street Cleaning Problem in San Francisco; Report of the Committee on Street Improvement*. 1909.

Michigan. Citizen's Research Council. *Report on Street Cleaning and Refuse Collecting, Department of Public Works, City of Detroit*. February 1917.

New York American. Public Welfare Department. *Considerably More Than Too Much!* New York: McConnell Printing Co., 1915.

New York City. Board of Aldermen. Committee on Administration of the Department of Street Cleaning. *Report on the Administration of the Department of Street Cleaning of the City of New York*. 1906.

———. Board of Health. *A Report as to the Existing Conditions on Barren Island*. 1899.

———. Citizens' Committee of Twenty-one. *Statement and Report of the Citizens' Committee of Twenty-one Respecting the Efforts to Procure Reform in the System of Cleaning the Streets of the City of New York*. 1881.

———. Department of Health. *Annual Report*. 1907–15.

———. Department of Sanitation. *Outline History of the Department of Sanitation*. 1954

———. Department of Street Cleaning. *Annual Report*. 1886–1917.

———. ———. *Report of Commissioner Andrews to His Honor the Mayor*. 1893.

———. ———. *Report of the Commission on Street Cleaning and Waste Disposal*. 1907.

———. ———. *Report of the Exhibition and Tests of Street Cleaning Appliances*. 1914.

———. ———. *Unsightly Streets and Careless People: Control of the Loose Paper Nuisance*. 1914.

———. ———. Bureau of City Betterment. *Some Phases of the Work of the Department of Street Cleaning of N.Y.C.* 1906.

———. Street Cleaning Committee. *An Examination of the Subject of Street Cleaning in the City of N.Y. Made at the Request of Hon. Hugh J. Grant, Mayor*. 1891.

———. Woman's Municipal League. *Campaign Bulletin*. November, 1903.

————. ————. *Yearbook*. 1911–14.

New York Ladies' Health Protective Association. *Memorial of the New York Ladies' Health Protective Association, to the Hon. Abram S. Hewitt, Mayor of New York, on the Subject of Street-Cleaning*. 1887.

New York Municipal Society. *Report of a Committee of the New York Municipal Society*. 1878.

New York State Assembly. Committee on the Affairs of Cities. *Report to the Assembly of the State of New York, April, 1880, as to the Present System of Street Cleaning in the City of New York, and the Means Whereby a More Efficient and Economical Method of Doing the Work May Be Secured*. 1880.

Official Proceedings of the League of American Municipalities. 1899–1903.

Ohio State Board of Health. *Report of a Study of the Collection and Disposal of City Wastes in Ohio*. 1910.

Osborn, I. S. *Disposal of Garbage in the District of Columbia*. U.S. Congress. House. 64th Cong., 1st session, 1915. H. Doc. 661.

Philadelphia. Bureau of Health. *Annual Report*. 1891–1904.

————. Bureau of Municipal Research. *Municipal Street Cleaning in Philadelphia*. June 1924.

————. Department of Public Health and Charities. *Annual Report*. 1906–13.

————. Department of Public Works. *Annual Report*. 1889–1917.

Pittsburgh. Civic Club of Allegheny County. *Fifty Years of Civic History, 1895–1945*. Compiled by H. Marie Dermitt. 1945.

————. Commission on Garbage and Rubbish Collection and Disposal. *Report on Methods of Garbage and Rubbish Collection and Disposal in American Cities*. 1918.

————. Department of Public Health. *Annual Report*. 1915.

————. Department of Public Works. *Annual Report*. 1890.

Proceedings of the American Society for Municipal Improvements [ASMI]. 1897–1917.

Proceedings of the League of American Municipalities. 1903.

Proceedings of the League of California Municipalities. 1911.

Saint Louis. Civic Improvement League. Public Sanitation Committee. *Disposal of Municipal Waste*. 1906.

————. ————. *Keep Our City Clean*. 1902.

————. Department of Health. *Annual Report*. 1894–96.

San Francisco. Citizens' Health Committee. *Eradicating Plague from San Francisco*. Prepared by Frank Morton Todd. March 31, 1909.

Staniford, Charles W. *Report on the Disposal of City Wastes*. New York: New York City, Department of Docks and Ferries, 1913.

Stearns, Frederick L. *The Work of the Department of Street Cleaning*. New York: Municipal Engineers of the City of New York, 1913.

Transactions of the American Society of Civic Engineers. 1886–1928.

U.S. Bureau of the Census. *Characteristics of the Population*. Vol. 1 of *Census of Population: 1960*. Washington, D.C., 1961.

————. *Statistics of Cities Having a Population of 8,000 to 25,000: 1903*. Bulletin no. 45. Washington, D.C., 1906.

————. *Statistics of Cities Having a Population of over 25,000: 1902–1903*. Bulletin no. 20. Washington, D.C., 1905.

U.S. Committee on Interstate and Foreign Commerce. *Hearings on Bill to Prevent the Dumping of Refuse Material in Lake Michigan at or Near Chicago*. 1910.

U.S. Department of Commerce [and Labor]. Bureau of the Census. *General Statistics of Cities: 1909*. Washington, D.C., 1913.

————. ————. *Statistics of Cities Having a Population of over 30,000: 1907*. Washington, D.C., 1910.

————. ————. *Statistics of Cities Having a Population of over 3,000: 1905*. Washington, D.C., 1907.

U.S. Department of Health, Education, and Welfare. Public Health Service. Environmental Health Service. Bureau of Solid Waste Management. *Solid Waste Management: Abstracts and Excerpts from the Literature*. Publication no. 2038. 2 vols. Washington, D.C., 1970.

U.S. Department of the Interior. Census Office. *Report on the Social Statistics of Cities in the United States, Eleventh Census, 1890*. Compiled by John S. Billings. Washington, D.C., 1895.

————. ————. *Report on the Social Statistics of Cities, Tenth Census, 1880*. Compiled by George E. Waring, Jr. Washington, D.C., 1886.

U.S. Department of Labor. *Bulletin no. 24*. September, 1899.

————. *Bulletin no. 30*. September, 1900.

————. *Bulletin no. 36*. September, 1901.

————. *Bulletin no. 42*. September, 1902.

U.S. Environmental Protection Agency. *Guidelines for Local Governments on Solid Waste Management*. Publication no. 2084. Washington, D.C., 1971.

————. *Legal Compilation: Statutes and Legislative History, Executive Orders, Regulations, Guidelines and Reports*. Supplement 2. Vol. 1, *Solid Waste*. Washington, D.C., 1974.

U.S. Food Administration. *Garbage Utilization, with Particular Reference to Utilization by Feeding*. Washington, D.C., 1918.

Washington, D.C., Department of Health. *Report to the Health Officer*. 1880–1900.

————. Department of Street Cleaning. *Report of the Superintendent*. 1899–1911.

Books, Pamphlets, and Articles

Addams, Jane. *Twenty Years at Hull-House*. 1905. Reprint. New York: New American Library, 1961.

Allen, William H. "Sanitation and Social Progress." *American Journal of Sociology* 8 (March 1903): 631–43.

American Child Health Association. Research Division. *A Health Survey of 86 Cities*. New York: American Child Health Association, 1925.

American Garbage Cremation Co. *Cremation of Garbage*. Boston, n.d.

American Public Health Association [APHA]. *A Half Century of Public Health*. Edited by Mazyck P. Ravenel. New York: APHA, 1921; reprint New York: Arno Press and New York Times, 1970.

American Public Works Association [APWA]. *History of Public Works in the United States, 1776–1976*. Edited by Ellis L. Armstrong, Michael C. Robinson, and Suellen M. Hoy. Chicago: APWA, 1976.

———. *Municipal Refuse Disposal*. 3d ed. Chicago: APWA, 1970.

———. *Solid Waste Collection Practice*. 4th ed. Chicago: APWA, 1975.

———. *Street and Urban Roan Maintenance*. Chicago: Public Administration Service, 1963.

———. *Street Cleaning Practice*. Edited by Rodney R. Fleming. 3d ed. Chicago: APWA, 1978.

American Society for Municipal Improvements [ASMI]. *The American Society for Municipal Improvements*. Lakeland, Fla.: ASMI, 1925.

Antunes, George E., and Halter, Gary. "The Politics of Resource Recovery, Energy Conservation, and Solid Waste Management." *Administration and Society* 8 (May 1976): 55–78.

Babbitt, Harold W. *Sewerage and Sewage Treatment*. New York: John Wiley and Sons, 1922; reprint 1953.

Baker, M. N. *Municipal Engineering and Sanitation*. New York: Macmillan Co., 1902.

Banner, Lois W. *Women in Modern America: A Brief History*. New York: Harcourt Brace Jovanovich, 1974.

Baskerville, Charles, ed. *Municipal Chemistry*. New York: McGraw-Hill Book Co., 1911.

Baum, Bernard, et al. *Solid Waste Disposal*. Vol. 1. Ann Arbor, Mich.: Ann Arbor Science Publishers, 1974.

Beard, Charles A. *American City Government: A Survey of Newer Tendencies*. New York: Century Co., 1912.

Beard, Mary Ritter. *Woman's Work in Municipalities*. New York: D. Appleton and Co., 1915.

Benarde, Melvin A. *Our Precarious Habitat*. New York: W. W. Norton and Co., 1970.

Blair, Thomas S. *Public Hygiene*. Boston: Richard G. Badger, Gorham Press, 1911.

Blake, John B. *Public Health in the Town of Boston, 1630–1822*. Cambridge, Mass.: Harvard University Press, 1959.

Blum, Barnard, et al. *Solid Waste Disposal*. Ann Arbor, Mich.: Ann Arbor Science Publishers, 1974.

Bolduan, Charles F. Over a Century of Health Administration in New York City. New York: New York City, Department of Health, 1916.

Bowditch, Henry I. *Public Hygiene in America*. Boston: Little, Brown Co., 1877.

Branch, Joseph G. *Heat and Light from Municipal and Other Waste*. St. Louis: W. H. O'Brien, 1906.

Bridenbaugh, Carl. *Cities in Revolt: Urban Life in America, 1743–1776.* New York: Alfred A. Knopf, 1955. Reprint. 1965.

———. *Cities in the Wilderness: The First Century of Urban Life in America, 1625–1742.* New York: Ronald Press, 1938.

Briggs, Asa. *Victorian Cities.* New York: Harper and Row, 1963.

Brooks, Robert C. *A Bibliography of Municipal Problems and City Conditions.* 1901. Reprint. New York: Arno Press and New York Times, 1970.

Bruttini, Arturo. *Uses of Waste Materials: The Collection of Waste Materials and Their Uses for Human and Animal Food, in Fertilizers, and in Certain Industries, 1914–1922.* London: A. S. King and Sons, 1923.

Buhler, Franchot. "Is There Gold among the Garbage?" *Sky: Delta Air Lines Inflight Magazine* (April 1979): 11–16, 18.

Burg, David F. *Chicago's White City of 1893.* Lexington, Ky.: University Press of Kentucky, 1976.

Cain, Louis P. "Raising and Watering a City: Ellis Sylvester Chesbrough and Chicago's First Sanitation System." *Technology and Culture* 13 (July 1972): 353–72.

Callahan, Raymond E. *Education and the Cult of Efficiency: A Study of the Social Forces That Have Shaped the Administration of the Public Schools.* Chicago: University of Chicago Press, 1962.

Capes, William Parr, and Carpenter, Jeanne Daniels. *Municipal Housecleaning.* New York: E. P. Dutton and Co., 1918.

Cargo, Douglas B. *Solid Wastes: Factors Influencing Generation Rates.* Research paper no. 174. Chicago: University of Chicago, Department of Geography, 1978.

Caris, Susan L. *Community Attitudes toward Pollution.* Research paper no. 188. Chicago: University of Chicago, Department of Geography, 1978.

Cassedy, James H. *Charles V. Chapin and the Public Health Movement.* Cambridge, Mass.: Harvard University Press, 1962.

———. "The Flamboyant Colonel Waring: An Anti-Contagionist Holds the American Stage in the Age of Pasteur and Koch." *Bulletin of the History of Medicine* 36 (March–April 1962): 163–76.

Chamber of Commerce of the United States of America. Construction and Civic Development Department. *Refuse Disposal in American Cities: A Report.* Washington, D.C., 1931.

Chapin, Charles V. *Municipal Sanitation in the United States.* Providence, R.I.: Providence Press, 1901.

Cipolla, Carlo M., ed. *The Industrial Revolution, 1700–1914.* Vol. 33 of *The Fontana Economic History of Europe.* London: Harvester Press, 1976.

Clarke, Robert. *Ellen Swallow: The Woman Who Founded Ecology.* Chicago: Follett Publishing Co., 1973.

Cochran, Thomas C., and Miller, William. *The Age of Enterprise: A Social History of Industrial America.* New York: Macmillan Co., 1942. Reprint. 1961.

Cohen, Mrs. Julius Henry. *What We Should All Know about Our Streets: Prepared for the Use of Our Young Citizens in the City Schools.* New York: Women's Municipal League of the City of New York, 1916.

Cook, Ann; Gittell, Marilyn; and Mack, Herb, eds. *City Life, 1865–1900: Views of Urban America.* New York: Praeger, 1973.

Corfield, Henry. *The Treatment and Utilization of Sewage.* 3d ed. London: Macmillan Co., 1887.

Cremin, Lawrence A. *The Transformation of the School: Progressivism in American Education, 1876–1957.* New York: Alfred A. Knopf, 1961.

Crohurst, Harry R. "The Collection and Disposal of Municipal Wastes." In *Selected Readings in Municipal Problems,* edited by Joseph Wright, pp. 593–611. Boston: Ginn and Co., 1925.

Culver, Edgar L. *Value of City Waste: Treating on the Subject of Sanitation, Incineration, Reduction, Gathering, and Commercial Value.* Kansas City, Mo.: Co-Coal-Co., 1916.

Day, Albert C. *The Garbage Question: A Profitable Solution.* N.p., 1902.

Degler, Stanley E. *Federal Pollution Control Programs: Water, Air, and Solid Wastes.* Rev. ed. Washington, D.C.: Bureau of National Affairs, 1971.

Devlin, Thomas C. *Municipal Reform in the United States.* New York: G. P. Putnam's Sons, 1896.

DeWitt, Benjamin Parke. *The Progressive Movement: A Non-Partisan Comprehensive Discussion of Current Tendencies in American Politics.* New York: Macmillan Co., 1915.

Dial, Timothy. "Refuse Disposal and Public Health in Atlanta during the Progressive Era: A Continuing Crisis." *Atlanta Historical Bulletin* 17 (Fall–Winter 1972): 31–40.

Duffy, John. *A History of Public Health in New York City, 1866–1966.* New York: Russell Sage Foundation, 1974.

———. *A History of Public Health in New York City, 1625–1866.* New York: Russell Sage Foundation, 1968.

Dyck, George E. *The Treatment of Garbage.* Chicago, 1916.

Dyos, H. J., and Wolff, Michael, eds. *The Victorian City: Images and Realities.* London: Routledge and Kegan Paul, 1973.

Evinger, Morris Irwin, and Faber, Daniel C. "The Collection and Disposal of City Refuse." *Bulletin of Iowa State College of Agriculture and Mechanical Arts* 14 (1 January 1915).

Fairlie, John A. *Essays in Municipal Administration.* New York: Macmillan Co., 1908. Reprint. 1910.

———. *Municipal Administration.* New York: Macmillan Co., 1901. Reprint. 1906.

Fein, Albert. *Frederick Law Olmsted and the American Environmental Tradition.* New York: George Braziller, 1972.

Fenton, Richard. "Current Trends in Municipal Solid Waste Disposal in New York City." *Resource Recovery and Conservation* 1 (1975): 167–76.

Flack, J. Ernest, and Shipley, Margaret C., eds. *Man and the Quality of His Environment.* Boulder: University of Colorado Press, 1968.

Folwell, A. Prescott. *Municipal Engineering Practice*. New York: John Wiley and Sons, 1916.

Gardner, Fletcher, and Simonds, James Persons. *Practical Sanitation: A Handbook for Health Officers and Practitioners of Medicine*. St. Louis: C. V. Mosby Co., 1914.

Gerhard, William Paul. *The Disposal of Household Wastes*. New York: Van Nostrand, 1890.

———. *Sanitary Engineering*. New York: By author, 1898.

———. *Sanitation and Sanitary Engineering*. 2d ed. New York: By author, 1909.

Glaab, Charles N., and Brown, A. Theodore. *A History of Urban America*. 2d ed. New York: Macmillan Co., 1976.

Goldfield, David R., and Brownell, Blaine A. *Urban America: From Downtown to No Town*. Boston: Houghton Mifflin Co., 1979.

Goodrich, Walter Francis. *The Economic Disposal of Towns' Refuse*. New York: John Wiley and Co., 1901.

———. *Modern Destructor Practice*. London: C. Griffin and Co., 1912.

———. *Refuse Disposal and Power Production*. Westminster: Archibald Constable and Co., 1904.

Gould, Lewis L., ed. *The Progressive Era*. Syracuse, N.Y.: Syracuse University Press, 1974.

Green, Constance McLaughlin. *Washington: Village and Capital, 1800–1878*. Princeton, N.J.: Princeton University Press, 1962.

Griffith, Ernest S. *History of American City Government: The Colonial Period*. New York: Oxford University Press, 1938.

———. *A History of American City Government: The Conspicuous Failure, 1870–1900*. New York: Praeger Publishers, 1974.

———. *A History of American City Government: The Progressive Years and Their Aftermath, 1900–1920*. New York: Praeger Publishers, 1974.

Gunnerson, Charles G. "Debris Accumulation in Ancient and Modern Cities." *Journal of the Environmental Engineering Division, ASCE* 99 (June 1973): 229–43.

Habakkuk, H. J., and Postan, M. *The Industrial Revolutions and After: Incomes, Population and Technological Change*. Vol. 6 of *The Cambridge Economic History of Europe*. Cambridge: Cambridge University Press, 1966.

Haber, Samuel. *Efficiency and Uplift: Scientific Management in the Progressive Era, 1890–1920*. Chicago: University of Chicago Press, 1964.

Hagerty, D. Joseph; Pavoni, Joseph L.; and Heer, John E., Jr. *Solid Waste Management*. New York: Van Nostrand Reinhold Co., 1973.

Hammond, Kenneth A.; Macinko, George; and Fairchild, Wilma B., eds. *Sourcebook on the Environment: A Guide to the Literature*. Chicago: University of Chicago Press, 1978.

Hays, Samuel P. *Conservation and the Gospel of Efficiency: The Progressive Conservation Movement, 1890–1920*. New York: Atheneum, 1959. Reprint. 1972.

Hering, Rudolph. "Disposal of City Refuse." *Transactions of the Fifteenth International Congress on Hygiene and Demography* 4 (1913).

————, and Greeley, Samuel A. *Collection and Disposal of Municipal Refuse.* New York: McGraw-Hill, 1921.

Hodges, Laurent. *Environmental Pollution: A Survey Emphasizing Physical and Chemical Principles.* New York: Holt, Rinehart, and Winston, 1973.

Holli, Melvin G. *Reform in Detroit: Hazen S. Pingree and Urban Politics.* New York: Oxford Univeristy Press, 1969.

Hoy, Suellen M., and Robinson, Michael C. *Recovering the Past: A Handbook of Community Recycling Programs, 1890–1945.* Chicago: Public Works Historical Society, 1979.

Institute of Gas Technology. *Symposium Papers: Clean Fuels from Biomass and Wastes.* Orlando, Fla.: Institute of Gas Technology, 1977.

James, Herman G. *Municipal Functions.* New York: D. Appleton and Co., 1917.

Kaplan, Justin. *Lincoln Steffens: A Biography.* New York: Simon and Schuster, 1974

Kelly, Katie. *Garbage: The History and Future of Garbage in America.* New York: Saturday Review Press, 1973.

Kemper, Peter, and Quigley, John M. *The Economics of Refuse Collection.* Cambridge: Ballinger Publishing Co., 1976.

Klein, Maury, and Kantor, Harvey A. *Prisoners of Progress: American Industrial Cities, 1850–1920.* New York: Macmillan Co., 1976.

Korbitz, William E., ed. *Urban Public Works Administration.* Washington, D.C.: International City Management Association, 1976.

Kramer, Howard D. "The Germ Theory and the Public Health Program in the United States." *Bulletin of the History of Medicine* 22 (May–June 1948): 233–47.

Kranzberg, Melvin, and Pursell, Carroll W., Jr. *The Emergence of Modern Industrial Society, Earliest Times to 1900.* Vol. 1 of *Technology in Western Civilization.* New York: Oxford University Press, 1967.

Larsen, Lawrence H. "Nineteenth-Century Street Sanitation: A Study of Filth and Frustration." *Wisconsin Magazine of History* 52 (Spring 1969): 239–47.

Layton, Edwin T., Jr. *The Revolt of the Engineers: Social Responsibility and the American Engineering Profession.* Cleveland, Ohio: Press of Case Western Reserve University, 1971.

Leavitt, Judith Walzer, and Numbers, Ronald L., eds. *Sickness and Health in America: Readings in the History of Medicine and Public Health.* Madison: University of Wisconsin Press, 1978.

League of Women Voters. *Federal Environmental Law and You.* Washington, D.C.: League of Women Voters Education Fund, 1978.

Leary, William M., Jr., and Link, Arthur S., eds. *The Progressive Era and the Great War, 1896–1920.* 2d ed. Arlington Heights, Ill.: AHM Publishing Corp., 1978.

Lovejoy, Luther E. "Garbage and Rubbish." *Proceedings of the Academy of Political Science* 2 (1911–12): 62–69.

Lubove, Roy. "The Twentieth Century City: The Progressive as Municipal Reformer." *Mid-America* 41 (October 1959): 195–209.

―――. *Twentieth-Century Pittsburgh: Government, Business, and Environmental Change*. New York: John Wiley & Sons, 1969.

McCullough, Ernest. *Engineering Work in Towns and Small Cities*. Chicago: Technical Book Agency, 1906.

MacDowell, R. F. "The Disposal of Municipal Wastes in Small Cities and Villages." *Ohio State Board of Health Monthly Bulletin* (November 1912): 423–29.

McKenzie, Garry D., and Utgard, Russell O., eds. *Man and His Physical Environment: Readings in Environmental Geology*. Minneapolis, Minn.: Burgess Publishing Co., 1972.

McShane, Clay. "Transforming the Use of Urban Space: A Look at the Revolution in Street Pavements, 1880–1924." *Journal of Urban History* 5 (May 1979): 279–307.

Mantell, C. L. *Solid Wastes: Origin, Collection, Processing, and Disposal*. New York: John Wiley and Sons, 1975.

Marx, Wesley. *Man and His Environment: Waste*. New York: Harper and Row, Publishers, 1971.

Mathews, Ernest Romney. *Refuse Disposal*. London: C. Griffin and Co., 1915.

Maxey, Chester C. *An Outline of Municpal Government*. New York: Doubleday, Page, and Co., 1924.

―――. *Urban Democracy*. Boston: D. C. Heath and Co., 1929.

Maxwell, William Henry. *The Removal and Disposal of Town Refuse*. London: Sanitary Publishing Co., 1898.

Melosi, Martin V. " 'Out of Sight, Out of Mind': The Environment and the Disposal of Municipal Refuse, 1860–1920." *Historian* 35 (August 1973): 621–40.

―――. *Pragmatic Environmentalist: Sanitary Engineer George E. Waring, Jr.* Washington, D.C.: Public Works Historical Society, 1977.

―――. "Urban Pollution: Historical Perspective Needed." *Environmental Review* 3 (Spring 1979): 37–45.

―――, ed. *Pollution and Reform in American Cities, 1870–1930*. Austin: University of Texas Press, 1980.

Merriman, Mansfield. *Elements of Sanitary Engineering*. New York: John Wiley and Co., 1898; 2d ed. 1899.

Merritt, Raymond H. *Engineering in American Society, 1850–1875*. Lexington: University of Kentucky Press, 1969.

Metcalf, Leonard, and Eddy, Harrison P. *Sewerage and Sewage Disposal*. New York: McGraw-Hill, 1920. Reprint. 1930.

Miller, Zane L. *The Urbanization of Modern America: A Brief History*. New York: Harcourt Brace Jovanovich. 1973.

Morgan, H. Wayne. "America's First Environmental Challenge, 1865–1920," in *Essays on the Gilded Age*, edited by Margaret F. Morris, pp. 87–108. Austin: University of Texas Press, 1973.

Morse, William F. *The Collection and Disposal of Municipal Waste*. New York: Municipal Journal and Engineer, 1908.

————. *The Disposal of Refuse and Garbage*. New York: J. J. O'Brien and Sons, 1899.

————. *The Street Cleaning Department of New York City under Tammany Administration*. N.p., 1901.

Mumford, Lewis. *The City in History: Its Origins, Its Transformation, and Its Prospects*. New York: Harcourt, Brace and World, 1961.

National Academy of Sciences–National Research Council. Committee on Pollution. *Waste Management and Control*. Washington, D.C.: NAS-NRC, 1966.

National Bureau of Municipal Research. *Making Money out of Garbage*. Compiled by W. C. Howland. N.d.

National League of Cities and United States Conference of Mayors. Solid Waste Management Task Force. *Cities and the Nation's Disposal Crisis*. Washington, D.C.: National League of Cities–United States Conference of Mayors, 1973.

Noble, David F. *America by Design: Science, Technology, and the Rise of Corporate Capitalism*. New York: Alfred A. Knopf, 1977.

Opie, John, ed. *Americans and Environment: The Controversy over Ecology*. Lexington, Mass.: D. C. Heath and Co., 1971.

Parsons, H. de B. "City Refuse and Its Disposal." *Journal of the Society of Chemical Industry* 27 (30 April 1908): 376–79.

————. *The Disposal of Municipal Refuse*. New York: John Wiley and Co., 1906.

Patton, Clifford. *Battle for Municipal Reform: Mobilization and Attack, 1875–1900*. Washington, D.C.: American Council on Public Affairs, 1940.

Perry, Stewart E. *San Francisco Scavengers: Dirty Work and the Pride of Ownership*. Berkeley: University of California Press, 1978.

Peterson, Jon A. "The City Beautiful Movement: Forgotten Origins and Lost Meanings." *Journal of Urban History* 2 (August 1976): 415–34.

————. "The Impact of Sanitary Reform upon American Urban Planning, 1840–1890." *Journal of Social History* 13 (Fall 1979): 83–103.

Petulla, Joseph M. *American Environmental History: The Exploitation and Conservation of Natural Resources*. San Francisco: Boyd and Fraser Publishing Co., 1977.

Phelps, Earle B. *The Principles of Public Health Engineering*. New York: Macmillan Co., 1925.

Pierce, Bessie Louise. *The Beginning of a City, 1673–1848*. Vol. 1 of *A History of Chicago*. Chicago: University of Chicago Press, 1937. Reprint. 1975.

Pomerantz, Sidney I. *New York, an American City, 1783–1803: A Study of Urban Life*. Port Washington, N.Y.: Ira J. Friedman, 1938. Reprint. 1965.

Pumpelly, Josiah C. *Clean Streets*. N.p., 1894.

Purcell, Arthur H. *The Waste Watchers: A Citizen's Handbook for Conserving Energy and Resources*. Garden City, N.Y.: Anchor Press, 1980.

Rice, Bradley Robert. *Progressive Cities: The Commission Government Movement in America, 1901–1920*. Austin: University of Texas Press, 1977.

Richards, Ellen H. *Conservation by Sanitation*. New York: John Wiley and Sons, 1911.

Richman, Julia, and Wallach, Isabel Richman. *Good Citizenship*. New York: American Book Co., 1908.

Riis, Jacob. *How the Other Half Lives*. 1890. Reprint. New York: Hill and Wang, 1957.

Riordan, William L. *Plunkitt of Tammany Hall*. New York: E. P. Dutton and Co., 1963.

Roosevelt, Theodore. *Theodore Roosevelt: An Autobiography*. New York: Charles Scribner, 1924.

Roper, Laura Wood. *FLO: A Biography of Frederick Law Olmsted*. Baltimore, Md.: Johns Hopkins University Press, 1973.

Rosen, George A. *A History of Public Health*. New York: MD Publication, 1958.

Rosenberg, Charles E. *The Cholera Years: The United States in 1832, 1849, and 1866*. Chicago: University of Chicago Press, 1962.

Rosenkrantz, Barbara G. *Public Health and the State: Changing Views in Massachusetts, 1842–1936*. Cambridge, Mass.: Harvard University Press, 1972.

Ruckelshaus, William D. "Solid Waste Management: An Overview." *Public Management* (October 1972).

Russel, Robert R. *A History of the American Economic System*. New York: Appleton-Century-Crofts, 1964.

Salveson, Kenneth, and Chun, Laurel, eds. *Biomass Energy for Hawaii*. Vol. 3 of *Mixed Municipal Refuse*. Stanford, Calif.: Stanford University, Institute for Energy Studies, 1977.

Savas, E. S. *The Organization and Efficiency of Solid Waste Collection*. Lexington, Mass.: D. C. Heath and Co., 1977.

Schiesl, Martin J. *The Politics of Efficiency: Municipal Administration and Reform in America, 1820–1920*. Berkeley: University of California Press, 1977.

Schultz, Stanley K., and McShane, Clay. "To Engineer the Metropolis: Sewers, Sanitation, and City Planning in Late-Nineteenth-Century America." *Journal of American History* 65 (September 1978): 389–411.

Schurr, Sam H., and Netschert, Bruce C. *Energy in the American Economy, 1850–1975*. Baltimore, Md.: Johns Hopkins University Press, 1960.

Sedgwick, William T. *Principles of Sanitary Science and the Public Health*. New York: Macmillan Co., 1918.

Selfridge, Harry G. *Suggestions on the Problem of Cleaning the Streets of Chicago*. Chicago: City Homes Association, 1901.

Shaheen, Esber I. *Environmental Pollution: Awareness and Control*. Mahomet, Ill.: Engineering Technology, 1974.

Shaw, Albert. *Life of Col. Geo. E. Waring, Jr.: The Greatest Apostle of Cleanliness*. New York: Patriotic League, 1899.

Singer, Charles, et al., eds. *The Industrial Revolution, 1750 to 1850*. Vol. 4 of *A History of Technology*. New York: Oxford University Press, 1958.

Skitt, John. *Disposal of Refuse and Other Waste*. New York: Halsted Press, 1972.

Skolnik, Richard. "George Edwin Waring, Jr.: A Model for Reformers." *New York Historical Society Quarterly* 52 (October 1968): 354–78.

Small, William E. *Third Pollution: The National Problem of Solid Waste Disposal.* New York: Praeger Publishers, 1970.

Smillie, Wilson G., et al, "The Great Pioneers of Public Health in America, 1610–1925." *American Journal of Public Health* 43 (September 1953): 1077–84.

———. *Public Health: Its Promise for the Future.* New York: Macmillan Co., 1955.

———. *Public Health Administration in the United States.* 3d ed. New York: Macmillan Co., 1947.

Smilor, Raymond W. "Cacophony at 34th and 6th: The Noise Problem in America, 1900–1930." *American Studies* 28 (Spring 1977): 23–38.

Soper, George A. *Modern Methods of Street Cleaning.* New York: Engineering News Publishing Co., 1909.

Stewart, George R. *Not so Rich as You Think.* Boston: Houghton Mifflin Co., 1967.

Still, Bayrd. *Milwaukee: The History of a City.* Madison: State Historical Society of Wisconsin, 1948.

Stone, Donald C. *The Management of Municipal Public Works.* Chicago: Public Administration Service, 1939.

Sutherland, Douglas. *Fifty Years on the Civic Front: A History of the Civic Federation's Dynamic Activities.* Chicago: Chicago Federation, 1943.

Sydenstricker, Edger. *Health and Environment.* New York: McGraw-Hill Book Co., 1933.

Talbot, Marion. "Sanitation and Sociology." *American Journal of Sociology* 2 (July 1896): 74–81.

Tarr, Joel A. "From City to Farm: Urban Wastes and the American Farmer." *Agricultural History* 49 (October 1975): 598–612.

———. "The Separate vs. Combined Sewer Problem: A Case Study in Urban Technology Design Choice." *Journal of Urban History* 5 (May 1979): 308–39.

———. "Urban Pollution: Many Long Years Ago." *American Heritage* 22 (October 1971): 64–69, 106.

———, and McMichael, Francis Clay. "Decisions about Wastewater Technology, 1850–1932." *Journal of the Water Resources Planning and Management Division, ASCE* 103 (May 1977): 47–61.

Tchobanoglous, George; Theisen, Hilary; and Eliassen, Rolf. *Solid Wastes: Engineering Principles and Management Issues.* New York: McGraw-Hill Book Co., 1977.

Tolman, William Howe. *Municipal Reform Movements in the United States.* New York: Fleming H. Revell Co., 1895.

Turk, Amos; Turk, Jonathan; and Wittes, Janet T. *Ecology, Pollution, Environment.* Philadelphia: W. B. Saunders Co., 1972.

U.S. News and World Report. *Our Poisoned Planet: Can We Save It?* Washington, D.C.: Books by US News and World Report, 1970.

Upson, Lent D. *Practice of Municipal Administration.* New York: Century Co., 1926.

Van Tassel, Alfred J., ed. *Our Environment: The Outlook of 1980.* Lexington, Mass.: Lexington Books, 1973.

Venable, William Mayo. *Garbage Crematories in America.* New York: John Wiley and Co., 1906.

Walsh, Edward J. *Dirty Work, Race, and Self-Esteem.* Ann Arbor: University of Michigan–Wayne State University, Institute of Labor and Industrial Relations, 1975.

Waring, George E., Jr. *The Causation of Typhoid Fever.* Cambridge, Mass.: Riverside Press, 1878.

———. *The Disposal of Sewage, and the Protection of Streams Used as Sources of Water Supply.* Philadelphia: W. J. Dorman, 1886.

———. *Draining for Profit and Draining for Health.* New York: D. Judd and Co., 1867.

———. *Earth-Closets: How to Make Them and How to Use Them.* New York: Tribune Association, 1868.

———. *The Elements of Agriculture.* New York: D. Appleton and Co., 1854.

———. *How to Drain a House.* New York: Henry Holt and Co., 1885.

———. *Modern Methods of Sewage Disposal.* New York: D. Van Nostrand Co., 1894.

———. *The Sanitary Condition of City and Country Dwelling Houses.* New York: D. Van Nostrand Co., 1877.

———. *Sewerage and Land-Drainage.* New York: D. Van Nostrand Co., 1889.

———. *Street-Cleaning and the Disposal of a City's Wastes: Methods and Results and the Effect upon Public Health, Public Morals, and Municipal Prosperity.* New York: Doubleday and McClure Co., 1898.

———. "Suggestions for the Sanitary Drainage of Washington City." *Smithsonian Miscellaneous Collections* 26 (1880).

———. *Village Improvements and Farm Villages.* Boston: J. R. Osgood and Co., 1877.

———. *Whip and Spur.* Boston: J. R. Osgood and Co., 1875.

Warner, Sam Bass, Jr. *The Private City: Philadelphia in Three Periods of Its Growth.* Philadelphia: University of Pennsylvania Press, 1968. Reprint. 1975.

———. *Streetcar Suburbs: The Process of Growth in Boston, 1870–1900.* New York: Atheneum, 1962. Reprint. 1973.

———. *The Urban Wilderness: A History of the American City.* New York: Harper and Row, 1972.

Waserman, Manfred. "The Quest for a National Health Department in the Progressive Era." *Bulletin of the History of Medicine* 49 (Fall 1975): 353–80.

Welling, Richard. *As the Twig is Bent.* New York: G. P. Putnam's Sons, 1942.

Whinery, S. *Municipal Public Works: Their Inception, Construction, and Management.* New York: Macmillan Co., 1903.

Wilcox, Delos F. *The American City: A Problem in Democracy.* New York: Macmillan Co., 1904. Reprint. 1906.

———. *Great Cities in America: Their Problems and Their Government.* New York: Macmillan Co., 1910.

Willard, Charles Dwight. *City Government for Young People*. New York: Macmillan Co., 1906.

Williams, Ralph Chester. *The United States Public Health Service, 1798–1950*. Washington, D.C.: U.S. Public Health Service, Commissioner Officers Association, 1951.

Worster, Donald. *American Environmentalism: The Formative Period, 1860–1915*. New York: John Wiley and Sons, 1973.

Wylie, J. C. *The Wastes of Civilization*. London: Faber and Faber, 1959.

Zink, Harold. *Government of Cities in the United States*. Rev. ed. Macmillan Co., 1948.

Zueblin, Charles. *American Municipal Progress*. Rev. ed. New York: Macmillan Co., 1916.

Periodicals and Newspapers

American Architect and Building News. 1893–99.

American City. 1910–17.

American Journal of Public Health. 1897–1922.

American Municipalities. 1915–17.

Annals of the American Academy of Political and Social Science. 1914.

Annals of Hygiene. 1892.

APWA Reporter. 1977–81.

Better Roads and Streets. 1915.

Bulletin of the New York City Women's Municipal League. 1903–1908.

Canadian Engineer. 1914.

Century Illustrated Monthly Magazine. 1894.

Charities Review. 1898.

City and State. 1898.

City Club Bulletin of Chicago. 1911–13.

City Club Bulletin of Philadelphia. 1909–12.

City Government. 1896–1900.

City Hall: Bulletin of the League of American Municipalities. 1901–10.

City Manager Magazine. 1924.

Civic Club Bulletin of Philadelphia. 1908–13.

Contract Record and Engineering Review. 1914.

Cosmopolitan Magazine. 1898–1907.

Engineering and Contracting. 1912–14.

Engineering Magazine. 1895–97.

Engineering News. 1890–1917.

Engineering Record (formerly *Sanitary Engineer*). 1885–1915.

Fire and Water Engineering. 1913.

Forum. 1893–1901.

Garden and Forest. 1896.

Harper's Weekly. 1891–98.

Independent. 1917.

Journal of the American Medical Association. 1885–1915.
Journal of the Association of Engineering Societies. 1892–1915.
Journal of the Franklin Institute. 1874–1904.
Journal of Home Economics. 1915–17.
Literary Digest. 1900–17.
McClure's Magazine. 1897.
Municipal Affairs. 1897–1900.
Municipal Engineering. 1898–1915.
Municipality and County. 1895.
Municipal Journal and Engineer. 1900–17.
Municipal Record and Advertiser. 1897.
Munsey's Magazine. 1900.
Nation. 1898.
National Municipal Review. 1912.
New York Times. 1895–98.
North American Review. 1883–96.
Outlook. 1898–1914.
Pacific Municipalities (formerly *California Municipalities*). 1900–15.
Popular Science Monthly. 1891–1902.
Public Improvements. 1899–1900.
Review of Reviews. 1897.
St. Louis Civic [League] Bulletin. 1910–12.
Sanitarian. 1879–99.
Sanitary Record [London]. 1898.
Science. 1888–1911.
Scientific American. 1891–1916.
Scribner's Magazine. 1877–1903.
Survey (formerly *Charities and the Commons*). 1906–17.
Time. 1978–80.

Index